D0990751

**PRODUCTION
PLANNING
AND
INVENTORY
CONTROL**

PRODUCTION PLANNING AND INVENTORY CONTROL

SECOND EDITION

JOHN F. MAGEE
Vice-President

DAVID M. BOODMAN
Arthur D. Little, Inc.
Cambridge, Massachusetts

.

McGRAW-HILL Book Company
New York • St. Louis • San Francisco
Toronto • London • Sydney

WINGATE COLLEGE LIBRARY
WINGATE, N. C.

Production Planning and Inventory Control

Copyright © 1958, 1967 by McGraw-Hill, Inc. All Rights Reserved.
Printed in the United States of America. No part of this publication may be
reproduced, stored in a retrieval system, or transmitted, in any form or by any
means, electronic, mechanical, photocopying, recording, or otherwise, without
the prior written permission of the publisher.

Library of Congress Catalog Card Number 67–17199
39488

1 2 3 4 5 6 7 8 9 0   M P   7 4 3 2 1 0 6 9 8 7

PREFACE

The pressure for operating capital, since World War II, has made business increasingly aware of inventory as a form of earning investment. In turn, this has stimulated extensive work in business, research, and academic circles to build an understanding of the function of inventory and design techniques for improved management control.

This book is designed to introduce operating executives, students of business, and engineers of planning and control systems to the concepts and methods which have been developed, emphasizing the functions inventories serve and the pressures and costs bearing on inventory and planning decisions. The aim is to bring the range of concept and technique to a point of useful application in the practical design of production planning and inventory control systems. For this purpose, mathematical formulation of concepts and techniques has been excluded as far as possible in the main text. Graphs and numerical examples are used extensively to illustrate concepts and methods. Appendixes are included to introduce mathematical methods having general application in production planning and inventory control. Procedural and equipment detail has been held to a minimum to emphasize basic analysis and system-design technique.

35441

Members of operating management concerned with inventory and planning decisions will be primarily interested in Chapters 1 to 3, which outline functions of inventories and planning, and policies and costs bearing on these, and in Chapter 11 on system design. Chapters 4 to 10 will be of interest primarily to industrial engineers and others concerned with detailed design of planning and control systems.

The aim of the second edition is similar to that of the first: to provide an introduction to the principles of production planning and inventory control to those who have an administrative, an operating, or an academic interest in the subject. The approach continues to be quantitative, but to the greatest extent possible does not include mathematical manipulations and formalisms.

The objectives of the revision have been to clarify the presentation of material and to expand the treatment of certain topics, which use had shown to be desirable. Certain new material, developed since the original edition, has been incorporated and has facilitated this expansion and clarification. To add to the usefulness of the book as a teaching text, problems and discussion questions have been provided; a glossary has been added; and a bibliography has been incorporated at the end of chapters to assist those interested in pursuing the subject in greater depth.

The concepts and methods described are drawn primarily from the work of the Operations Research Group of Arthur D. Little, Inc. Other ideas have been drawn from a wide variety of sources working in this general area. Where at all possible, we have tried to acknowledge indebtedness specifically in the text. In many cases, however, similar concepts have developed essentially simultaneously in many places in response to similar problems. Particular material first appeared in a series of articles in the *Harvard Business Review;* we wish to thank the editors for permission to use the material here.

We wish to acknowledge the outstanding contributions of Miss Marian Carter and Miss Martha Ann Palmer in the preparation and editing of the text.

John F. Magee
David M. Boodman

CONTENTS

1

INVENTORY CONTROL: OBJECTIVE, PROBLEMS, AND SYSTEMS

INTRODUCTION

This book deals with the production process and the modern methods available for controlling it. The aim of a production activity is the timely manufacture of the desired product of specified quality in proper quantities at least possible cost. Manufacturing is fundamentally a process of converting money into money, successful manufacturing yielding an increase in money to those risking the original resources in the venture.

But there are exceedingly complex interactions among the factors involved in production. Even for the simplest production operations, the decisions that must be made by production managers about when to produce goods, at what rate, or in what quantities, can be troublesome. To achieve the production goals stated above, the production manager must simultaneously attempt to maintain stable operations, provide customers with adequate service, and keep investment in stocks and equipment at reasonable levels. Beyond the problems of planning, scheduling, and expediting production and the problems of inventory and distribution management there are the action questions that businessmen must face. The questions are stated, unsurprisingly, in the characteristic terms of decisions to be made or actions to be taken: Where shall we maintain how much stock? Who will be responsible for it? What shall we do to control balances or set proper schedules? A manager necessarily thinks of problems in production planning in terms of people and their responsibilities.

However, action questions are not enough by themselves. In order to get at the answers to these questions as a basis for taking action, it is necessary to step back and ask some rather different kinds of questions: Why do we have inventories? What affects the inventory balances we maintain? How do these effects take place? From these questions a picture of the inventory problem can be built up which shows the influence on inventories and cost of the various alternative decisions which the management may ultimately want to consider.

This type of analysis or functional question has been answered intuitively by businessmen in the past with considerable success. Consequently, most of the effort toward improved manufacturing management has been aimed at more efficient means for recording, filing, or displaying information, better ways of doing the necessary clerical work. These are important, but the growing inadequacy of intuition combined with efficient data handling has recently become evident.

The basic problem of inventory policy is to strike a balance between operating savings and the costs and capital requirements associated with larger stocks. Striking this balance is easier to say than to do. In the past, businessmen have been able, and quite successfully, to achieve a reasonably balanced inventory policy largely through an intuitive understanding of the needs of their businesses. However, as business grows it becomes more complex, and as business executives become more and more specialized in their jobs or farther removed from direct operations, achieving an economical balance intuitively is increasingly difficult. That is why more and more businessmen are finding the concepts and mathematics of the growing body of inventory theory to give direct practical help.

Business management now has a wide range of techniques for attacking production control and inventory control problems. These are more than new developments in clerical methods for keeping track of orders and inventory balances. They are methods for analyzing the place of inventories in an individual business organization and for designing production and inventory control systems which will be truly responsive to management policies on investment, customer service, employment, and cost reduction. These techniques have been developed over a period of many decades. For example, development of methods for fixing manufacturing run lengths or purchase quantities was studied by industrial engineers at least as early as the mid-twenties.

Since World War II, a combination of influences has led to rapid development of these methods to cover a broad variety of production and inventory planning problems. The pressure for capital and the growth of return on investment as a measure of business performance have made business management increasingly conscious of the importance of inventories as a cost element. The trend toward heavy fixed investment to reduce direct-labor cost and growing pressure from labor for employment stability have combined to force more careful future planning. Production-planning and logistics problems have received the greatest amount of attention of all classes of business-management problems in the course of development of industrial operations research since 1950. Universities and other research groups have shown a greatly expanded interest, since World War II, in the development of new quantitative methods for studying industrial problems, and much of this attention has been focused on production-planning problems. These trends have combined to yield a growing body of technique and concept, tested by experience, for studying management's inventory problems and designing efficient systems for resolving them.

Some of these techniques are described in following chapters. They include, for example, methods for fixing manufacturing runs or purchase quantities, setting safety stocks and order points, and deciding which item to make, when, to keep inventories in balance. They include techniques ranging from simple graphical methods to more complex numerical techniques for planning production operations in the face of seasonal demand and for adjusting operating levels to reflect demand fluctuations. They include methods for designing inventory-control and reorder systems for branch-warehouse operation or for planning operations in a complicated series of manufacturing steps. Many of these techniques employ concepts and language foreign to the line executive, drawn from fields of mathematical statistics, automatic-control theory, and other research and engineering fields. Nevertheless, they are far from being either clerical devices or from having only academic interest; they are aimed at helping the businessman make better policy decisions and getting his people to follow policy more closely. As such, these techniques are worth time and thought commensurate with the central importance of production planning and inventory policy in business operations.

SCOPE OF THE PROBLEM

The problem of planning, scheduling, and controlling production in the face of uncertain market conditions and of maintaining reasonable levels of inventories of all types is almost universal in business. The production-planning problem arises from the need to manage strictly internal operations of producing a good or service in the face of outside demands and limitations (such as the demand for goods or services, the availability of materials, the availability of funds for financing operations). The objective of sound production planning, scheduling, or control of inventories is to minimize frictions in these internal-external relationships or to adapt them to the advantage of the company.

The problem of planning and scheduling production or inventories pervades all operations concerned with the manner of production versus time, the interaction between production and distribution, and the location and size of physical stocks. The problems occur at almost every step in the production process, whether purchasing, production of in-process materials, finished production, distribution of finished product, or service of customers. In procuring materials or supplies, questions arise with reference to how much raw stock to maintain, and how much to buy in a given order in the face of required inventory investments, possible quantity discounts, and possible uncertainty in delivery times. Production departments must allocate a given demand or number of orders among production facilities to avoid bottlenecks while still arriving at a minimum level of cost, and they must determine the size of physical facilities to meet a highly seasonal product demand. In multiplant operations, both production planning and scheduling include decisions with reference to the amount of each item to be made in each of the several plants. This may extend to specification of the warehouses to be served from individual plants in their demand for individual products. Finally, cascaded production systems, in which the product passes from the raw-material stage to the finished-product stage through a series of production departments or plants, with major in-process stocks maintained between all production operations, illustrate other types of production planning and scheduling problems and problems in the control of inventory.

Inventory and production management problems involve some factors which are relatively exact, such as cost factors; other factors considered are subject to chance errors. Sales forecasts and actual sales experience fall into the latter category. Still other factors are quite intangible. The cost to be imputed against capital tied up in inventories is frequently difficult to ascertain and depends on broad financial policy. The level of customer service to be specified frequently cannot be determined by objective means but must be arrived at by management judgment in view of other, more tangible factors which can be evaluated. The need for consideration of the many uncertain or intangible factors and the necessity for balancing conflicting objectives are reasons both for the difficulty which business organizations typically have had in resolving these problems and for the potential value of new methods for attacking them.

ECONOMIC AND SOCIAL IMPLICATIONS OF INVENTORY MANAGEMENT

Inventories are another type of industrial asset. Far from earning no profit, inventories serve definite functions, discussed in Chapter 2, and if efficiently used, earn return like other assets, a return expressed ultimately in terms of increased human productivity. Inventories may mean lowered labor and training costs, lessened requirements for other capital assets such as production capacity, or improved ability to meet consumer needs; in most cases, inventory is as essential to the operation of a production-distribution system as are plant, machines, and transport equipment. However, management of and plans for assets in inventory are as important as plans for other types of assets if they are to contribute fully to human productivity.

Inventory accumulation and depletion have long been recognized as a major contributing factor to fluctuations in business activity. Indeed, the unwitting and tardily recognized build-up of excess stocks is often recognized as a major cause of the 1920–1921 depression. Four of the major business downturns in the post-World War II period to 1961 have been attributed to inventory fluctuations.[1] Today the number of notes on inventory conditions appearing in business magazines and newspapers shows how seriously businessmen and business economists treat the effect of inventory fluctuations on business conditions. More and more economic-research and market-research groups in business find that they have to take into account the inventory picture in distribution channels in estimating future sales and in making manufacturing plans.

Businessmen as individuals cannot expect to eliminate entirely the effect of inventory fluctuation—inventory build-up or depletion—when forecasts on which production plans are based are in error. But they can protect their part of the economy from the costs of extreme fluctuations, first, by keeping inventories well under control and, second, by fixing inventory levels and plans based on clear assessment and balancing of risks. Both serve to reduce the likelihood that inventories will absorb excessive assets and to minimize the need for forced inventory liquidation.

Inventories serve important social functions. For example, inventories permit the consumer to be master of an economy made up of highly integrated and often inflexible production units. Inventories give business the flexibility at reasonable cost to meet the whims of consumers. The rigidities and lack of consumer freedom have been clear on occasions like war or

[1] T. M. Stanback, Jr., "Inventory Changes and the Business Cycle," *Challenge*, April, 1962.

mobilization build-ups when inventories have been depleted and the economy producer-controlled.

Inventories also permit business to help stabilize employment and increase the utilization of skilled employees. Inventories help by absorbing fluctuations in demand—some predictable, like seasonal buying patterns, others unpredictable. The importance of employment stability on community well-being is receiving full attention from political and economic groups. Efficient inventory management and production planning are an essential part of a business program to achieve employment stability.

SOME PRODUCTION AND INVENTORY POLICY QUESTIONS AND PROBLEMS

Business management's questions in dealing with inventory policy and management can be summarized in deceptively simple terms: How big should inventories be? The question is easy to state but not so simple to answer. The difficulty in getting an answer arises in part because each individual within the management group will answer the question from his own point of view. The goals underlying production planning, scheduling or control problems, and related inventory-management problems in any company involve balancing of conflicting objectives, such as minimum purchase or production cost, minimum storage and distribution costs, and minimum inventory investment, while maintaining maximum service to customers. Ultimately the objective of production planning and inventory control usually takes one of two forms—either maximum return on investment, or minimum cost, subject to some imputed charge for invested capital. In either case, the objective of customer service may be included by including the cost of poor service (in the form of excessive paper work and lost business or good will) as one element of the total cost of production and inventory control, or by setting an objective of maintaining a given degree of customer service in terms of the proportion of orders filled upon receipt or within a specified period of time and minimizing other costs or maximizing return on investment within this limit.

Part of the difficulty in resolving policy conflicts arises because each part of management may recognize only some of the costs which are really important and may fail to recognize costs outside of their usual field of activity. The sales organization is well aware of the cost of poor service and may take the point of view that the company must never make a customer wait. The production organization, on the other hand, sees the need for long manufacturing runs to cut setup and change-over costs and is aware of the effect of fluctuating operating levels on employment, overhead, and facilities cost. The financial management recognizes that inventories are draining off cash which could be used elsewhere to make a profit. Each of these types of cost is legitimate and has a real effect on the company profit-and-loss statement.

Unfortunately, however, the effect of these costs on profit and loss is not usually apparent from normal profit-and-loss accounts. Many costs, such as setup or purchasing costs, are hidden in the accounting records. Others, such as inventory capital costs, may never appear at all. Each cost bearing on inventory policy is felt by the operating manager most concerned. As it is a "hidden" cost, however, its importance may not be clear at all to other members of management who are not directly involved. The resulting confusion over costs may make it difficult indeed for reasonable men jointly to weigh the importance of costs and arrive at a consistent policy. With embarrassing frequency, the result may be endless wrangling over the importance of unclearly recognized costs, leading to harmful vagaries in the policy governing schedules and inventories.

One fundamental job in getting control over inventories is to identify clearly and state explicitly the costs which are really influenced by inventory levels so that all the costs can be recognized by each element of management and so that management, in turn, can arrive at a conscious balance of costs for the good of the company as a whole. Some types of cost and principles of cost definition appropriate to inventory-control questions are discussed in Chapter 3.

Sometimes inventory problems arise because of a tendency to think of inventories in isolation from production or sales operations. Sometimes field inventories are thought of as important to the sales organization but of no direct interest to production management. All that the production people are supposed to do is fill field-replenishment orders as they come in. Sometimes factory inventories are viewed too narrowly as the concern of production management alone, and the influence of demand forecasts, customer-order handling and field-reordering methods on inventory requirements at the factory is overlooked.

Production planning and control problems must in the end be solved from the point of view of the company as a whole. These problems cut across every phase of business operation, including sales, production, and finance. A solution to these problems most advantageous from the point of view of any one of the branches of the business without regard for the interests of the others would be undesirable and might be disastrous. Ultimately, what is required is a statement of policy on production and inventory by the top management of the firm. The allowable variations in production rates and the level of service that the firm intends to provide its customers must be stated as matters of policy. The intangibles involved in each make it difficult to fix these policies precisely by a detailed cost analysis. Open competition among the various departments of a production organzation cannot be relied on to produce the desired allocation of the firm's resources among inventory and production.

Often businessmen blame their inventory and scheduling difficulties on small orders and product diversity: "You can't keep track of 100,000 items. Forecasts mean nothing. We're just a job shop." Many businessmen seem to feel that their problems in this respect are unusual; in fact, the problems faced by a moderate-sized manufacturing organization with a widely diversified product line are almost typical of business today. It is true, however, that under the methods of organization presently used in many areas, the costs of paper work, setup, and control, in view of the diversity of products sold, represent an extremely heavy drain on the company's profit and a severe cost to its customers.

The fact is that the principles of good inventory control and production planning apply just as much to a job-shop operation as to a large-scale mass-production system. Although the problem is more difficult, on the surface at least, because of the variety of end products, the number of special cases and exceptions, and the complicated flow of product through manufacturing stages, companies facing all of these conditions have found that the techniques discussed in following chapters for analyzing inventory requirements and setting up control systems apply in a very direct, practical fashion to their circumstances. This has proved true because inventories, whether in a job shop or on a mass-production line, serve basically the same functions as outlined in Chapter 2. The analysis techniques which have been developed are designed to help individual companies analyze their own inventory requirements in the light of their own particular manufacturing processes, costs, and policies, rather than to be used as "cookbook" procedures for handling the clerical job which grows out of production and inventory control.

Businessmen sometimes view inventories with distaste, as an apparently necessary drain on resources, something that no one has been able to eliminate, but hardly a "productive" asset like a new machine or tool. Inventories are as productive of earnings as other types of capital investment; in fact, they serve as the lubrication and springing for a production-distribution system which keeps it from burning out or breaking down under external shocks.

The same basic criterion governs investment in inventories as in other capital assets: added earnings or cost saving plus intangible benefits must be balanced against investment and maintenance costs. A new processing unit or machine tool may offer labor-cost savings plus cleaner working conditions or better quality, at the cost of tying up capital and requiring added maintenance. Inventory in the same plant may permit saving in overtime and training costs and may help level employment fluctuations, again at the cost of capital investment plus warehousing. Investment in machine tools will not pay off if made indiscriminately, and inventory investment needs the same careful consideration to find the type and amount of inventory justified by cost and other savings in view of existing financial policies.

Arriving at the right balance point in inventory investment is often more difficult than in other capital decisions. Inventory functions are more complex, the advantages more subtle, and the balance of gains and costs much more difficult to find. Inventory decisions have been based, as a result, more on intuition than on logic and arithmetic; intuition-based policies are not always easy to administer or to keep up to date. Many businessmen's deep concern over inventory policy is not that they think they are wrong but that they do not know whether they are right or not.

PRACTICAL USEFULNESS OF ANALYSIS TECHNIQUES

The notion that techniques developed through research and mathematical analysis, despite their limitations, can help business managements obtain better control over inventory policies and administration is by no means academic. Many companies have found that analysis of the functions of inventories, measurement of the proper level of stocks, and development of inventory and production control systems based on the sorts of techniques described in following chapters can be profitable indeed. For example:

The Transformer Department of Westinghouse Electric Corporation has successfully applied these techniques to balance its stocks of 500 varieties of transformers among 30 regional warehouses through a system of centralized inventory control. Better stock availability is now achieved with inventory 20 per cent lower than the original level.[2]

Successful applications of these system principles to the management of the production and distribution functions in oil, agrichemicals, paint, and household appliances manufacture have been documented.[3]

[2] C. C. Holt, F. Modigliani, J. F. Muth, and H. A. Simon, *Planning Production, Inventories, and Work Force,* Prentice-Hall, Inc., Englewood Cliffs, N.J., 1960.
[3] R. E. McGarrah, *Production and Logistics Management: Text and Cases,* John Wiley & Sons, Inc., New York, 1963.

The American Thread Company, as a supplier to the fashion-goods industry, was plagued with large in-process inventories, day-to-day imbalances among production departments, labor turnover, and customer-service difficulties. They found in these methods the key to improved scheduling and control procedures. These improved procedures helped keep an inventory of tens of thousands of items in balance and smoothed out production operations even in the face of demand showing marked erratic fluctuations due to fashion changes.[4]

The Lamp Division of the General Electric Company used these methods to survey its finished-inventory functions and stock requirements in view of operating costs and characteristics.[5] This survey indicated how an improved warehouse reorder system would yield inventory cuts at both factories and warehouses, and pointed to the reorder system characteristics that were needed, leading to the installation of a new reorder and stock-control system offering substantial opportunities for stock reduction.

An industrial-equipment manufacturer used these methods to investigate inventory and scheduling practices and to clear up policy ambiguities in this area as a prelude to installing an electronic computer system to handle inventory control, scheduling, and purchase requisitions.

The Procter and Gamble Company has described how analysis of its factory-inventory functions and requirements using these methods has pointed out means for improved scheduling and more efficient use of finished stock.[6] The analysis indicated how the company could take advantage of certain particular characteristics of its factories to cut stocks needed to meet sales fluctuations while still maintaining its long-standing policy of guaranteed annual employment.

CONTROL-SYSTEMS APPROACH

Control over inventories means good long-range and intermediate planning of production operations, good production scheduling, and good methods of control. A comprehensive and integrated control system, including produc-

[4] C. G. McGee, "Operations Research in the American Thread Company," *Operations Research*, vol. 4, no. 5, pp. 587–598, October, 1956.

[5] William E. Davidson, "Applications of Operations Research to Long Range Planning, Inventory Control, and Allocation of Sales Effort." Discussion at Case Institute of Technology's Conference, Apr. 5, 1955: What Is Operations Research Accomplishing in Industry?

[6] Discussion: "A Specific Operations Research Study at the Procter and Gamble Company," *Proceedings, Operations Research Conference*, Sept. 29–30, 1955, New York, Society for Advancement of Management.

tion planning, scheduling, and control, must be closely coordinated with other planning and control activities, such as cash planning, capital budgeting, and sales forecasting, since it impinges on a wide range of production, sales, and financial policy and operating decisions. The specific planning steps and timing will vary from one company to another, depending on product and process requirements, but the essentials of an inventory-control system can be grouped into three broad classes:

1. *Long-range planning* to budget capital for facilities and inventory invest-ment, to arrive at a balanced capital budget in view of long-range busi-ness forecasts *and possible errors in these forecasts.*
2. *Intermediate policy making and planning* as a basis for short-term sched-uling. Decisions must be made on what money is currently worth, what current service requirements are. General plans must be laid out for using existing facilities in the light of sales forecasts, e.g., to determine what level of stocks may need to be built up in advance of sales peaks to stay within plant capacity, to keep employment fluctuations at an acceptable level, or to balance inventory and production costs. This type of planning lays the ground rules for short-term scheduling consistent with inventory policy.
3. *Short-term scheduling* of work assignments to keep facilities and men employed and stocks balanced in view of the demand for output as it actually materializes. This must be done within a consistent framework of policies governing the level of production and employment to be main-tained, the size of inventory investment, and the service to customers, warehouses, or later production units to be maintained.

Inventories serve as cushions in each of these stages of planning, to absorb the shocks of demand-forecast errors, to permit more effective use of facil-ities and staff in the face of demand fluctuations, and to isolate one part of the system from the next to permit each to work more effectively.

Figure 1.1 shows the three basic planning functions, in boxes, with the arrows indicating the flow of information shown to and from the analysis. These steps may be done unconsciously or as part of an explicit, carefully organized program; they may be done by hunch or by use of the powerful methods now available (some of which are described in subsequent chap-ters), with calculations performed by hand or possibly justifying use of a high-speed computer.

As Figure 1.1 illustrates, the long-range plan makes use of demand fore-casts (with error or range estimates) and preliminary policy decisions—on capital allocation and value and on the amount of risk to be assumed—to show the implications of policy choices and help refine these, and then to

12

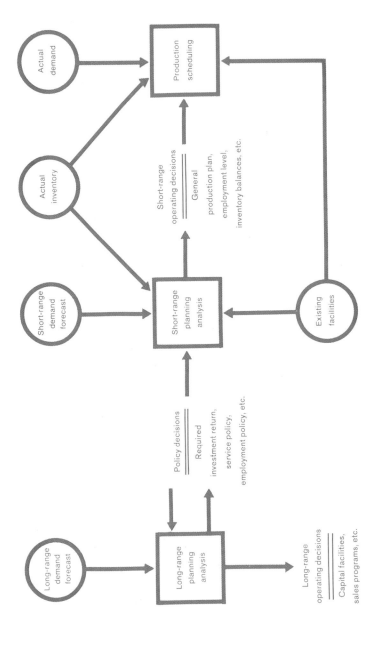

FIGURE 1.1 Schematic diagram of inventory planning

provide a basis for long-range operating decisions on, for example, construction, purchase or sale of facilities, or adjustment of sales and promotion programs. The analysis results may also lead to further forecasting effort by showing the production and capital costs resulting from poor forecasts. The techniques used in the analysis may be the type described in later chapters, particularly Chapters 5, 7, and 8. They are basically similar to those used in later stages, but will deal with broader, less detailed problems and thus may use cruder but more comprehensive mathematical pictures, such as linear programing.

At the intermediate stage, policy decisions, short-term demand forecasts, existing facilities, manpower, and inventories are the raw materials. This is the stage where questions about the general allocation of resources, isolation of bottlenecks, fixing of lead times, determination of raw-materials requirements and manning requirements are resolved. Some of the questions may be: How fast should we build up inventories to meet seasonal peaks? Is capacity adequate to meet forecast demand? How much inventory should be accumulated in view of the uncertainties in the sales picture? What target levels or goals for inventories and production operations should be defined? What raw materials will be needed, when, and can we get them? Can we expect to operate on one shift? Will overtime be necessary, or should we plan extra-shift operations? If so, when should they start? How does the demand forecast by product group match manufacturing capacity? Where are the tight spots?

The purpose of production planning is to resolve these and other general planning questions within the limitations of operating resources, with the objective of maximizing profit or return on investment rather than to define precisely how much of what item is to be made on what machine. The outputs are bases for short-range operating decisions: the general production plan to follow, adjustments in the employment rate, and corrections in inventory balances. These set the framework within which detailed schedules can be made up to react to demand as it actually materializes. Lot-size calculations, reorder rules, and production rate adjustment rules like those discussed in Chapters 4, 6, and 8, and seasonal planning techniques such as those described in Chapter 7, make up part of the analysis equipment. The nature of production-planning questions dictates that techniques must be flexible; i.e., they must be adaptable to variations from time to time in policy decisions and must be usable to demonstrate the impact of alternative decisions or policies. They must be comprehensive in accounting properly for all major factors—sales, finance, and production—which affect the plan.

Production scheduling covers the detailed handling of orders or require-

WINGATE COLLEGE LIBRARY
WINGATE, N. C.

ments—the decisions as to how many of an item should be made at what time at what operating center. Production scheduling by nature is characteristically very short run. The job is to make a schedule subject to conditions which are then known to exist, and good practice generally means that the only detailed schedules made are those which have to be frozen at the moment to meet delivery commitments.

Control means, first, keeping track of the degree with which plans or schedules have been met, or the extent to which circumstances have caused departures of actual production or demand from plan, and, second, having systematic procedures for deciding how to adjust future plans and schedules to take account of departures from planned production or inventory which have built up. Many presumably well-conceived production-planning or scheduling techniques fall down because adequate control systems are lacking in one or another of the following respects. Control systems fail when information requirements for control have been inadequately examined or when the procedures for making control decisions do not follow the rules, however well-intentioned, or have not been carefully thought through. Good inventory or production control means that control decisions are made routinely and automatically, with rare exceptions. Thus inventory-control systems must obey the laws governing design of good automatic controls as much as any mechanical or electrical control over a physical process.

Individual approaches to inventory planning vary widely depending on circumstances, though each company makes the same basic decisions and similar techniques are useful. For example, a major chemical company, in an expanding, rapidly changing market, makes long-range (18 months to 3 years) demand forecasts every 6 months. These are analyzed by linear-programing methods to determine raw-material requirements and to let contracts for surplus processing time or by-products, as well as to adjust plant, transport, and warehouse facilities. The analysis also gives information useful in setting the return demanded on inventory investment and policy concerning the risk of extra unusable equipment versus the risk of unfillable orders to be assumed.

Short-range forecasts are made and analyzed monthly, to plan raw-material deliveries, to set plant and related packaging operating levels, and to adjust field and plant inventory balances in view of existing stocks. Here again, production rate control schemes have been found useful along with safety-stock calculations and waiting-line theory, for studying transport requirements. Scheduling is done daily; it consists of adjusting flow rates on raw-material inputs and selecting specific transport equipment to handle each order.

A furniture manufacturer of moderate size holds quarterly meetings of a group of executives to forecast demand by general product line for the coming year. The group acts largely on "feel," setting forecasts by knowing style trends, competitive actions, and pricing or other merchandising plans. In these meetings, annual production rates are set by line to yield uniform employment. Biweekly calculations of department work loads and raw and process parts requirements are made by line. Scheduling is done irregularly to handle replenishment orders for finished products and component parts as they arise. Replenishment-order quantities and reorder points are set by methods similar to those described in Chapters 4 and 6.

This inventory-control system is generally workable but needs many feasible improvements. There is, for example, a tendency for the executive committee to overcorrect for past forecast errors. This tends to accentuate inventory and employment fluctuations. And the system does not make full use, in controlling component stocks, of information on what has been used versus what has been ordered or is in a later processing stage.

A manufacturer of small home appliances, with two factories and several branch warehouses and several products with strong seasonal-demand patterns, makes a long-range forecast by product line once each year. Control charts similar to quality-control charts are used to analyze deviations and indicate need for forecast review or modification. Analysis of this forecast, by methods like those described in Chapters 5 and 6, is used to set desired inventory levels and factory operating rates by product line for the coming sales year. Warehouses check item-replenishment quantities quarterly in view of current costs and shipping rates. Warehouse managers periodically estimate demand by individual items and set base-stock levels, using the concepts and methods described in Chapter 6. Monthly the factories adjust their operating levels by department. Each week the warehouses report to the factories what has been shipped out to jobbers and retailers. The factories use these reports of goods shipped (plus warehouse orders to change base stocks) to schedule production of replenishment supplies. When the cumulative depletion in a warehouse of items made in one factory reaches an economical shipping quantity, the factory ships a replenishment order having the same stock mix as the warehouse's reported shipments out.

This system illustrates a moderately complex production and inventory control system which lets individual warehouses and factories take responsibility for their own operations but sets the framework so that decisions made are responsive to general policy changes. The system makes use of modern analytical techniques to attain smooth operation at economical inventory levels.

THE ROLE OF FORECASTING

Forecasts, as Figure 1.1 indicates and as later chapters show in detail, are essential in inventory and production management. The forecasts may be crude, intuitive, or even hidden, but they are there. Whether forecasts are needed or possible is not the question; they are made formally or informally every time a decision is made—no matter how routine—whether to replenish or build inventory. The question is whether the necessary forecasts are being made as well as they might be if formally recognized and if available statistical and market-research techniques were used. Types of forecasts required and some approaches to forecasting are discussed in Chapter 5.

The important forecasting period is that just ahead, the time needed to make any current production or purchasing decisions effective—the lead time. Of course, in seasonal items a forecast at least through the next cycle is needed if stocks are to be built in anticipation. Sometimes forecasts and sales goals or quotas are confused, but economical plans depend on realistic estimates of need. Forecast errors cost money; the bigger the errors, the bigger must inventories be to guard against them. But forecast errors always exist, and a single estimate, without specifying an estimated error or limits of error, is not enough. Sometimes specifying a maximum sales forecast, the maximum which the production and distribution organization will be required to service, is a satisfactory way of accounting for forecast error. Often a comparison of past forecasts and sales is hard to find, in part because of informal forecasts and in part because old forecasts are quickly discarded and hopefully forgotten. However, since forecast errors bear so importantly on inventory economy, systematic review of forecast errors and improvement in technique are an important part of the job of keeping the inventory-control system up to date.

Since forecast errors will always exist, inventory-control methods must be flexible and responsive to unforeseen conditions. Uncertainty requires that there be procedures for action and control which are flexible to meet conditions as they in fact develop, but sometimes the need for flexibility is used as an excuse for indefiniteness: "We can't count on a thing. We have to play the situation by ear." In a sizable organization, when people at the factory level start "playing by ear," one can be almost morally sure that management policy will not be regularly translated into practice. It is possible to have inventory controls which are both flexible and carefully designed and explicit. Designing this kind of control system to be efficient in a complicated business is a task which defies logic and arithmetic as the only analytical tools. If this task is to be approached with any degree of assurance, methods are needed for taking direct account of uncertainty, for measuring the response characteristics of the system, and for relating these to costs.

LIMITATIONS OF INVENTORY CONTROL

Efficient inventory-control methods can reduce but not eliminate business risk. Risk, in business as elsewhere, is essentially a measure of uncertainty concerning the future. Inventory planning and control procedures can only help the businessman assess the risk and plan a strategy, as far as production and purchasing plans are concerned, to accept it on the most favorable terms consistent with the basic policies and objectives of the business.

The power of improved inventory management is limited further by the basic nature of the conflict among the objectives of a business. Better sales through improved service to customers, lower costs through smoother production operations, and lower investment needs through reduced inventories are all legitimate business aims, but they are in fundamental conflict. The best an inventory-control system can do is make the conflict evident in order to force a business decision which balances objectives, and then assure that the balance arrived at will be faithfully observed in day-to-day operations. But making decisions more intelligently and making action respond to them does not mean that the decisions are necessarily easier, that the basic conflicts are eliminated, or that the essential risk of the business is reduced.

DISCUSSION TOPICS AND PROBLEMS

1. Many familiar physical systems are designed as quantity-control systems. A home heating system, for example, is designed to control the heat content of a living space. Identify the features of a heating system that correspond to those of a stock-control system, such as demand, forecasts, order quantity, order costs, and lead time.
2. Does the inventory-control analogy serve to explain why most houses are heated in pulses rather than continuously to balance heat losses? Describe how.
3. Describe how the production superintendent, the sales manager, and the controller of a firm that manufactures and distributes hospital supplies might each define the objectives of his department's activities. What are the cost considerations in each of their objectives? Show how the departmental activities could conflict with each other and how such a conflict could be resolved.

BIBLIOGRAPHY

Biegel, John E.: *Production Control: A Quantitative Approach,* Prentice-Hall, Inc., Englewood Cliffs, N.J., 1963.

Bowman, Edward H., and Robert B. Fetter (eds.), *Analyses of Industrial Operations,* Richard D. Irwin, Inc., Homewood, Ill., 1959.

Buffa, Elwood S.: *Models for Production and Operations Management,* John Wiley & Sons, Inc., New York, 1963.

Carr, Charles R., and Charles W. Howe: *Introduction to Quantitative Decision Procedures in Management and Economics,* McGraw-Hill Book Company, New York, 1964.

Eilon, Samuel: *Elements of Production Planning and Control,* The Macmillan Company, New York, 1962.

Geisler, M. A.: "A Study of Inventory Theory," *Management Science,* vol. 9, no. 3, pp. 490–497, April, 1963.

Holt, Charles C., Franco Modigliani, John F. Muth, and Herbert A. Simon: *Planning Production, Inventories, and Work Force,* Prentice-Hall, Inc., Englewood Cliffs, N.J., 1960.

Mills, E. S.: "Expectations and Undesired Inventory," *Management Science,* vol. 4, no. 1, pp. 105–109, October, 1957.

Moran, P. A. P.: *The Theory of Storage,* John Wiley & Sons, Inc., New York, 1959.

2

ANALYSIS
OF
INVENTORY
FUNCTIONS

DEFINITIONS: ITEMS, STOCK-KEEPING UNITS, STOCK POINTS, AND OPERATIONS[1]

Physical inventory in any business is made up of a number of *stock-keeping units*, or *items*. Two physical objects are the same item if they are fully interchangeable. The same-style shoe in two different sizes makes two items. Each combination of size and grade of steel rod in raw stocks constitutes a separate item. An oil company must regard each crude segregation as a separate inventory item. A soap company must view supplies of the same brand and size of soap package in two distinct warehouses as separate items, since they are not directly interchangeable; it takes time and money to move stock from one warehouse to another.

A stock-keeping unit is held in a *stock point*. A typical warehouse will have anything from a few to many thousand stock points, one for each item held. A manufacturing plant will also have a number of stock points where raw, partially converted, and finished items are held. Material is transferred from one stock point to another by means of an operation. An *operation* transforms one stock-keeping unit into another, either by changing it physically (as in machining), by assembling it with others (as on an assembly line), or by moving it (as from a plant to a field warehouse).

[1] See also Glossary, pp. 375–393.

Stripped to its essentials as far as inventory is concerned, an organization, whatever it may be, can be viewed as consisting of a number of stock points and a number of operations, together with a control system. Each stock point is fed by one or more operations and is drained by other operations, until the point is reached where the drain is the demand by customers on the finished products. In principle, a flow chart can be constructed showing the course of the flow from the sources of raw materials through the intermediate stock points to the customers. Except in rare cases, this flow is not steady. Operations are constantly being switched from feeding one stock point to feeding another, or the rate of flow through them is being increased, decreased, or interrupted. The control system governs the size of inventories in the various stock points by governing the rate and direction of flow through operations. The inventories in turn make it possible for the individual operations to run efficiently and for the production-distribution system as a whole to operate smoothly to give adequate service to the consumer of finished product.

FUNCTIONS OF INVENTORY: EFFECTS OF UNCERTAINTY

Basically, inventories serve to *decouple* successive operations in the process of making a product and getting it to consumers. For example, inventories make it possible to make a product at a distance from customers or from raw-material supplies or to do two operations at a distance from one another (even if only across the plant or room!). Inventories make it unnecessary to gear production directly to consumption or, alternatively, to force consumption to adapt to the necessities of production. In these and similar ways, inventories free one stage in the production-distribution process from the next, permitting each to operate more economically. The essential question is: At what point does the decoupling function of inventory stop earning enough advantage to justify the investment required?

The basic decoupling function of inventories has, in a sense, two aspects: (1) inventories necessary because it takes time to complete an operation and to move product from one stage to another—*process and movement inventories;* (2) inventories employed for *organizational* reasons—to let one unit schedule its operations more or less independently of another. These aspects or functions apply equally to a small candy store and to the General Motors Corporation, to coal mines and department stores, to pushcart vendors and railroads. The inventories may be as tangible as piles of iron ore, or they may be as intangible as airline reservations. They may be manufactured by the organization under study, or they may be purchased from some outside organization. They may be finished goods ready for sale, they may be parts or intermediate products, or they may be raw materials.

Movement inventories

These arise because of the time required to move stocks from one place to another. The inventory balances to fill this function are often not recognized or are confused with others, e.g., economical shipping quantities, discussed below. The average amount of movement inventory can be determined from the following mathematical expression:

$$I = ST$$

where I = movement inventory needed

$\qquad S$ = average sales rate

$\qquad T$ = transit time from one stage to the next

For example, if it takes 2 weeks to move materials from plant to a warehouse and if the warehouse sells 100 units per week, the average inventory in movement is 100 units/week times 2 weeks = 200 units. From a different point of view, when a unit is manufactured and ready for use at the plant, it must sit idle for 2 weeks while being moved to the next station (the warehouse); thus, on the average, stocks equal to 2 weeks' sales will be in movement.

The amount of movement stocks changes only when sales or the time in transit is changed. Time in transit is in large part a result of method of transportation, although improvements in loading or dispatching practices may cut transit time by eliminating unnecessary delays. Other somewhat more subtle influences of time in transit on total inventories will be described in connection with safety stocks.

Movement stocks are usually thought of in connection with movement between distant points, as from a plant to a warehouse. However, if transport is viewed as just another operation in the production-distribution system, movement stocks are fundamentally similar to process stocks, material being worked. Any plant usually contains substantial stocks in movement from one operation to another, e.g., the product moving along an assembly line. Movement stock is one component of the "float," or in-process, inventory in a manufacturing operation.

Organization inventories

Such inventories "buy" organization, in the sense that the more of such inventories carried between stages in a manufacturing-distribution process, the less coordination is required to keep the process running smoothly. Contrariwise, if inventories are already being used efficiently, they can be cut only at the expense of greater organization effort (greater scheduling effort to keep successive stages in balance) and greater expediting effort to work out of the difficulties which unforeseen disruptions at one point may cause in the whole process. Despite superficial differences among businesses in the nature and characteristics of the inventory they maintain, the following three inventory functions are very common:

1. *Lot-size inventories,* maintained wherever the user makes or purchases material in larger lots than are needed for his immediate purposes. For example, it is common practice to buy raw materials in relatively large quantities to obtain quantity price discounts, to keep shipping costs in balance, and to hold down clerical costs connected with making out requisitions, checking receipts, and handling accounts payable. Similar reasons lead to long production runs on equipment calling for expensive setup or to sizable replenishment orders placed on factories by field warehouses.

2. *Fluctuation stocks,* held to cushion the shocks arising basically from unpredictable fluctuation in consumer demand. For example, warehouses and retail outlets maintain stocks to be able to supply consumers on demand, even when the rate of consumer demand may show quite irregular and unpredictable fluctuations. In turn, factories maintain stocks to be in a position to replenish retail and field-warehouse stocks whenever customer demand makes this necessary. Short-term fluctuations in the mix of orders on a plant often make it necessary to carry stocks of parts or subassemblies, to give assembly operations flexibility in meeting orders as they arise, while freeing earlier operations, such as machining, from the need to make momentary adjustments in schedules to meet assembly requirements. Fluctuation stocks may also be carried in semifinished form to balance out the load among manufacturing departments when orders received during the current day, week, or month may put on individual departments a load which is out of balance with long-run requirements.

These so-called fluctuation stocks are not absolutely essential. A business could get along without them if it were willing and able to make its customers wait until the material they want could be ordered in, or until their orders could be scheduled into production in a convenient fashion. In some cases, stocks to fill this need are patently uneconomical, e.g., finished inventories of battleships for sale. In most cases, anticipating all fluctuations is uneconomical; back orders will arise at some time. Fluctuation stocks are part of the price we pay for a general business philosophy of serving the consumers' wants (and whims) rather than having them take what they can get.

3. *Anticipation stocks,* needed where goods or materials are consumed on a predictable but changing pattern through the year, and where it is desirable to absorb some of these changes by building and depleting inventories rather than by changing production rates, with attendant fluctuations in employment and additional capital capacity requirements. For example, many products show a seasonally changing demand. Or inventories may be built up to meet a special sale or fill needs during a plant shutdown. Alternatively, seasonal stocks may arise where materials, such as agricultural products, must be produced at seasonally fluctuating rates but where consumption may be reasonably uniform. The problems connected with producing and storing tomato catsup are a prime example.

As more and more of these three basic types of organizational inventory are carried, less coordination and planning are needed, less clerical effort is needed to handle orders, and greater economies can be achieved in manufacturing and shipping. The only difficulty is that these gains are not achieved in direct proportion to the size of the inventory. As inventories are increased, even if they are kept well balanced and properly located, the gains from additional stocks become less and less. On the other hand, the warehouse, obsolescence, and capital costs associated with maintaining inventories rise in proportion to, or perhaps even at a faster rate than, the inventories themselves.

To illustrate this point, suppose a plant needs 2,000 units of a specially machined part in a year. If these are made in runs of 100 units each, then 20 runs with attendant setup costs will be required each year. If the production quantity were increased from 100 to 200 units, only 10 runs would be required—resulting in a 50 per cent reduction in setup costs, with a corresponding 100 per cent increase in the size of a run and the resulting inventory balance carried. If, however, runs were further increased in length to 400 units each, five production runs during the year would be required. Thus an additional 200 per cent increase in run length, compared with the original run length of 100 units, would earn only a 25 per cent reduction in setup costs.

The basic problem of inventory policy connected with the types of inventories which relax organization requirements is to strike a balance between the increase in costs and the declining return from additional stocks. Striking this balance in a complex business is a problem that defies solution through intuitive understanding alone. Each of the above inventory components is set on the basis of an estimate of demand or usage rate of the item. The uncertainty of future requirements is a central feature of inventory operations and will be dealt with at greater length in Chapter 5.

DEMAND CHARACTERISTICS

Demand or usage characteristics which strongly influence the production and inventory control system (and the relative importance of the different inventory functions) include:

1. *The size and frequency of orders.* Are individual sales or withdrawals made in dozens, tons, or carloads? Are there a few large orders each day or each week, or is there a steady stream of small orders? Planning must take into account the characteristic size of orders. The same total volume sold in a large number of small orders can characteristically be supported by substantially less inventory than if sold in a few large orders, unless special measures are taken to reduce the uncertainty about the time when individual large orders will be placed.

2. *Uniformity or predictability of demand.* Does demand show predictable seasonal fluctuations? Or does it show large short-term fluctuations, uncontrollable or self-imposed (as by special sales campaigns)? Handling large unpredictable fluctuations requires flexibility and additional capacity in inventory production as well as carefully designed rules for adjusting or controlling inventory balances. But where fluctuations are predictable, advance planning techniques can be used.

3. *Service requirements, or allowable delay in filling orders.* Where allowable delays are small, inventories and production capacity must be correspondingly greater; care is required to be sure the control system is really responsive to needs.

4. *The distribution pattern.* Do shipments go direct from factory to customer or through field warehouses, through jobbers, retailers, or consignment? The more stages there are, characteristically, the more inventory is required. Field inventories in fact serve basically to improve service to jobbers or retailers and thereby to remove from them some of the burden of keeping stocks.

   Where the product moves through several stages of handling from factory to ultimate consumer, prompt reports or estimates of movement, as close to the consumer level as possible, are important in minimizing the amount of uncontrollable fluctuation in demand which the factory has to contend with. Often the reordering habits of retailers and jobbers can seriously exaggerate the basic uncertainty in consumer demand for a product, and thereby can compound the inventory and production control problems of the plant.

5. *The accuracy, frequency, and detail of demand forecasts.* Fluctuation stocks exist basically because forecasts are not exact. Thus the inventory problems of a business are directly related to its inability to forecast demand with precision. This does not mean that lack of precise demand forecasts is an excuse for sloppy control. In fact, a principal purpose of almost any well-conceived control system is to account for forecast errors and keep these from causing serious trouble. But the responsibility of forecast errors for inventory needs should be clearly recognized, and the control system should be adapted to the types of forecasts and forecasting accuracy that are possible.

PRODUCTION CHARACTERISTICS

The production characteristics which influence the scheme of production and inventory control are:

1. *The form of production organization.* Job-shop-type organization is an expensive way of getting flexibility; a company using it should be sure it really needs that degree of flexibility. The inventory and production control scheme can be considerably simpler under a product-line organization than in a job shop.
2. *The number of manufacturing stages.* Where a number of stages in manufacturing exist, the inventory-control scheme can often be set up to take advantage of differences in cost and obsolescence risk which are likely to exist. The control system must also provide for smooth adjustment of early operating stages and inventories to fluctuations in finished stock.
3. *The degree of specialization of the product at specific stages.* Is each end product distinct from the raw-material stage on, or are the different products more or less the same up to the final processing, assembly, and packaging? Where the latter is true, economies are often possible in keeping the right balance of stocks in the semifinished state and by simplifying the control and scheduling of preliminary stages where the types of product are not diverse.
4. *Physically required processing times at each stage.* Processing times affect the length of delay, after issuance of a replenishment order or adjustment of a production rate, before the action becomes effective. This replenishment lead time, in turn, directly influences the size of the inventory needed. Lead time is fundamentally important in determining inventory

requirements. Its influence on stock levels will be shown explicitly in the analyses of various types of inventories in later chapters.

5. *Production flexibility.* How rapidly and at what cost can management vary production rates, shift personnel among product lines or departments, and change equipment from one product to another? Changing an assembly line or an intricate machine tool from one product to another may be very expensive and time-consuming. Most automatic packaging lines, however, appear to absorb moderate changes in package size or type or in product type readily; and personnel are often readily interchangeable among lines.

Management of inventories and production is basically a question of striking a balance among production flexibility and capacity, inventory levels, and customer-service needs. No company is free to pick all three at will. A realistic inventory-control system must be set up to recognize limitations in flexibility and to take advantage of those elements of flexibility which exist.

6. *Capacity of production and warehousing stages.* Production capacity in any operation sets one limit on flexibility. In the manufacture of products with seasonal sales, such as toys or building materials, it may not be economical to maintain operating capacity to match peak sales rates. The control system must provide for orderly and balanced build-up of stocks in advance of the peak. Capacity for heating-oil production in an oil refinery is governed in part by total through-put capacity and in part by the ability of the distribution system to absorb other refined products, such as gasoline components, produced simultaneously. However, in some petrochemical operations, the processing unit can economically be built with large through-put relative to average usage, and production rates can be adjusted easily and at low out-of-pocket cost. Warehouses also have limited capacity, although in many companies warehouse capacity is large relative to need or can be increased by temporary changes in stocking methods at modest cost. However, in some cases—refrigerated storage of food products, storage of chemicals under pressure, or tank storage of petroleum products—the cost of storage facilities is high enough to set a severe limit on capacity.

7. *Kind of processing.* Are batches of materials of a certain size needed in production? Some chemical, metallurgical, or blending operations are done on equipment requiring a fixed batch size. If so, the quantities and combinations must obviously be taken into account in scheduling for production.

8. *Quality requirements, shelf-life limits, or obsolescence risks.* These set important upper limits on the extent to which inventories can be used to

buy flexibility and free production operations from fluctuations in demand.

MEASURES OF INVENTORY PERFORMANCE

The inventory in a stock point will be depleted as demand is placed on it. In a well-run system all normal demand on a stock point will be filled within some specified time, the *service time*. At some time the control system will operate to place a demand for replenishment on the operation feeding the stock point. This may be on a unit-for-unit basis (as one unit is removed from the stock point, a replacement is ordered), or the demand may call for replenishment in an "economical" batch. The operation in turn will demand stock from the stock points feeding it. In a sense, every inventory is a link in a chain of inventories stretching from the point of raw-material extraction to the point of consumption.

The operation cannot proceed until all the items demanded are available. It will have to wait a time equaling the longest of the service times of the stock points feeding it. Then, after all materials are ready, the operation itself will take some time—the *processing time*. The *lead time* of the original stock point which is being replenished equals the sum of the processing time plus the longest service time among the stock points from which the replenishing operation draws items.

No single index serves to describe the performance of an inventory. Three interrelated factors must be considered in rating the performance:

1. The size of the inventory
2. The cost of replenishment
3. The degree to which it provides stock when demanded

Inventory can, of course, be reduced if the firm is willing to buy or produce in small replenishment quantities at an increased total cost of replenishment *or* if the firm is willing to tolerate a high degree of stock-out. Similarly, a high degree of stock availability can be maintained and replenishment cost can be reduced if large replenishment orders are issued, at an increased cost of carrying the higher resultant inventory. A complete measure of inventory performance requires specification of all three factors for the period of concern:

1. Size of inventory—dollar or unit amounts, averaged over the period
2. Costs of replenishment—total reorder cost for purchased goods or setup cost for manufactured goods over the period

3. Service level—average stock availability in dollars or units; amount of stock available when demanded usually expressed as a fraction of amount demanded

The commonly used *turns ratio*, the ratio of total sales to average inventory for the period, is an incomplete measure of performance unless the service level is specified.

DISCUSSION TOPICS AND PROBLEMS

1. A pharmaceutical manufacturer produces a broad line of drug products, one of which is a sunburn remedy, most of which he sells during the first 2 months of summer of each year. An inventory of this item is built in advance of the heavy selling season since market demand far exceeds the manufacturer's available capacity to produce it during those two months. Describe the nature of the decoupling that the inventory of this sunburn remedy produces and identify some of the economic considerations that make such decoupling desirable for the manufacturer.
2. The wheat in a loaf of bread existed as inventory of various forms in its cycle from farm to consumer: first as bulk wheat in a silo or warehouse; later as bread at the bakery and the supermarket; and ultimately as bread on the consumer's premises. Identify other inventories in this wheat cycle and describe their functions and economic considerations.
3. Discuss the inventory features of the following:

   a. The queue of automobiles awaiting service at a car wash
   b. The water in a reservoir
   c. The oil in the tank of a home heating system
   d. The cash in a supermarket cash register at the start of the business day
   e. The stock of a popular brand of cigarettes in a vending machine

   What considerations determine the size of each of the above inventories?

BIBLIOGRAPHY

Hadley, G., and T. M. Whitin: *Analysis of Inventory Systems*, Prentice-Hall, Inc., Englewood Cliffs, N.J., 1963.
Hadley, G., and T. M. Whitin: "An Optimal Final Inventory Model, August, 1960," *Management Science*, pp. 179–183, January, 1961.

Hanssmann, Fred: *Operations Research in Production and Inventory Control,* John Wiley & Sons, Inc., New York, 1962.

McGarrah, Robert E.: *Production and Logistics Management: Text and Cases,* John Wiley & Sons, Inc., New York, 1963.

Moran, P. A. P.: *The Theory of Storage,* John Wiley & Sons, Inc., New York, 1959.

3

COST
FACTORS
IN
PRODUCTION
AND
INVENTORY
CONTROL

THE IMPORTANCE OF COSTS

Costs, and the balancing of opposing costs, lie at the heart of all production and inventory control problems. The cost elements essential to a production or inventory problem are characteristically not those reported in summary accounting records. Cost information often can be obtained from accounting records, but typically it requires a reorganization or restatement of the accounting costs to arrive at cost definitions suitable to the particular problem at hand. There are, at times, costs which must be derived by experimental method or statistical means. Frequently a major part of the organizational problem in the inventory-production area is to demonstrate to company management the importance of these costs and the distinction to be drawn between *accounting costs* for historical and financial reporting and *operational*, or *functional costs* to be used in arriving at policy or day-to-day management decisions. However, because accounting and operational costs are often confused, and because accounting organizations and records are usually a major source of cost information in production-scheduling problems, an essential early step in the analysis of production and inventory problems is the development of an acquaintance with, and an understanding of, the cost-accounting system employed in the particular process under study. This includes methods for collection of direct costs, the definition and allocation of overhead, the method for valuing inventories at book cost, and the method by which responsibility for various cost elements is assigned to management units. A friendly but firm position with reference to the truth or validity of accounting costs is essential.

PRINCIPLES OF COST DEFINITION

It is not the purpose of this book to discuss in detail the various types of cost-accounting systems which may be encountered in practical situations.[1] However, in any discussion of cost in business operations it is essential at the outset to recognize the distinction between accounting and operational costs.

Accounting conventions

Accounting costs are derived under principles of accounting developed over many years and are strongly influenced by tradition. In any particular business the specific methods and the degree of accounting skill and refinement will vary, but in all of them the basic objective of accounting procedures is to provide a fair, consistent, and conservative valuation of assets and a picture of the flow of values in the business. Accounting methods have traditionally been strongly influenced by the objective of making a record, or "accounting," of the flow of assets through the business. Modern accounting is also affected by legal and tax considerations and the desire to maintain "conservative" values in the face of price-level fluctuations. In recent years, accountants have tended to emphasize the "control" use of costs in making operating decisions and exercising operating control. However, there has not been as broad a recognition of the need for flexible definition of costs to suit the varied needs of decision making and control.

Accounting systems typically distinguish two or three types of costs: direct costs, indirect costs, and overhead. *Direct costs* are those which can be directly associated with a specific job, order, batch of material, or item, e.g., raw materials, the wage cost of workers directly operating production equipment such as machine tools or of workers assigned to a production line. *Indirect costs* may include the cost of supplies used to service a machine or line, wages of process operators where operator time is not directly related to specific jobs, or auxiliary help, such as setup men, sweepers, etc. The items included as indirect cost vary widely. *Overhead items* include factory

[1] See references at end of chapter.

overhead, such as building and equipment depreciation and factory supervision, and general overhead, such as administration, selling, etc. Again, the breakdown of overhead between factory and general overhead varies widely among companies.

While many variations exist, two basic types of accounting system can be distinguished, one based on *actual costs* and one on *standard costs.* Under an actual-cost system, product costs are based on an accumulation of the actual direct costs incurred on a given job or in making a given item during a given period of time (e.g., by the use of labor time cards, periodic physical-inventory counts, or material requisitions). Thus the cost of a given item under an actual system will vary from batch to batch or from time to time. Under a standard-cost system, product costs are based on *standards,* or desired norms of direct labor and materials cost which remain fixed for substantial periods. Under a standard-cost system, actual costs will also be collected to varying degrees of detail as a check on the reliability of the standards and as a control device. The standard costs are generally used to value material in semifinished (in-process) or finished inventory or in-process material used in a following operation; differences or *variances* between actual and standard cost are considered as additions to or subtractions from current profits rather than being included as adjustments to inventory value.

Actual- or standard-cost systems may in turn be based on *direct* or *absorption costing.* Under direct costing, only direct (plus allocated indirect) costs are included in the value placed on products in inventory. Under absorption costing, the value includes not only direct costs but also allocated overhead charges (usually only factory overhead). A variety of overhead allocation bases are used; the establishment of "fair" methods of overhead allocation has received a great deal of attention by accountants. At the present time, absorption costing is the more generally used.

Methods of overhead absorption are based, first, on the assignment of expected overhead charges in total to work centers and, second, on the allocation of the overhead charge in each work center to the work done in the center, based on an overhead rate. For example, the overhead may be assigned to products in proportion to the direct labor charge incurred on each. The overhead rate—the dollars of overhead charged per dollar of direct labor cost—is conventionally set in advance, based on an expected or "normal" level of activity in the work center. If, after the overhead rates are set, the actual level of activity exceeds expected, more overhead will be charged to the product than was assigned to the center; overhead will be "overabsorbed." If actual activity is less than expected, overhead will be "underabsorbed."

Overabsorption has come in some quarters to denote "good operation" and underabsorption the opposite, for reasons independent of production planning or scheduling. However, sometimes overhead-absorption considerations will be drawn into discussions of production planning. For example, sometimes there is a tendency to balance production between two plants of different efficiencies "to absorb overhead" in the less efficient plant, independent of other reasons. At the other extreme, production may sometimes be shifted to the plant operating at a high level because of its low average costs resulting from spreading plant overhead over a larger volume. Either type of overhead fallacy must be avoided.

This brief discussion of accounting methods is designed to serve merely as an introduction to the notes on cost which follow, indicating the general character of costs as defined in accounting, to help distinguish them from operational costs in production planning and inventory control.

Functional and operational costs

Contrasting with the principles and sought-for consistency underlying accounting costs, the definition of costs for production and inventory control may vary from time to time, depending on circumstances and on the length of time being planned. These costs are defined subject to the criteria:

1. *The costs shall represent out-of-pocket expenditures, i.e., cash actually paid out, or foregone opportunities for profit.* Overtime premium payments are out-of-pocket expenditures; depreciation on equipment on hand is not. To the extent that storage space is available and cannot be used for other productive purposes, no out-of-pocket cost of space is incurred. To the extent that storage space is rented (out-of-pocket) or could be used for other productive purposes (foregone opportunity), a suitable charge is justified. The charge for investment is based on the out-of-pocket investment (in inventories or added facilities), not on the "book" or accounting value of the investment. The rate of interest charged on out-of-pocket investment may be based either on the rate paid banks (out-of-pocket) or, alternatively, on the rate of profit that might reasonably be earned by alternative uses of investment (foregone opportunity), depending on the financial policies of the business. In some cases a bank rate may be used on short-term seasonal inventories and an internal rate for long-term minimum requirements.

2. *The costs shall represent only those out-of-pocket expenditures or foregone opportunities for profit whose magnitude is affected by the schedule or plan.* Many overhead costs, such as supervision costs, are out-of-pocket,

but neither the timing nor the size is affected by the schedule. Normal material and direct labor costs are unaffected in total; thus they are not considered directly. However, these costs as well as some components of indirect and overhead cost do represent out-of-pocket investment and thus enter indirectly through any charge for capital.

These comments are illustrative rather than complete. They show how the basis of cost definition in production and inventory control problems differs from that of accounting. Indeed, the cost definitions may well vary in the same organization, depending on the time scale of the particular question. In the short run, few costs are controllable out-of-pocket costs; in the long run, all are.

Accounting and operational costs also differ in detail requirements. Accounting systems are noted for their meticulous concern with precise detail. There are many sound reasons for this. However, production and inventory control decisions are typically relatively insensitive to small variations in cost factors; indeed, many cost elements cannot be determined accurately, even by detailed accounting methods. While great precision in cost information is not required, this is no justification for careless use of cost data.

COST FACTORS RELEVANT TO PRODUCTION AND INVENTORY CONTROL

Costs dependent on order quantity

The most frequently encountered and best-known costs associated with production and inventory control are related to the quantity ordered, either from an outside source or as an internal manufacturing run.

When material is purchased, *quantity discounts* may be allowed; i.e., the unit price of the item may be adjusted depending on the quantity purchased. Quantity discounts are conventionally quoted in terms of *price breaks* or *brackets,* volume limits within which fixed unit prices apply, or in terms of a discount schedule, a statement of percentage allowances granted on orders or quantities of given amounts or over. They are sometimes quoted in terms of free goods, prepaid shipment, deferred payment or other allowance offered for quantity purchase. These allowances can usually be converted to an equivalent discount rate or amount.

Quantity discounts are in most cases subject to legal restraint; they are presumed to reflect demonstrable differences in cost of manufacture or handling rather than the purchaser's economic power. The differences in cost may result from reduction of paper work or machine setup incident to an order, differences in manufacturing method, economies in shipping or packing, or even administrative or selling economies.

On contract bids or special-order inquiries, sometimes purchasers attempt to obtain estimates of quantity price reductions by asking for bids based on small, medium, and large lots or orders. Unfortunately, such data may be less than informative, since it may be compiled half-heartedly and in a routine manner, and will often fail to give the potential buyer an understanding of actual quantity influences or method and cost which might influence his purchasing practices. Likewise, despite the generally recognized importance of order-handling costs, rarely are prices quoted based on a fixed minimum to cover clerical and warehousing costs independent of order size.

Figures 3.1 and 3.2 illustrate a typical unit price–quantity relation from a discount schedule and the corresponding total cost–quantity relation.

Setup cost in internal manufacturing operations is similar in effect. Equipment or process-setup costs arise, for example: in adjusting machine tools— a lathe or drill—at the start of a manufacturing operation; in batch-mixing operations, like mixing paint, dyes, or special chemicals; in changing over an assembly line to a new item, or shifting paper, textile, and similar equipment to a different size or weight. *Clerical costs*, including order reading, pricing, shop order production scheduling and expediting, form an important class of setup costs on orders which are only recently coming to be recognized as important and identifiable.

Time and cost studies of a variety of manufacturing, processing, and clerical operations indicate that the relation between the total cost (in time or dollars) of doing a job and the size of the job, the quantity produced, can often be expressed mathematically as

$$C = a + bq \tag{3.1}$$

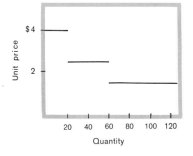

FIGURE 3.1   Unit price—quantity relation (discount schedule)

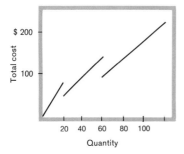

FIGURE 3.2 Total cost—quantity relation (discount schedule)

where a and b are fixed costs or coefficients possibly depending on the characteristics but not the quantity, q, of the item ordered. The cost component, a, represents the setup cost, that portion of total cost independent of run size. The fixed cost of a manufacturing run may include the wage paid the operator during the setup if, but only if, the setup requires that he work longer hours than he otherwise would. It may include the wage cost of a special setup man—again, if and only if, setup wages are variable. Where a plant or process is operating at capacity and an added setup results in a cut in productive time, the setup cost may include the loss in profit (the difference between sales revenue and out-of-pocket cost) on the product that otherwise might be made, or the added cost of making up this time on overtime.

Costs obtained from accounting data must be checked carefully where setup is likely to be important. Conventional accounting practice frequently makes use of unit costs based on a fixed-run quantity. The "standard" accounting organization may be unaware of the source of the unit costs used, having obtained them from the industrial engineering department. In such cases, industrial-engineering records should be reviewed.

Variation in unit manufacturing cost cannot always be traced to the existence of a simple setup cost. In machine-tool operations several alternate manufacturing processes may be available. For example, the coefficients in Eq. (3.1) may vary depending on the nature of the tooling and setup used. A very few pieces may be made essentially by hand; the setup cost may be negligible, as indicated by line (1) in Figure 3.3, or may be entirely clerical cost. A larger number of pieces or longer run may be made on equipment with higher setup costs but lower unit costs, such as ordinary machine tools, line (2) in Figure 3.3. Very long runs may justify expensive special tools, e.g., punch-press dies, in view of low unit costs, line (3) in Figure 3.3. The heavy line, the lower bound of these alternates, is the effective relation between cost and quantity produced.

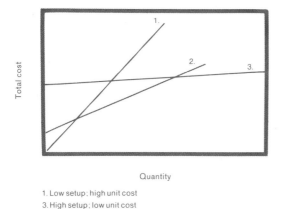

Quantity

1. Low setup; high unit cost
3. High setup; low unit cost

FIGURE 3.3 Total cost—quantity relation (varying cost elements)

Shipping costs form another class of costs dependent on order quantity. Table 3.1 illustrates the variability of freight costs with size of shipment.

TABLE 3.1 Cost of shipping automobile parts, New York–Pittsburgh (1966)

Size of shipment	Cost per 100 lb
t.l.: Truckload (30,000 lb and over)	$1.33
l.t.l.: Less than truckload (24,000 lb)	1.42
c.l.: Carload (30,000 lb and over)	1.36
l.c.l.: Less than carload (under 30,000 lb)	2.57

Frequently, shipping companies will impose a minimum charge on freight shipments; for example, all shipments of 100 pounds or under may pay the 100-pound rate.

Production cost factors

Production costs, other than setup or change-over costs, important to production and inventory control are the abnormal or nonroutine costs whose incidence may be affected by the planning or control methods. Normal or standard raw-material costs, for example, must be borne if a given quantity of product is to be made and sold. The principal types of abnormal costs are overtime, inefficiency, hiring and training, and employee-turnover costs.

Setup costs associated with a product run have been discussed. At times, however, another type of cost is connected with starting up or changing equipment—a "shakedown" or "learning" cost. Output during the early part of a run may be deficient in quantity or quality. Where this is so the comments on setup costs also apply; any out-of-pocket costs due to labor inefficiency must be accounted for. Where material spoilage results, an added material cost is incurred. These costs may effectively be considered as additions to the direct setup cost of the run.

Industrial engineers have developed generalized learning curves which appear to be widely useful in a variety of machining, assembling, and similar operations where process improvements, methods changes, and training as work progresses have an important bearing on the time required to complete a unit of work. One learning curve takes the following form:[2,3,4]

$$\hat{T}(q) = \frac{H}{q^h} \qquad 0 \leq h \leq 1 \qquad\qquad (3.2)$$

where $\quad q = $ number of units produced

$\hat{T}(q) = $ cumulative average time per unit over the first q units

$H = $ time for producing the first unit

The term h is a learning parameter which has the effect of decreasing the time required to perform the task as the task becomes familiar. If h approaches unity, the learning is rapid. When h is 0, the cumulative average is unchanged; i.e., there is no learning taking place. The relation (3.2) between the cumulative average time per unit and the number of units is shown graphically in Figure 3.4. In the example shown, the average time per unit is cut in half when the size of the run is increased fourfold; e.g., a run of 4 takes an average of 10 hours per unit, while a run of 16 takes an average of 5 hours per unit. The total time to make q units, $T(q)$, is given by

$$T(q) = Hq^{1-h}$$

and the time for the qth unit is given by

$$t(q) = T(q) - T(q-1)$$
$$= H[q^{1-h} - (q-1)^{1-h}]$$

[2] F. J. Andress, "The Learning Curve as a Production Tool," *Harvard Business Review*, vol. 32, no. 1, January-February, 1954.
[3] James E. Howell and Daniel Teichroew, *Mathematical Analysis for Business Decisions*, Richard D. Irwin, Inc., Homewood, Ill., 1963.
[4] Winfred B. Hirschmann, "Profit from the Learning Curve," *Harvard Business Review*, January-February, 1964.

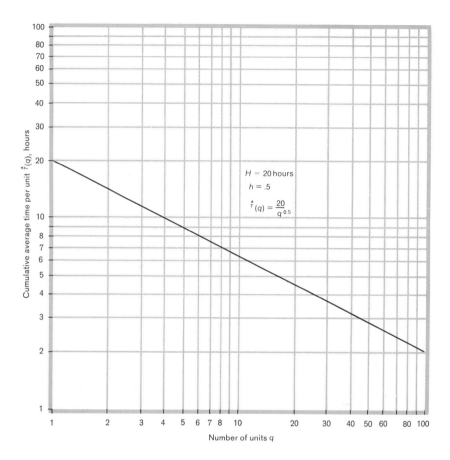

FIGURE 3.4 Learning-curve illustration: Cumulative average hours per unit

Overtime cost is frequently important. Overtime premiums paid workers are typically 50 per cent of basic payments on hours worked over 8 per day or 40 per week. The added overtime premium is frequently an out-of-pocket cost directly associated with planning and scheduling decisions. Where production planning includes deciding whether or how long to operate second or third shifts, shift premium may be encountered and the extra cost of premium payments must be considered.

The impact of overtime or extra-shift operation on supervisory and other normally fixed costs varies substantially from case to case. Furthermore, in addition to direct premium payments, there are important indirect labor costs, such as social security, workmen's compensation, pension, and similar benefit payments to be considered; additional indirect payments incurred because of premium payments should be included as part of the premium cost. Finally, overtime or extra-shift operation may cause losses due to inefficiency, fatigue, unskilled supervision, or special lunch or rest benefits. In one case, for example, output per hour on extra shifts is found to be 5 per cent below normal one-shift rates; thus labor costs per unit of product were increased 5 per cent before any consideration of shift premium payments.

The *cost of undercapacity* operation may at times be encountered, e.g., where a basic labor force must be maintained independently of volume. Frequently, however, it is simpler to consider the cost of the basic force or facility as independent of the schedule and treat all labor costs of production beyond the basic capacity as a form of overtime cost. For example, Figure 3.5 shows a possible relation between direct labor cost and volume per unit time, with a fixed basic labor force.

The shaded area under the curve in Figure 3.5 might be classed as "under time" cost. However, as shown in Figure 3.6, this can be restated for scheduling purposes as "no-cost" production up to quantity Q_1 and added cost production on quantities beyond.

A related condition was found in one contract packaging operation. The company contracts with an outside packing plant to package its output, paying b dollars per ton plus a penalty of h dollars per ton on the amount by which production is less than 50,000 tons in any month. For scheduling purposes this contract can be interpreted as yielding a packing cost of:

1. A fixed charge of 50,000h per month.
2. An out-of-pocket cost per ton of $(b - h)$ up to 50,000 tons per month.

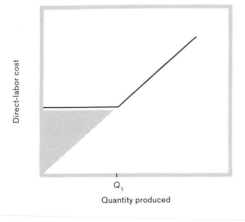

FIGURE 3.5 Direct-labor cost versus quantity produced

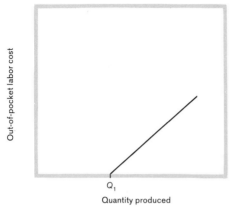

FIGURE 3.6 Out-of-pocket labor cost versus quantity produced

3. An out-of-pocket cost per ton of b beyond 50,000 tons per month; i.e., whenever the production schedule calls for packing in excess of 50,000 tons in a month, an added out-of-pocket cost of h per ton *over* 50,000 is incurred.

Hiring and training costs frequently are important, but are rarely available from normal records, in production planning. Direct hiring costs may include interviewing, paper work and tests, and special training. Indirect costs may

FIGURE 3.7 Clerical-operations learning curve: skill versus time on job

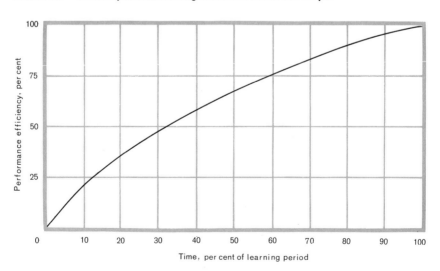

include inefficiency costs during early work. Extensive studies of a wide variety of clerical and handling operations indicate that worker efficiency as a function of time employed can be expressed as shown in Figure 3.7, where the scale of the abscissa depends on the type of job.

The indirect cost of hiring (and layoff) may extend well beyond the immediate job affected. In one case it was estimated that the training loss on an individual job equaled roughly 40 hours (at a cost of $2 per hour, or $80), but, because of union seniority rules, filling one job might cause as many as three moves of individual workers (a total cost of $240). On a lay-off, "bumping" may cause the reverse, yielding a substantial training cost due to layoffs! Layoff costs may also include termination pay, exit interview and related costs, and increased unemployment insurance premiums. In another instance, analysis of personnel records indicated that for every two employees laid off a third employee left (presumably to seek more stable work before being laid off)—layoffs causing labor instability beyond plan. Some companies have also speculated that fluctuations in employment or variations in the length of the work week have led to hidden personnel costs, due to inability to attract and hold qualified permanent employees when labor policies have been less stable than in other companies in the same area.

Inventory cost factors

Inventory costs related to production planning, scheduling, and inventory control may include costs of handling product in and out of inventory, storage costs such as rent and heat, insurance, and taxes and shrinkages of a variety of forms. Obsolescence is also a form of inventory cost of a rather different character. Costs of capital in inventories are considered in the next section.

The normal *costs of handling* product in and out of inventory are typically excluded from direct consideration in inventory problems, just as normal direct labor costs are. However, in some cases the cost per unit of handling may depend on the magnitude of inventories held. For example, high inventories may result in inefficient stacking or crowding. Sometimes, as inventories build up, secondary warehousing space must be used, with higher-than-normal handling costs. In one instance, limitations in factory warehouse space required the use of secondary storage considerably removed from manufacturing lines whenever inventories exceeded rather low levels. Costs of loading, trucking, and unloading products into these warehouses were substantial. Such costs over and above normal handling costs, like production costs over and above normal, represent out-of-pocket costs directly affected by the schedule and must be considered.

Storage costs such as rent, heat, and light are frequently fixed. A given amount of warehouse space is available and must be heated and maintained. Therefore, up to the point where inventories exceed the capacity of this space there is no out-of-pocket cost directly affected by inventory planning. In some cases, however, warehouse space is rented, or owned space might be released for other income-producing uses. The amount of space required, and therefore the cost of such space, may depend either on the average size of the inventory (if short-term variation in space is possible) or on the maximum amount of space made available for inventories. In either case, where inventory space is rented or might be used for other productive purposes, a cost directly associated with inventory control is borne, either as an out-of-pocket cost or as a foregone opportunity for profit.

The *taxes* on inventory are sometimes overlooked as an inventory cost; they can be important. Property taxes in some states are assessed on one day during the year against the inventory which is on hand on that particular day. This may create a distortion in inventory planning which can have considerable impact. Manufacturers strive to deplete their inventories by the assessment date and build them up thereafter.

Inventory shrinkage costs may take several forms:

1. Outright spoilage.
2. The risk that a particular product, either as a component or an end item, will become (*a*) technologically unsalable except perhaps at a discount or as spare parts, or (*b*) go out of style.
3. The product may otherwise become out of date.
4. Pilferage, breakage, evaporation, etc.

In the first case, the cost, equal to the cash investment in the goods, may be borne wholly at some fixed period of time after manufacture. Thus, when inventories exceed the equivalent of sales over this time, all additional inventories become unsalable. On the other hand, certain inventories, such as style goods, may in effect spoil at the end of a season, with only a reclaim or dump value obtainable. This may frequently happen in highly seasonal goods. For example, toys may be expected to remain in style for from 9 to 12 months of the year, but once the toy convention is held in early spring of each year, last year's merchandise stands a good chance of being obsolete and is substantially lowered in value. Some goods, such as technical equipment or spare parts, are subject to a relatively constant risk of obsolescence, and their value in stock will, in effect, decay with life. An exponential decay of value due to obsolescence has been used on occasion in such situations. For some such goods a known or estimable life is sometimes available instead, e.g., date of release of new models (not always a periodic event). Finally, some goods are subject to theft and misappropriation; some are subject to breakage or other accidental losses. In either case, an inventory shrinkage results with the attendant cost equal to the cash investment in the goods.

Other costs to the firm

CAPITAL COSTS

Inventory and production planning problems require consideration of the use of capital. Capital differs from expense in that it represents cash tied up which we expect ultimately to get back. The cost of capital is therefore not the capital loss but the cost of obtaining capital for use in supporting or financing operations. This cost may be based on either or both of the following: the cost of borrowing funds from the bank; or the cost of diverting capital from other possible uses, i.e., the cost of foregone opportunities for profitable use. Capital cost is based on out-of-pocket capital investment and a rate charged per dollar of capital invested per unit time. The rate of return earned on capital investment is the ratio of additional profit earned as a result of the investment to the additional out-of-pocket investment made. Capital investment as related to inventory or production planning problems breaks down to investment in inventory or in facilities.

Inventory investment is the out-of-pocket or avoidable cash cost for material, labor, and overhead of goods in inventory—to be clearly distinguished from the "book" or accounting value of inventory. For example, raw materials are normally purchased in accordance with production schedules; and if the production of an item can be postponed, buying and paying for raw materials can likewise be put off. The raw-material cost component normally, then, represents a part of the out-of-pocket inventory investment in finished goods. However, if cash must be disbursed to purchase raw materials when they are available—e.g., agricultural crops available only in limited seasons—regardless of the production schedule, the raw-material component of finished-product cost does not represent avoidable investment and therefore should be struck from the computation of inventory value for planning purposes.

Normally, maintenance and similar factory-overhead items are paid for the year round regardless of the timing of production scheduled; thus these elements of burden should not be counted as part of the product investment for planning purposes. Sometimes, of course, the maintenance costs, as for supplies, may actually vary directly with the production rate and should be included. Supervision, at least general supervision, is usually a fixed monthly cost which the schedule will not influence. Depreciation is another type of burden item representing a charge for equipment and facilities already bought and paid for. The timing of the production schedule cannot influence these past investments; therefore, while they represent a legitimate cost for accounting purposes, they should not be counted as part of the inventory investment for inventory and production planning purposes.

The definition of unit capital investment differs from the definition of unit production costs for scheduling and planning purposes as well as from normal unit accounting costs, since the unit capital investment in inventory includes all cash costs associated with production, even if these are normal costs. The capital costs in inventory and the size of the inventory investment are determined by the duration of time over which inventories are held—i.e., the average time goods remain in inventory before they are sold—and by the cash investment recovered from the customer.

Investment in inventory may be relatively permanent or short-term. For example, safety or protective inventory stocks may be fixed in size for a long time, with the level determined by inventory planning and control policies. The inventory investment is still defined in the same way, namely, the cash out-of-pocket expenditure required to produce goods. Seasonal stocks—i.e., inventories built up to anticipate high sales at one time during the year— are relatively short-term. Care in defining the cash investment is needed in such cases; raw materials, mentioned above, form a case in point.

The evaluation of crude and semirefined stocks in petroleum refineries illustrates the problems of defining inventory investment. Refineries may hold huge stocks of oil as crude buffers to protect against fluctuations in crude delivery or as processing stocks to help iron out the effects of processing imbalances. Where the refinery is a unit in an integrated company producing and marketing crude as well as refining and marketing finished products, the evaluation of the investment in crude and semirefined stocks must take foregone opportunities into account. The argument is sometimes made that the value of the crude itself should not be considered as part of the oil investment, since the company already owns the crude and if it were not in the refinery it would be in the ground. Under this line of argument, only the cash investment in production, transportation, and processing would be included. On the other hand, it can be argued that if the oil were not in the refinery, the company could have sold it beforehand as crude. Therefore the oil-stocks investment in the refinery should be valued at the current market price of crude plus out-of-pocket transportation and processing costs. The difference in assumption about what could have been done with the crude can make orders of magnitude differences to the value assigned to the inventory investment. The proper value to assign for planning purposes can vary from time to time as crude-marketing conditions vary.

The *cost of capital invested in inventories* is the product of three factors:

the capital value of a unit of inventory, the time a unit of product is in inventory, and the charge or imputed interest rate placed against a dollar of invested cash. The first factor was mentioned above. Inventory-policy decisions might be described as fixing the second factor—the time a unit of product is in inventory. But these decisions can be made economically only in view of the third factor. The third factor depends directly on the financial policy of the particular business.

The *rate of imputed interest* or of desired return on investment may be based on the cost of obtaining funds for investment from a bank, on the return that could be earned by alternative uses of internal funds, or on both, for different parts of the inventory. The proper choice depends strongly on the financial policy of the company.

Sometimes businessmen make the mistake of thinking that cash tied up in inventories costs nothing, especially if the cash to finance inventory is generated internally through profits and depreciation. However, this implies that the cash in inventories otherwise would sit idle. In fact, the cash could be invested in government bonds, at least, if not in inventories. And if it were really idle, the cash very likely should be released to stockholders for profitable investment elsewhere.

Determination of the rate of return based on alternative uses of funds is normally not easy. In some cases, companies have established rates which the management desires to earn on various types of investment. However, it might be argued that a complete study of the company's operations would be required to establish a realistic rate based on alternative uses. This is not necessarily true. Investigation of company financial and investment policies and estimation of current over-all return on investment will provide touchstones which can be used.

Sometimes businessmen think of inventory as short-term investment and thus relatively liquid and riskless. "After all, we turn our inventory investment over six times a year." Inventory investment may or may not be short-term or riskless. The point is, no broad generalization of this sort is possible. Each case must be decided on its own merits. The following cases are examples.

Much inventory carried in business is as much a part of the permanent investment as the machinery and buildings. The inventory must be maintained to make operations possible as long as the business is a going concern. The cash investment released by the sale of one item from stock must be promptly reinvested in new stock, and the inventory can be liquidated only when the company is closed. How much more riskless is this than other fixed manufacturing assets?

Inventory in fashion lines or other types of products having high obsolescence risk is hardly riskless. Its value depends only on the company's ability to sell it. If sales are insufficient to liquidate the inventory built up, losses result, and considerable risk may be entailed as a result in inventory investments.

Inventory in stable-product lines built up to absorb short-term seasonal fluctuations might be thought of perhaps as bearing the least risk, since this type of investment is characteristically short-term. But even in these cases, if peak seasonal sales do not reach anticipated levels, substantially increased costs of storage and obsolescence may be incurred before the excess inventory can be liquidated, over the time up to the next sales peak.

The rate of return charged may depend on the *type of investment*. For example, permanent investment (as in facilities or relatively permanent inventories) may be financed internally at a relatively high rate, while seasonal inventory stock may be financed by a bank line of credit at a relatively low rate. Furthermore, depending on the nature of financial arrangements, where the investment varies substantially from one time of the year to another, the capital cost of inventory investment may at times be based on the average inventory investment; in other cases it may be based on the maximum amount of funds tied up. The latter basis may be appropriate where cash released during low-inventory periods cannot be profitably invested elsewhere.

Where tax rates are progressive, as in the case of an excess-profits tax, a higher-than-average rate must be earned on incremental investment to maintain the average over-all return. When tax rates are high, the cost of borrowed capital—a deductible cost—represents a substantially lower cost to stockholders than the cost of internal funds imputed at equivalent gross rates. A substantially higher return must be earned on internal capital to maintain the same return on investment after taxes.

It is generally accepted that *average* or *expected* earnings which merely equal capital costs are not enough in risk-bearing circumstances; something additional is required to compensate for assuming the risk. Manufacturing and merchandising organizations are in business to bear the risks of these activities and to earn the resulting entrepreneur's or risk taker's profit. When the question of an appropriate rate of return to charge against investment is raised, company officers sometimes suggest a bank rate—i.e., 3 to 5 per cent annually—when this rate is, in fact, inconsistent with financial policy. It is important that the inconsistency be pointed out, since the use of a bank rate, when in fact the company is not inclined to use outside funds, typically results in a much lower rate of imputed interest and a much higher drain on capital than is consistent with true company policy. One wonders, therefore, how many businessmen are really satisfied with uses of their companies' capital funds which earn only a bank or a lender's rate of return on investment.

When inventory or related facilities investment is normally financed internally, a rate of return or imputed interest rate between 10 and 30 per cent is not unreasonable. In choosing a truly appropriate rate—a matter of financial policy—the businessman must answer some questions:

1. Where is the cash coming from—from inside earnings or outside financing?
2. What else could we do with the funds, and what could we earn?
3. When can we get the investment back out, if ever?
4. How much risk of sales disappointment and obsolescence is really connected with this inventory?
5. How much of a return do we want, in view of what we could earn elsewhere, or in view of the cost of money to us and the risk the inventory investment entails?

The use of a capital cost based either on external or on internal interest rates is not a cost typically found in accounting records. It is, however, implicit in many problems which arise in inventory control. Capital cost illustrates the type of operational cost which must be established entirely outside the normal accounting framework.

Valuation of *investment in facilities* is generally important only in long-run planning problems. Where facilities already exist and are not usable for other purposes, and planning or scheduling do not contemplate changing these existing facilities, investment is not affected. The question of facilities investment may come up in a planning problem where increases in productive or warehouse capacity are being considered. Facilities investment may also be important where productive capacity is limited, and the form of the plan or schedule will determine the amount of added capacity which must be installed, either to meet the plan itself or for alternative uses. In such cases, considerable care is necessary in defining the facilities investment to be consistent with the principles noted above; namely, facilities investment should represent out-of-pocket investment or, alternatively, foregone opportunities for out-of-pocket investment elsewhere.

MARKETING COSTS

An important objective in most production planning and inventory control systems is maintenance of reasonable customer service. An evaluation of the worth of customer service or, alternatively, the loss suffered through lack of customer service, is an essential aspect of the derivation of a minimum-cost scheduling or inventory-control system. The cost of customer-service limitations must be weighed against the production and capital costs incurred in improving service. It is typically very difficult to obtain a commitment on the value of customer service from sales organizations. Indeed the usual reaction will be that customer service is of immense importance and that, if any value can be put on it, the value is extremely high. Experience has shown that it is sometimes necessary to indicate what value placed on ability to fill orders is consistent with given levels of production and capital cost—in effect, to show how much must be paid to achieve a given degree of customer service. When this demonstration can be made, estimates of the value of customer service frequently become considerably more conservative.

Certain limits can be placed on the value of customer service directly in some cases. For example, in certain highly seasonal products the cost of being unable to fill an order immediately will vary from time to time during the year. During periods of slack sales, this cost may be very low—essentially the cost of extra paper work associated with a delayed order. During peak sales seasons, this cost is often at least as much as the total contribution to profit from the order. When an order is received at such a time and cannot be handled promptly, the sale may be lost completely. The contribution to profit which is lost is the difference between net sales revenue and out-of-pocket product cost. In some cases it may be possible to limit the back-order cost to the cost of producing this material on overtime or of purchasing the material from the outside. Where this is possible, the customer-service cost can be given a reasonably definite value.

In some cases it is not possible to arrive at a reasonable statement of the cost of being unable to fill an order. For example, the possible loss of customers, hence their sales, over a substantial period of time, sometimes estimable, may outweigh the cost of the direct loss in immediate business. In such cases it may be necessary to secure from the management a statement of a "reasonable" level of customer service, i.e., a statement of the degree of risk of running out of stock at a given time during the year which the management is willing to assume, as a matter of policy. In such cases the management can be aided in arriving at this estimate, since a given level of capital and production cost will be associated with a specified degree of customer-service protection. One function of a study of production or inventory control under these circumstances is to specify the cost, i.e., the insurance premium paid, of additional increments of customer-service protection.

CLERICAL COSTS

Clerical costs are one of the most difficult costs associated with production and inventory control to measure at the present time. Relatively little has been done in many companies to identify these costs clearly, to measure them, for example, by time-study or work-sampling methods, or to identify the work units or elements which generate clerical costs.

Clerical costs include such items as the cost of making out a requisition and placing an order, the cost of time of personnel required for scheduling, and the cost of periodic inventory reviews for reordering purposes. In the sections following, it will be noted that the level of production and capital cost in a given business situation can be reduced by more frequent or intensive scheduling or inventory review. For example, in some circumstances the amount of inventory carried in a warehouse is roughly proportional to the square root of the time between periodic inventory checks. It is therefore important to arrive at at least a rough determination of clerical costs to achieve a sound balance of production and capital cost against clerical detail.

That these costs can be isolated and measured has been demonstrated. Many companies have extended work measurement from the factory floor to include clerical labor. Studies in connection with the use of electronic internally programed data-handling systems have often required measurements of these functions.

Clerical costs connected with handling purchase orders, shipping requisitions, and manufacturing orders are usually particularly important but are frequently overlooked. Often, however, even when the costs have been identified and measured, they are still not reflected in scheduling decisions, like the choice of economical run lengths discussed in Chapter 4. One approach to measuring order-handling costs is to folow typical orders and requisitions through all the handling steps, noting the times required by individuals processing the item, supplies used, and direct costs incurred, such as telephone or postage. The time that individuals spend on handling orders may be estimated by watching to see how long it takes to process sample orders, by spot-checks to see how much of the time an individual is working on orders, or by counting to see how many orders each person handles in a day. Care is needed to be sure that order-handling time is distinguished from other duties the person may have and to see that fixed costs, such as machine rental, are properly accounted for. In some circumstances, the machines rented may be able to handle the conceivable maximum volume, and machine rental may be a fixed cost properly excluded. In other cases, machine rental may depend strongly on the volume handled.

Where clerical costs have not been measured by other means, statistical correlation methods like those described by Lyle[5] often can be used to get sufficiently accurate estimates. Where this approach is used, one must not be confused by large short-term fluctuations in the load of orders handled with no apparent change in cost. It is generally recognized that clerical

[5] Philip Lyle, *Regression Analysis of Production Costs and Factory Operations,* Oliver & Boyd, Ltd., London, 1946.

activities show an amazing capacity for absorbing load fluctuations. In two different days or weeks the load on the order-handling force may vary widely, by several hundred per cent. In both periods the orders may be handled by the same force in about the same time, and in both periods everyone will appear busy. This is deceptive, however; differences in clerical cost would show up if the load differences were sustained for any period. Normally, one wants to estimate the change in out-of-pocket cost resulting from a sustained change in order volume due, for example, to a change in inventory policy.

Estimates of clerical cost do not have to be precise to the last penny. The important points are that they be roughly correct and that they accurately reflect the types of out-of-pocket costs which would be affected.

Expediting cost is another type of clerical cost which is often extremely important. Many production systems which are either poorly designed or too loosely controlled require very extensive effort by expediters to push critical orders or materials through and to transmit scheduling policy and orders to operating people. In some job-shop plants, for example, very little paper-work control of production in process may be used. In such cases, however, there is often a substantial cost for expediting; this might be avoided by increasing expenditure on paper control, with a net saving.

DISCUSSION TOPICS AND EXERCISES

1. A *break-even point* in manufacturing operations is defined as the level of production at which the revenues on sales are precisely equal to the cost of manufacturing. It is the level of production below which losses are incurred and above which profits are made. Assuming a cost relationship such as that given in Eq. (3.1), what is the break-even point if on $5,000,000 of sales a profit of $600,000 is made when fixed costs were $2,000,000? What is the profit resulting from an additional $1,000 in sales?

2. In the manufacture of radio transceivers it is found that a learning effect similar to that described by Eq. (3.2) is experienced. Following the set-up for the manufacturing run, the first unit is produced in 25 hours. Assuming a learning parameter of 0.3, find:

   a. The total time required to produce the first 10 sets in a run
   b. The average time per unit when 10 sets are made in a run
   c. The per cent reduction in time required to make the tenth set relative to the first

3. The receivers in the preceding example are made to customer order. The price list shows a unit price for orders of one set. In view of the economies of manufacture due to learning, discuss how a discount on single orders for larger quantities could be granted to customers. What additional cost and other information would be needed to construct a proper price schedule?

BIBLIOGRAPHY

Dean, Joel: *Managerial Economics,* Prentice-Hall, Inc., Englewood Cliffs, N.J., 1951.

Heckert, J. Brooks, and Robert B. Miner: *Distribution Costs,* 2d ed., The Ronald Press Company, New York, 1953.

Hirschmann, Winfred B.: "Profit from the Learning Curve," *Harvard Business Review,* pp. 125–139, January-February, 1964.

Howell, James E., and Daniel Teichroew: *Mathematical Analysis for Business Decisions,* Richard D. Irwin, Inc., Homewood, Ill., 1963.

Levy, F. K.: "Adaption in the Production Process," *Management Science,* vol. 11, no. 6, pp. B–136–153, April, 1965.

Longman, Donald R., and Michael Shiff: *Practical Distribution Cost Analysis,* Richard D. Irwin, Homewood, Ill., 1955.

Lyle, Philip: *Regression Analysis of Production Costs and Factory Operations,* Oliver & Boyd Ltd., London, 1946.

Wright, Wilmer: *Direct Standard Costs for Decision Making and Control,* McGraw-Hill Book Company, New York, 1962.

4

ECONOMIC QUANTITIES OF MANUFACTURE OR PURCHASE

NATURE OF THE LOT-SIZE PROBLEM

Deciding how many of an item to buy or make for stock at one time is one of the most common and still frequently unresolved questions of inventory management that businessmen face. It happens also to be a question that has received continuing attention in the literature of inventory control ever since 1912, when the first full recognition of this problem first appeared.[1]

The lot-size problem arises, as mentioned earlier, because of the need to purchase or produce in quantities greater than will be used or sold at the moment. These purchases or manufactures create the inventories that permit the decoupling of vendors from distributors in a distribution system and of the successive states of production in a manufacturing process that was discussed in Chapter 2. Thus, specifically, businessmen buy raw materials in sizable quantities—carloads or even trainloads—in order to reduce the costs connected with purchasing and control, to obtain a favorable price, and to minimize handling and transportation costs. They replenish factory in-

[1] R. F. Mennell, "Early History of the Economic Lot Size," *APICS Quarterly Bulletin*, pp. 19–22, April, 1961. For an early discussion of this subject see Benjamin Cooper, "How to Determine Economical Manufacturing Quantities," *Industrial Management*, vol. 72, no. 4, pp. 228–233, 1926. The continued interest in this basic inventory problem is illustrated by W. E. Welch, "Economic Order Quantity Buying," *New York Purchasing Review*, p. 13, January, 1956.

process stocks of parts in sizable quantities to avoid, where possible, the costs of equipment setups and clerical routines. Likewise, finished stocks maintained in warehouses usually come in shipments substantially greater than the typical amount sold in one order, the motive again being, in part, to avoid equipment-setup and paper-work costs and, in the case of field warehouses, to minimize shipping costs.

Where the same equipment is used for a variety of items, the equipment will be devoted first to one item and then to another, in sequence, with the length of the run in any individual item to be chosen, as far as is economically possible, to minimize change-over cost from one item to another and to reduce the production time lost because of clean-out requirements during change-overs. "Blocked" operations of this sort are seen frequently, for example, in the petroleum industry, on packaging lines, or on assembly lines where change-over from one model to another may require adjustment in feed speeds and settings and change of components.

In all these cases the practice of replenishing stocks in sizable quantities compared with the typical usage quantity means that inventory has to be carried; it makes it possible to spread fixed costs (e.g., setup and clerical costs) over many units and thus to reduce the unit cost. However, one can carry this principle only so far, for if the replenishment orders become too large, the resulting inventories get out of line, and the capital and handling costs of carrying these inventories more than offset the possible savings in production, transportation, and clerical costs. Here is the matter, again, of striking a balance between these conflicting considerations.

NECESSITY OF QUANTITATIVE SOLUTION

Even though formulas for selecting the optimum lot size are presented in many industrial engineering texts,[2] few companies make any attempt to arrive at an explicit quantitative balance of inventory and change-over or setup cost. Why?

For one thing, the cost elements which enter into an explicit solution frequently are very difficult to measure or are only very hazily defined. For example, it may be possible to get a fairly accurate measure of the cost of setting up a particular machine, but it may be almost impossible to derive a precise measure of the cost of making out a new production order. Again,

[2] See, for example, Fairfield E. Raymond, *Quantity and Economy in Manufacture*, D. Van Nostrand Company, Inc., Princeton, N.J., 1931, and Franklin G. Moore, *Manufacturing Management*, 4th ed., Richard D. Irwin, Inc., Homewood, Ill., 1965.

warehouse costs may be accumulated separately on the accounting records, but these rarely show what the cost of housing an *additional* unit of material may be. It is generally true that the capital cost, or imputed interest cost, connected with inventory investment never appears on the company's accounting records.

Furthermore, the inventory is traditionally valued in such a way that the true incremental investment is difficult to measure for scheduling purposes. Oftentimes companies therefore attempt to strike only a qualitative balance of these costs to arrive at something like an optimum or minimum-cost reorder quantity.

Despite the difficulty in measuring costs—and indeed because of such difficulty—it is eminently worth while to look at the lot-size problem explicitly formulated. The value of an analytic solution does not rest solely on one's ability to plug in precise cost data to get an answer. An analytic solution often helps clarify questions of principle, even with only crude data available for use. Moreover, it appears that many companies today still have not accepted the philosophy of optimum reorder quantities from the over-all company standpoint; instead, decisions are dominated from the standpoint of some particular interest, such as production or traffic and transportation. Here, too, the analytic solution can be of help, even when the cost data are incomplete or imperfect.

ANALYTIC SOLUTION OF THE LOT-SIZE PROBLEM

Illustration

To illustrate how the lot-size problem can be attacked analytically—and what some of the problems and advantages of such an attack are—let us take a fictitious example. The situation is greatly oversimplified purposely to get quickly to the heart of the analytic approach.

Elements of the Problem. Brown & Brown, Inc., an automotive-parts supplier, produces a simple patented electric switch on long-term contracts. The covering is purchased on the outside at $0.01 each, and 1,000 are used regularly each day, 250 days per year.

The casings are made in a nearby plant, and B. & B. sends its own truck to pick them up. The cost of truck operation, maintenance, and the driver amounts to $10 per trip. The company can send the truck once a day to bring back 1,000 casings for that day's requirements, but this makes the cost of a casing rather high. The truck can go less frequently, but this means that it has to bring back more than the company needs for its immediate day-to-day purposes.

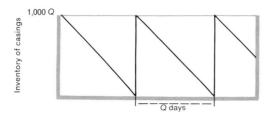

FIGURE 4.1   Pattern of inventory balance

The characteristic "saw-tooth" inventory pattern which will result is shown in Figure 4.1, where 1,000 Q casings are picked up each trip (Q being whatever number of days' supply is obtained per replenishment trip). These are used up over a period of Q days. When the inventory is depleted again, another trip is made to pick up Q days' supply, or 1,000 Q casings, once more, and so on.

B. & B. estimates that the cost of storing casings under properly controlled humidity conditions is $1 per 1,000 casings per year. The company wants to obtain a 10 per cent return on its inventory investment of $10 (1,000 times $0.01), which means that it should properly charge an additional $1 (10 per cent of $10), making a total inventory or carrying cost of $2 per 1,000 casings per year.

(Note that, in order to avoid undue complications, the inventory investment charge is made here only against the purchase price of the casings and not against the total delivery cost including transportation. Where transportation is a major component of total cost, it is of course possible and desirable to include it in the base for the inventory charge.)

Table 4.1 shows the variation of total annual cost of buying, storing, and

TABLE 4.1   Annual costs, various quantities

Quantity per trip	Annual acquisition cost delivery @ $10	Annual carrying cost @ $2 per 1,000 average inventory	Total annual cost
1,000	25.0 trips or $2,500	500 or $1	$2,501.00
10,000	2.5 trips or $250	5,000 or $10	260.00
100,000	2.5 trips or $25	50,000 or $100	125.00
1,000,000	0.25 trips or $2.50	500,000 or $1,000	1,002.50

moving (inventory plus acquisition cost) to Brown & Brown, Inc., with the quantity purchased. If 1,000 casings are purchased at a time, 250 trips will be made during the year, and the annual acquisition costs will be $2,500. Since the initial stock is 1,000 and the stock at the time of replenishment is zero, the average inventory will be 500 casings and the carrying cost will be $1. Hence, total annual cost for purchases of 1,000 is $2,501. As the quantity purchased per trip is increased, the annual acquisition cost decreases and the carrying cost increases. In Table 4.1, the last column shows the variation in total cost, suggesting that for some order quantity there is a minimum total cost. The variation of each of these costs is shown graphically in Figure 4.2. The total-cost curve shown in the solid line has a minimum at an order quantity of 50,000 casings per trip, requiring five trips per year. In this instance, the total trucking (or acquisition) cost and the total inventory and storage cost (carrying cost) are equal. Each is $50 per year and the total annual cost to Brown & Brown, Inc., is $100.

The economic lot size can be found without laborious tabulation and graphing. It can be shown,[3] in fact, that the minimum-cost order quantity under these assumptions can be expressed in mathematical terms as

$$x = \sqrt{\frac{2As}{i}}$$

[3] See Appendix A for a derivation of minimum-cost order-size formulas under various assumptions.

FIGURE 4.2   Annual cost of buying, moving, and storing casings compared with reorder quantity

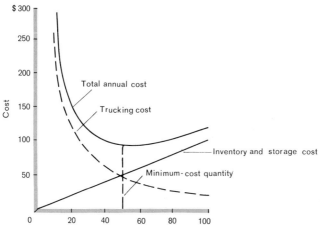

where x = quantity to be obtained on each order

   A = cost of placing or getting an order—e.g., the trucking cost in the B. & B. example

   s = annual usage in units

   i = annual cost of holding one unit in stock one year

In the B. & B. case, for example, the applicable values where A = \$10 per trip, s = 250,000 casings per year, and i = \$2 per 1,000 casings per year give

$$x = \sqrt{\frac{2 \cdot \$10 \text{ @ } 250,000/\text{year}}{\$2/1,000\text{-year}}}$$

$$= \sqrt{2.5 \times 10^9} = 50,000 \text{ casings per order}$$

Similarly, the minimum total annual cost is shown to be

$$C = \sqrt{2A \, si}$$
$$= \sqrt{2 \cdot \$10 \cdot 250,000/\text{year} \cdot \$2/1,000\text{-year}}$$
$$= \sqrt{10,000 \, (\$/\text{year})^2}$$
$$= \$100/\text{year}$$

Adjustments for changes in units

It is important to note the consistency of the dimensions in the above calculations. Sometimes other units of measurement are more convenient. For example, it may be more convenient:

1. To express usage in monthly rates
2. To express usage in terms of dollar value
3. To express inventory carrying cost as a ratio of value (e.g., inventory holding cost per year equal to 20 per cent or a fraction .20 of value)
4. To express the order quantity in dollars

It is important to be sure that the units used in the formula are consistent. The basic principles are:

1. The order quantity should be expressed in the same units as the usage rate, i.e., both in physical units or both in dollar units.
2. The usage rate and inventory cost should be based on the same time and material units. If usage is expressed on an annual basis, the inventory cost should be the cost of holding a unit 1 year. If monthly usage is used, the inventory cost should be the cost of holding 1 month. If usage is expressed in physical units, the inventory cost should be the inventory cost per physical unit. If usage is expressed in dollars, the inventory cost should be the cost per dollar in inventory.

For example, suppose it is more convenient to express the usage rate in physical units per month m, and the inventory cost i as a cost of holding a unit 1 year. Since the monthly measure of usage and annual measure of inventory cost are inconsistent, we must adjust one or the other in the formula. Either usage must be expressed as an annual rate equal to $12m$, or inventory cost must be expressed on a monthly basis equal to $i/12$. In either case the formula for the order quantity x would be

$$x = \sqrt{\frac{2A \cdot 12m}{i}} = \sqrt{\frac{2Am}{i/12}}$$

$$= \sqrt{\frac{24Am}{i}}$$

If it were convenient to express the usage rate in physical units per month and the inventory cost as an annual cost per dollar of value in inventory, r, these are clearly inconsistent. One way of adjusting would be to convert the inventory cost into a cost per physical unit by multiplying the cost rate by the value per unit, v: $i = rv$. Then the order quantity x would be given by

$$x = \sqrt{\frac{2A \cdot 12m}{rv}} = \sqrt{\frac{24Am}{rv}}$$

Another way would be to express usage as annual usage in dollars: $s = 12M \cdot v$, giving

$$x = \sqrt{\frac{24Amv}{r}}$$

Note, however, that in this case the order quantity x would be the *dollar* amount to purchase, since usage is expressed in dollar units.

Practical implementation of order-quantity calculations

The problem of Brown & Brown, Inc., though artificial, is not too far removed from the questions many businesses face every day in fixing re-order quantities.

Despite the simplifications introduced—e.g., the assumption that usage is known in advance—the method of solution has been found widely useful in industries ranging from mail-order merchandising (replenishing staple lines), through electrical equipment manufacturing (ordering machined parts to replenish stockrooms), to shoe manufacturing (ordering findings and other purchased supplies). In particular, the approach has been found helpful in controlling stocks made up of many low-value items used regularly in large quantities.

There are a variety of ways in which firms can use this approach to set economical purchase or manufacturing quantities, and there are a variety of short-cut techniques for calculating order quantities on individual items. Those concerned with the calculation of order quantities for the firm can use ordering tables, nomograms, slide rules, or charts for such purposes, and it is possible very rapidly to run off a long series of such calculations on desk calculators or electronic computers programed with a simple subroutine for such calculations. The mechanical and electronic computer methods are particularly useful for the firms interested in frequent revision of order quantities for a large number of items.

ORDERING TABLES

Where a large number of items are being ordered, it is not necessary to compute the order quantity individually for each item or order. Sometimes ordering tables can be used to short-cut the work of computing minimum-cost order quantities. Such tables incorporating various inventory charges and ordering costs can be readily computed by hand or mechanically and used as a reference, to look up order quantities for individual items.

For example, in warehouses handling a variety of purchased items, the cost of writing and issuing a purchase order may be fixed, and the annual unit inventory and storage cost of any item may be expressible as a constant percentage or fraction of the unit purchase price. To illustrate the use of ordering tables, suppose we are operating a warehouse and have estimated the ordering and inventory costs to be:

Ordering cost, $A = \$7$ per order placed
Annual inventory cost $= 20$ per cent, or .20 times the unit cost

If order quantities x are to be calculated in dollars from monthly usage rates in dollars m, the order-quantity formula can be written

$$x = \sqrt{\frac{24 \cdot \$7 \cdot m}{.20}} = \sqrt{840m}$$

or

$$x = 28.98\sqrt{m}$$

A table such as Table 4.2 can then be drawn up. This can be used to determine the order quantity for any item to which the ratio of ordering cost A to inventory cost i applies, once the monthly usage is determined.[4]

[4] The problem of determining usage rates is discussed in Chap. 5.

TABLE 4.2 Ordering-cost table

$$(A/i = 35.00; \ \sqrt{24A/i} = 28.98)$$

Monthly usage	Order amount	Monthly usage	Order amount
$ 1	$ 29	$ 500	$ 650
2	41	750	794
5	65	1,000	920
10	92	2,000	1,300
20	130	5,000	2,050
50	205	7,500	2,510
75	251	10,000	2,900
100	290	20,000	4,100
200	410	50,000	6,500

Where a single ordering table is appropriate, some companies have the table printed in semipermanent form, e.g., on stiff paper, for referral by inventory clerks. In other cases, the table may be printed on the back of the inventory ledger card on each item for ready reference.

In using such tables to reorder manufactured items, one must use care to be sure that the inventory charge is based only on that portion of standard cost affected by inventory-control policy[5] and that, where appropriate, the effect of production rate on order size, as described above, is accounted for.

The use of ordering tables is not restricted to circumstances where the same values of ordering cost A and inventory carrying cost i apply to all items. The minimum-cost order-quantity formula

$$x = \sqrt{\frac{2As}{i}}$$

can be written as

$$x = \sqrt{\frac{2A}{i}} \cdot \sqrt{s}$$

A series of ordering tables can be drawn up, each appropriate for some ratio of ordering cost A to inventory cost i. The values of A, i, and $2A/i$ appropriate to each item can be entered on the inventory ledger card for the item. Then when an order is to be placed, the inventory clerk can refer to the order table for that value of $\sqrt{2A/i}$.

Figure 4.3 illustrates how this can be done using a simplified ledger card. The use rate, the value of the inventory cost i, and the ratio A/i can be

[5] See Chap. 3.

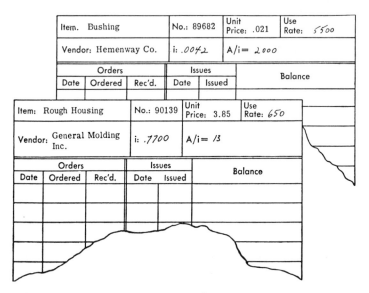

FIGURE 4.3 Ledger cards with posted A/i

inserted in erasable form. Then as the use rate is checked periodically, or as occasional changes in the rate charged against capital cause changes in i or A/i, the entries can be revised.

ORDERING CHARTS

Instead of using ordering tables, it is sometimes more convenient to use ordering charts, such as shown in Figure 4.4. This summarizes in a single chart the information on a series of ordering tables. To illustrate its use, we can use the two parts listed on the ledger cards in Figure 4.3.

1. Part 89682: The usage rate is 5,500, and the value of A/i is 2,000. The topmost line is for a value of A/i equal to 2,048, just higher than that which applies to this part but close enough for practical purposes. Reading from 5,500 on the horizontal scale to the top line and then across to the vertical scale, we find an indicated order quantity of 4,800.
2. Part 90139: The usage rate is 650. The value of A/i shown is 13, which indicates a value between that indicated by the line for $A/i = 8$ and $A/i = 32$, but close to the former. Reading from 650 on the horizontal scale to slightly above the line for $A/i = 8$, and across to the vertical scale, we find an indicated order quantity of about 130 units.

Ordering charts such as Figure 4.4 can be constructed readily, using log-log scale graph paper. Some companies find it useful to print these on the back of inventory records or requisition forms for ready reference; in other cases, a reference graph available to the inventory clerk works well.

The equivalent of ordering tables can be introduced into mechanized punched-card inventory systems in the form of a prepunched card deck. Often, especially where an internally programed computer is used, it is easier to compute the indicated order quantity directly, using the reorder formula. The data applicable to each inventory item—such as usage rate ordering cost, and inventory cost—can be carried as a part of the item record.

FIGURE 4.4   Ordering chart

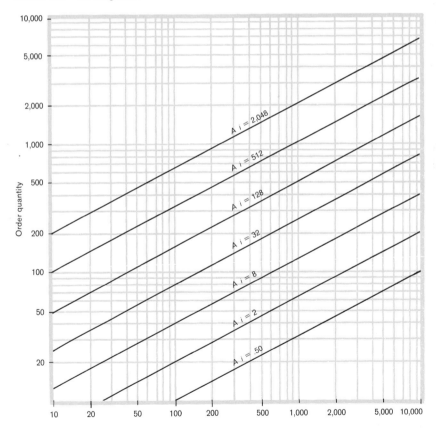

NOMOGRAMS

Nomograms are another useful type of computing aid to fixing reorder quantities in manual-control systems. A number of excellent books have been written on the theory and construction of nomograms.[6] The basic nomogram for order quantity calculations is illustrated in Figure 4.5.

[6] See, for example, A. S. Levens, *Nomography*, John Wiley & Sons, Inc., New York, 1948. The construction and use of simple nomograms in reorder calculation is discussed in detail in W. E. Welch, *Tested Scientific Inventory Control*, chap. VI, Management Publishing Corp., Greenwich, Conn., 1956.

FIGURE 4.5   Ordering nomogram

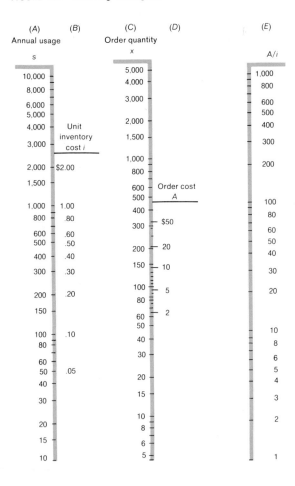

To use the nomogram to compute the order quantity, lay a straightedge along the line joining the appropriate values of inventory cost i (scale B) and order cost A (scale D), and make the point where this line intersects scale E. Then lay a straightedge through the point marked on scale E and the appropriate figure for usage rate s (scale A). The point on scale C where this second line intersects is the quantity to order. For example, suppose we want to compute the order quantity where

Inventory cost $i = \$.10$ per unit per year
Ordering cost $A = \$8$ per order
Annual usage $s = 3,000$ units per year

First we put a straightedge from .10 on scale B through 8.00 on scale D; this intersects scale E at the value 80.0. Next we connect the point 80.0 on scale E with the value 3,000 on scale A; this line intersects the order-quantity scale, C, just below 700, say at 690. The indicated order quantity, then, is about 690 units.

SENSITIVITY TO ERROR

The use of ordering charts, tables, nomograms, and other computation simplification devices for the routine calculation of order quantities will, in general, produce order quantities not noticeably different from optimal. For one thing, the round-off and reading errors in such devices can be made small; for another, the total cost function is not particularly sensitive to variations in lot size.[7] The total-cost curve of Figure 4.2 is typically relatively flat near the minimum-cost point. If, because of inaccuracies and errors, we have selected an order quantity x which is $(1 + a)$ times the true order quantity x_0, the resultant total annual cost C will be $1 + [a^2/2 \ (1 + a)]$ times the minimum cost C_0. Specifically, if an error is made which leads to an order quantity which is 40 per cent larger than the optimum, the effect on cost is, for $a = 0.4$,

$$1 + \frac{a^2}{2(1 + a)} = 1 + \frac{0.16}{2(1.4)} = 1 + \frac{0.16}{2.8} = 1.057$$

Hence, costs would be approximately 6 per cent higher than optimal.

[7] Joel Levy, "Loss Resulting from the Use of Incorrect Data in Computing an Optimal Inventory Policy," *Naval Research Logistics Quarterly*, vol. 5, no. 1, pp. 72–82, March, 1958.

LOT-SIZE CALCULATIONS FOR SPECIAL CASES

The Brown & Brown, Inc., example illustrates a somewhat idealized, but nonetheless frequently encountered, situation in which the withdrawal rate is reasonably constant over time, the replenishment is instantaneous, and the quantity ordered does not affect other costs and operations. Sometimes it is necessary to modify the results illustrated in the Brown & Brown, Inc., problem to account for extra handling costs of quantity discounts. At times, care must be taken to avoid pitfalls, for example, where total setup time in a department producing against economical-quantity orders may eat too deeply into available production time. Some of these cases are illustrated below.

Finite production rates in manufacturing runs

In determining the size of a manufacturing run (as contrasted with an order for purchase), it may be important to account explicitly for the fact that the item is produced over a period of time. For example, suppose the orders for some particular item over the course of a year will absorb a fair fraction of the total capacity of the equipment used to produce the item. Then when an order is placed and goes into production, the material produced may not arrive in inventory in one batch but in small quantities over the course of some time. In this case the inventory-balance pattern looks like Figure 4.6 instead of the saw-tooth pattern in Figure 4.1.

To illustrate, suppose Brown & Brown, Inc., instead of buying its casings outside, made them on a machine capable of turning out 3,000 a day. If a production order for 50,000 casings were written, it would take nearly 17 days to fill the order. If the order were put into production when the stock of casings on hand was fully depleted and if casing requirements were filled

FIGURE 4.6 Influence of production and sales rate on production-cycle inventory

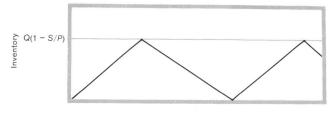

from current production, the total inventory at the end of the production run would not be 50,000 casings but 50,000 minus 17,000, or about 33,000 casings. The average inventory would be half this, or about 16,500 casings.

In general, if the amount ordered is Q units, if these are used at the rate of s units per day, and if p units are made each day of the production run, then:

1. The maximum inventory will be $Q(1 - s/p)$ units.
2. The average inventory will be $Q/2(1 - s/p)$ units.

Repeating the graphical analysis of Figure 4.2 using the same cost factors (thinking of the $10 fixed cost per order as a production setup rather than trucking cost) will show that the minimum-cost quantity would be 61,000 units per order. Note that since the annual inventory cost associated with any order quantity is only two-thirds the level of the previous example, this results in the larger minimum-cost order amount.

The mathematical expression for the minimum-cost order quantity, taking the production rate into account, is[8]

$$x = \sqrt{\frac{2As}{i(1 - s/p)}}$$

where s = rate of usage or sale
p = rate of production

Production cycled among several products

When a number of products are to be made on a regular cycle, one after another, on the same unit of equipment, the cycle length can be established in much the same way as described above. Usually in such cases the sequence of products in the cycle is determined by economy in change-over cost, depending on the equipment or product characteristics. For example, in paper making it is normally very desirable to go from fine to coarser grades on the same paper-making machine. The sequence may depend on going from lighter to darker colors in a dyeing operation, or on going through a regular sequence of carton or bottle sizes in a bottling operation.

Two points are worth keeping in mind: first, that the usage and production rates for all products in the sequence be expressed in common units and, second, that the cycle length for all products be set simultaneously. The most convenient unit is frequently *hours of production;* i.e., sales of each product in the sequence are expressed as a number of hours of production

[8] See Appendix A for mathematical derivation.

sold, e.g., per month or per year. Then, of course, the production rate is the same for all products—1 "hour" of product made each hour of operation on that product. The total cycle length—the time to go through the whole sequence—has to be set first, simply because an attempt to set order or run quantities on each product independently is almost sure to lead to incompatible run lengths—one product in the sequence supposed to be made three times a month and another twice, etc.

The basic approach to setting an economical cycle length is the same as in the case of one product: to find the cycle length or number of cycles per month or year which make the total of setup or change-over costs and inventory costs a minimum. The change-over costs increase with more cycles in a given period, while inventory costs tend to fall, since each batch, and thus the average inventory of all products, is smaller the more frequent the cycles. The resulting formula for total cycle length is very similar to that for the one-product situation.

When dealing with many products, it is somewhat easier to start with the total number of cycles per time period and work from there to the individual product run length. In the case of one product, the *frequency* of orders or runs n can be readily obtained from the length of individual runs x and the usage per unit of time, since

$$n = \frac{s}{x}$$

$$= \frac{s}{\sqrt{\dfrac{2As}{i(1 - s/p)}}}$$

$$= \sqrt{\frac{si(1 - s/p)}{2A}}$$

When a number of products are involved, the formula for the total number, n, of cycles (a cycle being one run through all *products*) is[9]

$$n = \sqrt{\frac{\displaystyle\sum_j s_j i_j (1 - s_j/p_j)}{2A}}$$

where s_j = usage or sales rate for each of the individual products
i_j = unit inventory cost for each of the products
p_j = production rate for each of the products
A = total setup or change-over cost for one cycle

The length of one run on an individual product x_j equals s_j/n.

[9] See Appendix A for derivation.

TABLE 4.3 Sales, rate of production, inventory, and change-over costs

Product	Sales/year	Production/day	Inventory cost/year/unit	Change-over cost
1	40,000	800	$0.010	$ 8.00
2	55,000	1,100	0.015	11.00
3	20,000	800	0.008	18.00
4	90,000	1,200	0.022	10.00
5	35,000	1,000	0.005	7.40

To illustrate, suppose we want to work out the cycle length on the group of products in Table 4.3. Expressing both sales rates and production rates for all products in common units—days of production per year—gives us Table 4.4. The production rate in the new unit is now the same for all products, since it takes the same time—one day—to produce a unit of any product. Note that the inventory cost per year is also expressed per "day of production." Carrying through the calculation of the formula given above results in Table 4.5. The minimum-cost operation is, therefore, to make five runs per year, each run lasting 47 days, producing one-fifth of the sales requirements each run.

VARIATIONS IN THE REGULAR CYCLE

Sometimes it may be desirable to consider variations in the regular cycle; e.g., one product might not be made every cycle if its sales rate were low and setup cost high. There is no simple way of arriving at the best cycle variation of this sort other than by trial. One rule of thumb can be applied, using the numbers in the last two columns, (4) and (5), of Table 4.5. If

TABLE 4.4 Sales, rate of production, inventory, and change-over costs as days of production per year (five products)

Product	s_j: Sales rate	p_j: Production rate	Inventory cost/year/unit	Change-over cost
1	50	250	$ 8.00	$ 8.00
2	50	250	16.50	11.00
3	25	250	6.40	18.00
4	75	250	26.40	10.00
5	35	250	5.00	7.40
	235			$54.40

TABLE 4.5 Determination of length of production cycle (five products)

Product	s_i/p_i (1)	$1 - s_i/p_i$ (2)	$s_i i_i$ (3)	$s_i i_i (1 - s_i/p_i)$ (4) = (2) × (3)	Setup: A (5)
1	.20	.80	400	320	8.00
2	.20	.80	825	660	11.00
3	.10	.90	160	144	18.00
4	.30	.70	1,980	1,386	10.00
5	.14	.86	175	151	7.40
				2,661	54.40

$$\frac{2661}{2 \times 54.40} = 24.5 \qquad \sqrt{24.5} = 5 \text{ cycles/year}$$

each type of product were being made independently, the minimum-cost number of cycles would be as shown in Table 4.6. If the value in column (6), the minimum-cost number of runs for the product alone, for any one or more products is less than half the value for all products, the product is a possible candidate for only occasional runs. For example, product 3, if made by itself, would be run only twice yearly, compared with five runs yearly for all products combined. Product 3 might then be made only occasionally, i.e., on every second or third cycle. If product 3 were eliminated from the group, the number of cycles for the remaining four products would be as shown in Table 4.7. If product 3 is excluded, the other four products would be made about six times a year, and product 3 by itself would be made twice yearly. Therefore a cycling which allowed for making product 3 on only one out of every three cycles appears feasible; i.e., the sequence of products made would run: 1–2–4–5–1–2–4–5–1–2–3–4–5.

TABLE 4.6 Minimum-cost number of runs (five products)

Product	From Table 4.5 (4)	From Table 4.5 (5)	(6) = $\dfrac{(4)}{2 \times (5)}$	Minimum cost number of runs $\sqrt{(6)}$
1	320	8.00	20	4.5
2	660	11.00	30	5.5
3	144	18.00	4	2
4	1,386	10.00	69.3	8.3
5	151	7.40	20.4	4.5
	2,661	54.40	24.5	5

TABLE 4.7 Minimum-cost number of runs (four products with highest usage rates)

	(4)	(5)	(6)	$\sqrt{(6)}$
All products	2,661	54.40		
Product 3	144	18.00		
Products 1, 2, 4, 5 combined	2,517	36.40	34.6	5.9

How much would this save? First, the total sales of products 1, 2, 4, and 5 equal 210 production days. If these were made in about six runs of equal length, each run would be 35 days long, with ideally a little less than 7 days between runs. If the individual runs of product 3 each took about 6 days, there would be no difficulty. Each run of product 3 could be fitted in between cycles of the other products without trouble. But product 3 calls for 25 days of production a year, now to be made in two runs of 12.5 days each. A run of product 3 will not fit between two cycles of the other four products without moving back the preceding cycle about 6 days. Ideally, products 1, 2, 4, and 5 would be sequenced as follows:

Time (days):	35	7	35	7	35	7	35	7	35...
Operation:	Prod. 4–5–1–2	Idle	4–5–1–2	Idle	4–5–1–2	Idle	4–5–1–2	Idle	4–5–1–...

However, because of the need for time to make product 3, the sequencing has to be:

Time (days):	35	7	35	1	35	12.5	35	7	35...
Operation:	Prod. 4–5–1–2	Idle	4–5–1–2	Idle	4–5–1–2	3	4–5–1–2	Idle	4–5–1–...

In effect, every third cycle—twice yearly—a full cycle of products 1, 2, 3, 4 has to be moved ahead 6 days. This amounts to carrying an unneeded full run of these products 6 days twice a year, or 12 out of the 250 days. Calculation will show that the resulting extra inventory carrying cost is $20. This is to be offset by savings in other costs. A comparison of costs under the original—full sequence—and proposed variation is shown in Table 4.8. The

TABLE 4.8   Cost comparison—full sequence versus varied cycle length

	Full sequence		Variation	
Setup costs	(5 × $54.40)	$272	(6 × $36.40)	$218
			(2 × $18.00)	36
Cycle inventory costs		272		254
Extra inventory cost				20
Total		$544		$528

proposed variation of making product 3 on only every third cycle does offer some modest economies.

Quantity discounts

The minimum-cost reorder formulas described earlier are based on the assumption that the unit purchase price is fixed. However, where quantity discounts are allowed, i.e., where lower unit prices apply to orders above fixed limits, a decision has to be made whether to buy the minimum-cost quantity at one price level or increase the order size to the minimum size for some lower unit price to take advantage of the price reduction. This question arises in any situation in which price is directly or indirectly affected by the quantity purchased. Indirect discounts are offered in a variety of forms. Freight allowances, free goods, extensions of credit, or other services have an equivalent cash value which can be expressed as a discount on the price paid for the quantity ordered.

EXAMPLES

To illustrate the basic problem, suppose a company buys 2,500 units of an item per year, using Table 4.9. Suppose the basic unit cost is $1, but discounts are given of 5 per cent for orders of 1,000 to 1,999 and 7 per cent (net) for orders of 2,000 or more. According to Table 4.9, the order quantity for $2,500 annual rate of usage is $500 (i.e., 500 units). If 1,000 units are purchased per order,

1. The company saves:

5 − 2.5 = 2.5 orders/year @ $10	=	$ 25
2,500 units @ $0.05 discount	=	125
		$150

TABLE 4.9 Specimen reordering table

Annual usage rate ($ at cost)	Order quantity (Annual unit inventory cost, $i = 20\%$ of price/year Ordering cost, $A = \$10$ per order placed)
$ 25	$ 50
50	70
100	100
250	160
500	225
1,000	315
2,500	500
5,000	710
10,000	1,000
25,000	1,580
50,000	2,240
100,000	3,160

2. The company incurs extra inventory costs[10] of

$$1,000/2 \times \$0.95 - 500/2 \times \$1 = \$225 @ 20\% = \underline{45}$$
Net saving $\$105$

Thus the company should buy at the additional discount price.

RULES OF THUMB

One quick method that has been suggested[11] for deciding on purchase discounts is as follows: The company can afford to take advantage of the price discount if the percentage price discount is more than the percentage increase in costs due to inventory charges. The inventory charge of 20 per cent per year equals 1.67 per cent per month. Taking advantage of the first price break increases the order by 500 units and the average inventory by 250 units, or 1.2 months' added supply. The increased inventory-cost percentage is 1.2 months $\times$ 1.67 per cent per month, or 2 per cent, compared with a percentage saving of 5 per cent. The company should buy at the discount. However, the second discount requires an added increase in inventory of 500 units, or 2.4 months' supply. Increased inventory cost of 2.4

[10] The inventory-cost differences are calculated on the assumption that inventory charge is based on value, e.g., capital charges, obsolescence risk, insurance, etc.
[11] Welch, *op. cit.*

months × 1.67 per cent, or 4 per cent, is not offset by the extra 2 per cent price discount. The company should not buy at this price. This scheme does not account for the reduction in order cost which results.

Whitin[12] cites a method devised by R. H. Wilson for handling quantity-discount decisions. This is essentially similar to Table 4.10, which is based

TABLE 4.10   Ordering-cost table

Inventory cost = 20% of unit price per year; ordering cost = $10

Annual usage	Order size								
	$100	$150	$200	$300	$500	$700	$1,000	$1,500	$2,000
$ 100	$120.00	$121.67	$125.00	$133.33	$152.00	$171.43	$201.00	$250.67	$300.50
250	114.00	112.67	113.00	115.33	122.00	129.43	141.00	160.67	180.50
500	112.00	109.67	109.00	109.33	112.00	115.43	121.00	130.67	140.50
1,000	111.00	108.17	107.00	106.33	107.00	108.43	111.00	115.67	120.50
2,500	110.40	107.27	105.80	104.53	104.00	104.23	105.00	106.67	108.50
5,000	110.20	106.97	105.40	103.93	103.00	102.83	103.00	103.67	104.50
10,000	110.10	106.82	105.20	103.63	102.50	102.13	102.00	102.17	102.50
25,000	110.04	106.73	105.08	103.45	102.20	101.71	101.40	101.27	101.30

on an order cost of $10 and an inventory cost of 20 per cent of unit purchase price per year. The entries in the table are the total costs (including price, order cost, and inventory cost) per $100 purchased. To illustrate the calculation, using the entry for $1,000 annual usage and $200 order size,

Purchase price   = $1,000
Order cost: $1,000/$200 = 5 orders @ $10   =   50
Inventory cost: $200/2 = $100 avg. inv. @ 20% =   20
                                                                                      $1,070

                        or $107/$100 purchased

To find the order size nearest the minimum-cost order size, for any rate of annual usage, read across the row in Table 4.10 corresponding to the rate of annual usage to find the column with the lowest entry. For example, if the annual usage rate is $2,500, the lowest cost shown is $104, at the order size of $500. This corresponds with the order size shown in Table 4.9.

Now, to test the value of a price discount (using the previous example of a 5 per cent discount on orders of $1,000 or more), the minimum order that must be placed to get the discount is $1,000. If we look in the column headed "Order size: $1,000" and in the row headed "Annual usage: $2,500,"

[12] Thomson M. Whitin, *The Theory of Inventory Management,* Princeton University Press, Princeton, N.J., 1953, p. 36.

we find an annual total cost of $105 per $100 purchased. This reduces the total cost to $99.95. Since this is less than the cost of $104 if the economical-order quantity at full price were purchased, it is worth while to take advantage of the 5 per cent discount. The net saving is $4 per $100 purchased, or $101.25 per year.

But is the additional 2 per cent discount allowed on orders of $2,000 or more worth while? Under the order size of $2,000 and opposite annual usage of $2,500, we find the total cost (at full price) is $108.50 per $100 purchased. This order amount is enough to earn the full net discount of 7 per cent, or $7 per $100 purchased. This reduces the total cost to $101.50. Since this net total cost when orders of $2,000 are placed is higher than net total cost when orders of $1,000 are placed—$100—the additional 2 per cent discount is not worth while.

Where the price is quoted as a fixed charge, e.g., for tooling, setup, etc., plus a price per unit purchased, this is sometimes looked at as a price discount. However, it can be handled directly as follows: Add the fixed (e.g., tooling) cost to the cost of placing the order to get a total fixed cost per order, and use the (direct or variable) price per unit to determine the usage rate.

SHIPPING COSTS AS DISCOUNTS

Methods for deciding on price discounts can also be used to decide among alternative shipping methods, e.g., truckload, less than truckload, carload, etc., where choice of method affects transportation cost. To illustrate, suppose we plan to use 30 tons per year of a raw material which can be purchased f.o.b. mill for $30 per ton. The total annual purchase cost is $900. This material can be moved to our plant at a cost of $5 per ton in quantities over 30 tons or at $7 per ton in smaller quantities. The cost of placing an order is $10, and the unit inventory holding cost, on an annual basis, is estimated to be 20 per cent of the purchase price. Thus we can use ordering-cost Table 4.10.

Since estimated annual usage in dollars is close to $1,000, we can use this row of the table as a good approximation. This row shows that the total cost is minimum when the material is purchased in $300 lots, or lots of 10 tons. This is not a large enough quantity to merit the lower freight cost.

The lower freight cost amounts to $2 per ton, or $6.66 per $100 worth of material purchased. To obtain the lower freight cost, we must order in 30-ton lots costing $900 or more. Looking across the $1,000 annual usage row, we find the annual total cost would fall somewhere between $108.43 and $111.00 per $100 worth of material purchased. We must subtract the freight saving of $6.66, giving a net delivered cost between $101.77 and

$104.34. This is lower than the total cost of $106.33 when $300 lots are purchased. It appears desirable, therefore, to buy the material in 30-ton lots, the net saving being about $20 to $30 annually.

DIRECT CALCULATION

The order quantity can be directly calculated if a discount schedule of prices versus quantity is known. Let us suppose that the unit price for a purchased item is stated as follows:

Less than 1 dozen	0% discount	$1.00 unit price
1–5 dozen	15% discount	$0.85 unit price
5–12 dozen	25% discount	$0.75 unit price
12 dozen and over	40% discount	$0.60 unit price

If we know in addition that usage of this item is 60 per year, that the order cost is $2.50 per order, and that the total cost to carry inventory is $0.25 per dollar per year, then our total costs of goods, ordering, and inventory storage are as shown in Table 4.11. To find the order quantity for which the total annual cost is a minimum, the procedure is as follows:

1. Find the economic lot size (as in pages 55–65) using the minimum unit price. It is a valid minimum-cost order quantity *if* it falls within the quantity range for which it is calculated.
2. If it does not fall in the proper range, find the total cost for each price-break quantity.

TABLE 4.11 Total annual costs

Quantity per order	Goods	Ordering	Inventory	Total
6	$60	$25	$ 0.75	$85.75
10	60	15	1.25	76.25
12	51	12	1.27	64.77
24	51	6.25	2.54	59.79
40	51	3.75	3.75	58.50
48	51	3.13	5.08	59.21
60	45	2.50	5.62	52.12
120	45	1.25	11.24	57.49
144	36	1.04	10.80	47.84
200	36	0.75	15.00	51.75

3. Calculate the minimum-cost order quantity (as in pages 55–65) for each unit price. Calculate the total cost for each valid lot size, that is, each lot size that falls within the quantity range for which it was calculated.
4. The valid lot size of lowest total cost is the minimum-cost order quantity.

Applying this stepwise procedure to our example:

Step 1.

Lot size at minimum price ($0.60) $= \sqrt{\dfrac{2 \times 2.50 \times 60}{0.25 \times 0.60}} = 45$

This is not a valid lot size since according to the price schedule we cannot order 45 units at $0.60 per unit.

Step 2.

Price-break quantity	12	60	144
Total cost	$64.77	$52.12	$47.84

Step 3.

Unit cost	$1.00	$0.85	$0.75	$0.60
Lot size	35	38	40	45
Valid?	No	Yes	No	No

As in step 1, the lot sizes for all unit prices except $0.85 are not valid because they cannot be purchased at those unit prices.

Step 4.

Repeating the total cost calculation shown in Table 4.9 for an order quantity of 38, the annual total for this order quantity is:

$C = \$51.00 + \$3.95 + \$4.04 = \$58.99$

Conclusion: Purchase of quantities of 144 (step 2) results in a lower total annual cost than the purchase of 38. Order quantities of 144.

EFFECT OF CAPACITY ON RUN LENGTH

Where change-over of manufacturing equipment takes a significant amount of time, it may not be possible to change equipment as frequently as consideration of setup cost and inventory charges would indicate. The load on the equipment, compared with capacity, may limit the time available for change-over. The extra inventories that must be carried because of longer-than-economical runs result in a cost chargeable to high capacity utilization. Where a number of alternative sources exist, as in multiple-plant operations, demand is sometimes allocated purely on the basis of transportation rates without regard for the effect of a high load on operating flexibility and inventory costs. It must be borne in mind that the firm's objective is the minimization of the *total* of manufacturing and distribution costs, not just of any one of these. The unrestrained optimization of any component cost can lead to serious diseconomies. An economical distribution of load, taking account of transportation as well as inventory costs, may often call for shifting demand to a plant with higher transportation or direct operating costs in order to reduce the load on a plant with lower direct costs, to give it greater flexibility and to cut inventory requirements and costs. The marginal costs used in transportation analyses should include the effect on inventory costs resulting from changes in load.[13]

COST FACTORS USED

The cost factors used in the computation of ordering quantities should be determined in a manner consistent with the concepts outlined in Chapter 3. In particular, ordering and inventory carrying cost estimates should be based on out-of-pocket or foregone opportunities costs, not necessarily full accounting costs. On the other hand, it is important to be sure that the ordering cost estimates used, e.g., in determining manufacturing-run quantities, include both machine setup or change costs and costs of making up and handling the necessary paper work.

GENERAL CONCLUSIONS

Analysis of inventories associated with order or batch quantities reveals certain relationships significant and useful to executives concerned with inventory management.

1. *The appropriate order quantity and the average inventory maintained do not vary directly with sales.* In fact, both of these quantities vary with the square root of sales. This means that with the same ordering and setup cost characteristics, the larger the volume of sales of an item, the less inventory per unit of sales is required. One of the sources of inefficiency in many inventory-control systems is the rigid adoption of a rule for ordering or carrying inventory equivalent to, say, one month's sales.

2. *The total cost in the neighborhood of the optimum-order quantity is rela-*

[13] See Appendix A for a more detailed discussion of the relation between load and marginal cost.

tively insensitive to moderately small changes in the amount ordered.
Figure 4.2 illustrates this proposition. Thus all that is needed is just to
get in the "right ball park" and a good answer can be obtained even with
fairly crude cost data. For example, suppose the company had estimated
that its total cost of holding 1,000 casings in inventory for a year was $1
when it actually was $2 (as in our illustration). Working through the
same arithmetic, the company would have arrived at an optimum-order
quantity of 70,000 casings instead of 50,000. Even so, the total cost
would have been (using the correct $2 annual carrying cost):

3.6 trips per year @ $10	= $ 36
35,000 casings average inventory @ $0.002 =	70
Total annual cost	= $106

Thus an error of a factor of 2 in one component cost results in only a
6 per cent difference in total cost.

Methods for calculating appropriate order or manufacturing lot sizes can
be elaborated in a variety of ways, as the preceding discussion illustrates.
The principal limitation, however, is the assumption that demand or usage
is known in advance. This assumption is sometimes reasonably valid. However, introduction of uncertainty in demand or usage raises new problems
of control, some which are discussed in Chapter 5.

PROBLEMS AND DISCUSSION TOPICS

1. An item used in the manufacture of surgical equipment has a steady
   annual usage rate of 1,200 dozen. Cost of the item is $3 per dozen. The
   manufacturer considers his cost of ordering these parts to be $5 per order
   and his annual cost of stored inventory to be 10 per cent. In what
   quantities should his purchasing agent order these items?
2. Additional uses have been found for the item of problem 1, with the
   result that the item's usage rate has doubled. In what quantity should
   this item be carried if this higher usage rate is expected to continue?
3. A distributor of a dated product sells 100,000 units annually costing
   $0.10 each. Because of the limited shelf life of the item, they are air-
   freighted to the distributor at his expense, bringing his order cost to $48
   per order, independent of order size. It costs the distributor $10 annually
   to store 1,000 units of the product and his cost of capital is believed to be
   14 per cent. Find:

a. The economic lot size
b. The total annual inventory and ordering cost
c. The economic lot size if the shelf life is 3 months

4. A plant producing a line of hydraulic valves can supply the factory warehouse at the rate of 750 per month. The warehouse ships 3,000 per year at a unit selling price of $250. Considering the plant's ordering and setup cost of $300 and its inventory carrying cost rate of 20 per cent, what quantities should the warehouse order from the plant?
5. The surgical-supply manufacturer in exercise 1 is offered a 10 per cent discount on his purchases if he will order no more than twice per year. Should he agree to this?

BIBLIOGRAPHY

Fabian, T., J. L. Fisher, M. W. Sasieni and A. Yardeni: "Purchasing Raw Material on a Fluctuating Market," *Operations Research,* vol. 7, no. 1, pp. 107–122, January-February, 1959.

Krone, L. H.: "A Note on Economic Lot Sizes for Multi-purpose Equipment," *Management Science,* vol. 10, no. 3, pp. 461–464, April, 1964.

Levy, Joel: "Loss Resulting from the Use of Incorrect Data in Computing an Optimal Inventory Policy," *Naval Research Logistics Quarterly,* vol. 5, no. 1, pp. 72–82, March, 1958.

Maxwell, William L.: "The Scheduling of Economic Lot Sizes," *Naval Research Logistics Quarterly,* vol. 11, no. 2, pp. 89–124, June, 1964.

Mennell, R. F.: "Early History of the Economic Lot Size," *APICS Quarterly Bulletin,* pp. 14–22, April, 1961.

Schupack, Mark B.: "Economic Lot Sizes with Seasonal Demand, March, 1958," *Journal of the Operations Research Society of America,* pp. 45–57, January-February, 1959.

Wagner, Harvey M., and Thomson M. Whitin: "Dynamic Problems in the Theory of the Firm," *Naval Research Logistics Quarterly,* vol. 5, no. 1, pp. 53–74, March, 1958.

Wagner, Harvey M., and Thomson M. Whitin: "Dynamic Version of the Economic Lot Size Model, February, 1958," *Management Science,* pp. 89–96, October, 1958.

**DEALING
WITH
UNCERTAINTY**

SOURCES OF UNCERTAINTY: DEMAND AND RESUPPLY

If all demands or requirements for product were known exactly in advance, deciding how much and when to buy or to make a product would be a relatively straightforward task made difficult only by the problems of defining and measuring costs. The principal limitations inhibiting the broad direct application of the methods of Chapter 4 are the assumptions connected with certainty of requirements and resupply. Generally one is not able to obtain his requirements immediately; there is some delay between placing an order and receipt of goods. For example, suppose, in the fictitious example of Brown & Brown, Inc.,[1] that the truckman had to make an all-day drive from the factory to the supplier. He would have to pick up by Monday morning an order needed on Tuesday, and another kind of inventory function would be introduced—transit stock needed to "buy" the time in transit from supply to need. Figure 5.1 illustrates the change in the total inventory because of the need for transit stock.

Transit delays in themselves cause no problem. All one has to do, if one knows how long delivery takes and how much stock will be used during the delivery period, is to order far enough in advance. However, variations in the delay, that is, in the resupply lead time, can and frequently do cause problems. The combination of the uncertainty in resupply time and the

[1] Chap. 4, pp. 55–58.

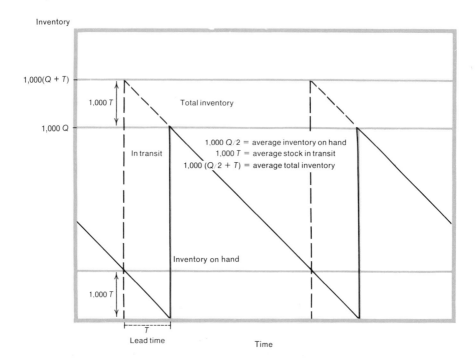

FIGURE 5.1 Total inventory on hand and in transit

uncertainty in demand causes the principal problems that businessmen face in managing their inventories. (Note that demand uncertainty by itself is likewise no problem when there is no replenishment delay, i.e., when one can fill any requirements immediately.)

The combination of transit delays and uncertainty can take a variety of forms. For example, demand for switch coverings may be entirely fixed by the processing capacity of the plant. However, perhaps the company's driver likes an occasional beer and may from time to time show up 3 days late. On the other hand, the driver may be the ultimate in responsibility, but the sales of switches, being strongly influenced by promotional programs, may double overnight while he is away. Brown & Brown's problem would then become much more complex, basically because of an inability to react immediately to random influences. Lacking ability to organize their manufacturing and sales activities thoroughly enough to control both the driver's and their customers' habits, the only way out is to carry some additional stock—safety stock.

SAFETY STOCKS AS A BUFFER AGAINST UNCERTAINTY

Safety stock is needed to cover the demand during the replenishment lead time in excess of the expected demand. The need results from a combination of the delay between the time a replenishment order is placed and the time the material is received and uncertainty as to how much material will be required during the replenishment lead time. In practice, the safety stock held by an inventory is the stock on hand at the time replenishment stocks are received.

The approach to eliminating difficulties resulting from exhaustion of stocks before a replenishment supply is received is clearly to keep some additional inventory on hand which can be drawn upon in case of emergency, but not to count on this inventory in determining when to place a replenishment order. The objective is to arrive at a reasonable balance between the amount of extra inventory (and its capital, storage, and other cost) and the protection obtained against stock exhaustion. As more and more inventory is set aside, either figuratively or in fact, as safety stock, the chance of stock exhaustion becomes ever less. However, the amount of protection which each additional unit of safety inventory buys characteristically drops as more inventory is added, and thus the return from increasing inventory balances diminishes rapidly. The question is: How much additional inventory as safety stock can be economically justified?

Safety stocks illustrate how inventories "decouple" one stage in a production and distribution system from the next, cutting the amount of over-all organization or control needed. Safety stocks separate one part of the production and distribution system from the uncontrollable shocks and uncertainties arising in another, e.g., as a result of sales fluctuations and transit or production delays.

Most reordering systems, whether for in-process materials, for replenishing raw materials, or for replenishing finished stocks in a warehouse, must be designed to take uncertainty in usage rates or in delivery times directly into account. In circumstances like the Brown & Brown case, where demand is fixed and constant, the result is a fixed amount reordered at fixed intervals. However, where usage or demand is uncertain or fluctuates, it is not possible to keep both the size of orders and the interval between orders fixed. A common way to approach reordering problems in the face of uncertainty is to fix the size of the order placed, by the means used in the Brown & Brown case, and then let the ordering frequency vary to take up fluctuations in usage. Another common method is to fix the ordering frequency or the length of time between orders and then let the size of orders vary with usage. In either case an extra amount of inventory, or safety stock, must be carried to fill unexpected surges in demand between placing and receiving orders.

Systems designed to handle uncertainty fall into two basic categories: those in which the order size is fixed but the order interval depends on actual demand, and those in which the inventory is reviewed periodically and restored to some predetermined level. The practice of ordering a fixed quantity when needed, essentially the "two-bin" system in common stockroom or factory use, assumes that individual inventories are under constant watch. The plan for ordering at fixed periods, i.e., monthly, weekly, or quarterly, is frequently used in warehouse control systems or for handling inventories involving a very large variety of items under some form of clerical control. While the two schemes are basically similar in concept, they produce somewhat different results, as will be seen. Other systems intermediate between these two offer the advantages of each in particular circumstances, while still others are designed to minimize effects of uncertainty through "explosion" techniques.

The details and features of the various control systems will be taken up in Chapter 6. Before doing so, it is of interest to examine the role of forecasting as a means of dealing with demand uncertainties.

ROLE OF FORECASTING IN PRODUCTION AND INVENTORY CONTROL

Characteristics of production-planning forecasts

It is a curious paradox that everyone in a responsible position in business management forecasts but, at the present time at least, few members of management are prepared to admit this. The forecasting function appears to be suspect; the methods are viewed as some form of applied black magic, partially as a result of bad experiences many businessmen have had in relying on forecast results, and partially because of reluctance to look into the various statistical and survey techniques, their assumptions and limitations, which are available to the present-day professional business economist and market-research staff.

Forecasts of customer demand are fundamental to the operation of a business. Any company is in business primarily to serve its customers' needs in some way. Its survival depends on its ability to adapt its operations to customers' needs, to demonstrate or stimulate the need, and to service it adequately and efficiently when it arises. The demand forecast is the link between the evaluation of external factors in the economy which influence the business and the management of the company's internal affairs. A forecast of demand of some type exists at least implicitly whenever the company management makes a decision in anticipation of future demand, whether this decision is to build a new plant or to manufacture another run of a particular item to restore inventory balances. The question whether demand forecasts are useful is not pertinent; the real problem is how to forecast demand reliably in order to cut planning and operating costs.

Since the mid-thirties more and more companies have come to recognize the need for formal forecasts of some type and to set up formal methods for obtaining them. These methods may cover procedures for organization and approval of the forecast, methods or programs for collecting data on which it will be based, or groups with technical facilities for analyzing the data as a basis for forecasting. These formal procedures in many cases, however, are restricted to rather broad, i.e., company-wide or division-wide, forecasts covering periods from a quarter to a year. Many times management fails to recognize that implicit forecasts are made at a great many levels in the production and inventory control system. Frequently, in fact, one finds forecasting decisions which have an important influence on production-planning operations being made by storekeepers or stockroom clerks with little or no procedural or policy guidance. Determination of the types of forecasts required and establishment of procedures governing generation of these forecasts are fundamental steps in the organization of a well-conceived production-control system.

There is a common belief that any forecast is a forecast. This does not happen to be true, unfortunately. Forecasts can be classified at least by use or function, time span they cover, and method of generation. Uses include directing sales effort, planning advertising programs, setting sales quotas, establishing expense budgets, establishing capital budgets, and guiding research programs. Our principal interest is with forecasts used for production planning, inventory contol, and guidance to purchasing. The use to which the forecast is to be put determines, or should determine, its form, content, and detail.

For production-planning purposes it is particularly important to distinguish between forecasts of demand and forecasts of sales. While forecasts of sales may be important for estimating revenue, cash requirements, and expenses, a production-planning system is designed primarily to react to customer demand. Demand may differ from sales for a variety of reasons. For example, there may be a substantial lag between customer orders and billings. Or sales may understate demand to the extent that the manufacturing and distribution system is unable to cope with the volume of customer orders placed. In short, sales represent demand as filtered by the manufacturing and distribution system. Sales represent an output from, rather than an input to, the production and inventory control system. The particular characteristics of demand forecasts which are pertinent to production and inventory control are the timing, detail and reliability of forecasts, and the assignment within the organization of the responsibility for making forecasts and controlling or improving their quality.

Forecast timing

From the point of view of production planning or inventory control, a demand forecast is only incidentally a forecast of commodity movement. Usually a forecast of orders for particular commodities is a necessary step to the real objective. But what is really required for planning purposes is a forecast of the demand customers will place on manufacturing and purchasing activities.

The merchandise a company sells may be looked at from many points of view, e.g., the utility it offers customers, the dollar revenue it represents, or the physical items themselves. From the point of view of production planning, the merchandise can best be viewed as capsules of time of employees and equipment and of purchased materials converted into storable form. The demand forecast needed, therefore, is a forecast of the demand customers will place for the time of types or pools of equipment, time of the manpower the company has or can make available, and quantities of materials the company is in a position to buy. The forecast of demand for each type of facility must necessarily cover a time span at least as long as the time needed to make decisions relative to that facility effective—the lead time—plus the time between reviews. Usually the lead time depends on physical processing considerations or suppliers' abilities and is beyond the control of the system.

To make these concepts more concrete, let us think for a moment of the problems of a grocery-products manufacturer. The grocery-products market in many lines has distinct seasonal patterns of demand. It is expanding but highly competitive. Retailers characteristically require very prompt service on orders, and the manufacturer whose service is poor faces the possibility of loss of outlet and exposure of his product to customers. Let us suppose that it takes a year to get a new plant or plant addition into operation, including design of facilities, architectural and construction work, and that the management of the company would like to limit the frequency of plant expansions to once every 2 years. Then a forecast is needed of customer demand for plant processing capacity of various types covering at least a 3-year span, since decisions made today would, in the normal course of events, establish the capacity available up to 3 years hence.

Now let us suppose further that one of the company's raw materials is vegetable oil purchased in crude form. This product is available only seasonally as crops are processed, and prices and quality depend strongly on the time of year when purchases are made. Then a forecast of gross requirements for vegetable oil as represented by customer demand is required covering at least one annual cycle ahead, in order that the company can intelligently plan its oil-buying and inventory policy. This does not, of course, commit the company irrevocably to any particular products or package sizes. However, to the extent that needs for vegetable oil may vary because of variations in the product mix, the company's oil-buying program must allow for inventory adequate to take up the swings in oil demand of the magnitude that may reasonably be expected.

The company may want to even out production in the face of seasonal demand in order to stabilize employment and make more effective use of plant capacity. The objective may be to build inventory during slack sales periods in anticipation of the peak in demand. In this case the company requires a forecast of production hours by major operating center at least a year ahead covering a complete demand cycle. This will permit the company to lay out a production plan making the right number of hours available each month to meet the demand. Since production hours in anticipation of demand will be "stored" in the form of physical inventory made up of particular items, at least a close estimate of breakdown of total demand by item is needed to keep seasonal inventories well balanced. Demand by item, however, does not need to be at all precise, since the company will have opportunity to adjust production rates on individual items to keep inventories in balance, provided the total amount of production time required is available.

Let us suppose that the company buys its packaging materials outside and that, because of the supplier's service time and time in transit, packaging materials must be ordered 4 weeks before they become available. Then the company needs a forecast by package type at least 4 weeks in advance. Note again, however, that this does not commit the company irrevocably to a particular production schedule over 4 weeks. In short, the company requires a forecast of maximum probable usage by package type covering a 4-week period so that packaging materials will be available if needed.

Union agreements in this industry frequently provide that the company will give employees firm notice of working hours at the end of 1 week covering the week ahead, and once this notice is given, the company is committed to pay the scheduled employees, come what may. This means that the company must have at the end of each week a forecast of required operating hours by employee pool, e.g., mixing center and packaging lines, for the coming week. Sufficient operating hours must be planned to meet customer demand in the light of inventory on hand.

Finally, a forecast of demand for individual products package sizes is needed only over the length of a characteristic production cycle or run. If the employees, packaging materials, and raw materials are available (as provided by the forecasts noted above), the plant can adjust the length of run in individual products almost from day to day to keep the inventory on hand in balance. Thus a means for forecasting maximum requirements for individual items and package sizes over a span as short as 2 or 3 days may be adequate for this purpose.

Figure 5.2 summarizes the illustrative types of forecasts identified as needed by this manufacturer. It indicates the purpose for which each forecast is to be used, the type of forecast required, and the time span which the forecast must cover.

The questions faced by a manufacturer of electrical components, such as switches and meters, illustrate these principles in a job-shop context. This hypothetical manufacturer makes a wide variety of end products assembled from a number of subassemblies and component parts. About half of the orders he receives are for special items or combinations of assemblies and parts, and the other half are for shelf or stock items. Customer-service requirements permit a 2-week delay in filling shelf items, and promise dates on special items are set to allow 2 weeks beyond engineering time needed to specify subassemblies and components. The rate of assembly operations is adjusted weekly, and it takes a maximum of a week to make any item once the parts are available.

In view of the allowed service time to customers, no forecast by item is needed to govern assembly operations, since the output requirements of the assembly group in any particular week can be defined in advance.

Suppose, however, that the company wants to set up to make economical runs of shelf items. Then the forecast of usage by item over the length of a production cycle is required to tell if a run is justified. For example, the inventory control or reorder procedure might indicate a run on some item equivalent to 2 months' demand at the current rate of usage. The question which must be answered, of course, is whether demand for the item is expected to hold up long enough to justify the inventory risk. The question may not be raised formally, but each time a run is made, a forecast is in effect implied.

If the company is not prepared to allow the level of assembly operations to fluctuate from week to week in full response to fluctuations in customer demand, a forecast of the expected level of demand and the range of variation from week to week in terms of assembly man-hours must be made. This

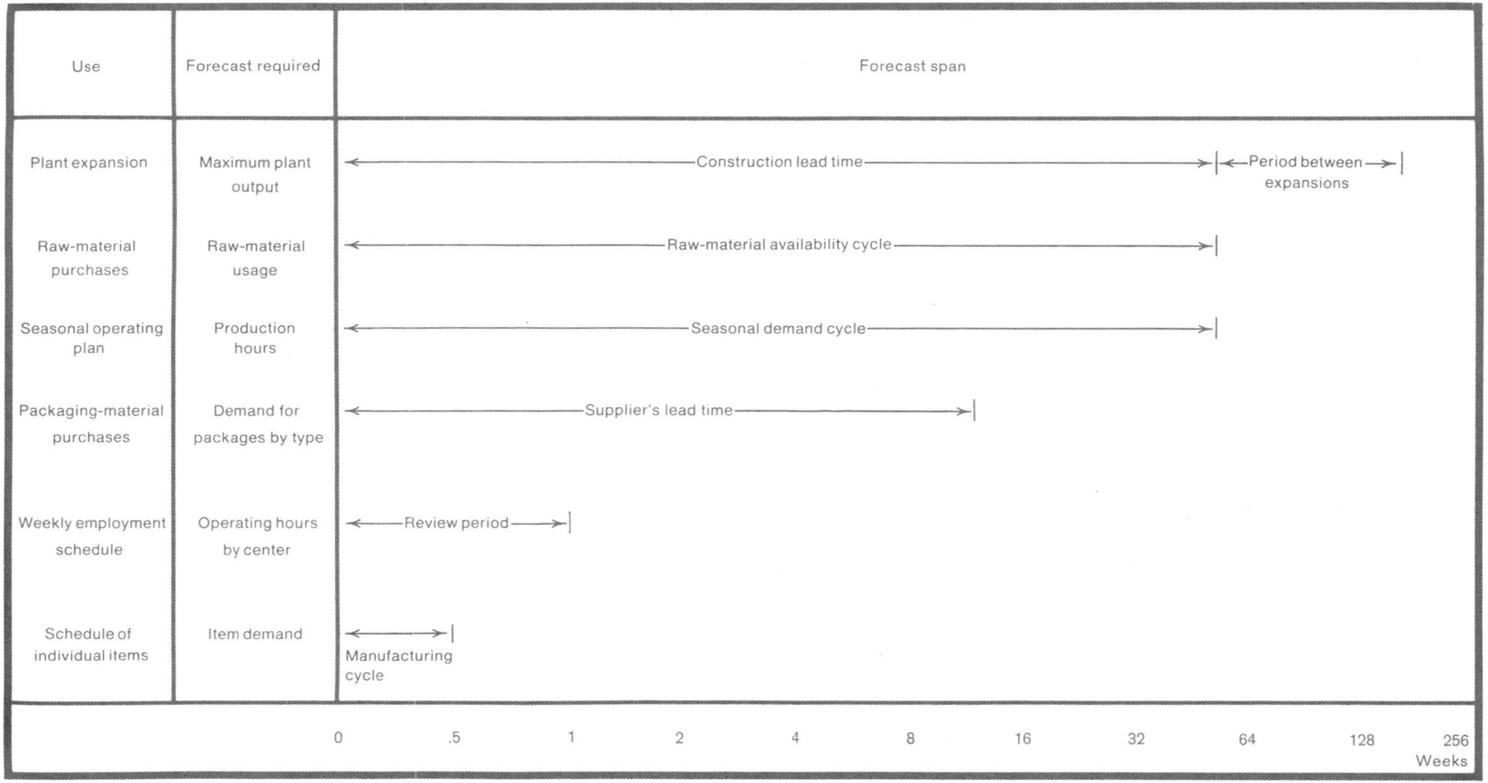

FIGURE 5.2 Illustrative schedule of required forecasts

is needed to set up a normal level of operation; and a procedure for adjusting this level must be set up which will be consistent both with the requirement of meeting customer demand and with the limits placed on employment fluctuations.

At any rate, the assembly operation can meet customer requirements only if the parts and subassemblies are available to make the items demanded. It it takes 2 weeks to make subassemblies and parts used in subassemblies, then the company requires a forecast of demand by subassembly uses extended at least 2 weeks beyond orders on hand. The forecast required is a forecast of customer demand, but not in terms of finished items; it should be, as noted above, a forecast in terms of subassemblies which those finished items represent. The company may in fact regulate the manufacture of subassemblies and parts by some type of conventional reorder-point system, as described in Chapters 4 and 6, but the point often overlooked is, again, that a reorder point implies the forecast of usage. Adequate control of subassemblies and parts requires that the forecasts implied by the reorder-point system be really consistent with current expectations.

To carry this point one step further, let us assume that some group of subassemblies requires a particular quality of wire which must be purchased on the outside with a 2-month lead time. In this case, a forecast of requirements for this type of wire, as represented by customer orders, is required covering at least 2 months plus 2 weeks in the future.

These examples serve to illustrate the point that a production-control system does not in fact rely on a single forecast covering a single span of time. A forecast is needed for each type of skill, capacity, or material that is used. Each forecast must cover a span of time equal at least to the lead time between the decision to procure the skill, capacity, or commodity and the time the skill, capacity, or material in question is available in the form of finished goods to fill a customer's need. This is not a definition of a useful or desirable time span but of an essential one. Whether the required forecasts are made explicitly or not, they are in fact made in any production and inventory control system no matter how designed. A fundamental question in designing a control system, therefore, is to decide how best to make the necessary forecasts over the required time spans, at what points these forecasts should be made by routine clerical extrapolation, and at what points they should be based on careful judgment and review.

Forecast detail

The preceding discussion of time requirements of forecasts indicates that the degree of detail of the forecast is closely allied to the question of time span. This goes back to the point that one can think of an end product the customer buys as representing a collection of times of employees and equipment and materials that the company has purchased. If one is attempting to control the level of operations at some stage in the manufacturing process, then what is needed is a forecast of the demands customers will place on that stage. For example, if one is attempting to control the level of employment in a punch-press department, it does no good to have a forecast in great detail of the items the company expects customers will order unless this forecast can somehow be converted into a forecast of time requirements in the punch-press department. If the forecast goes into greater detail than is needed for the particular operation being controlled, then the forecast of demand on that operation must be built up from the detail.

At this point it is worth while to distinguish between a forecast of demand on a particular operation for purposes of control and the detail to which it may be necessary to go in order to get this forecast. For example, a manufacturer of wire cable controlling the level of employment in stranding operations for making individual conductors needs to know demand for stranding-machine hours far enough in advance to plan stranding operations and employment so that he will have enough conductors stranded for assembly into cable. An estimate of dollar sales or dollar sales by product class is not enough. He may be able to get the forecast of required stranding-machine hours by a simple statistical extrapolation of past requirements. Or he may want to go through the steps of forecasting sales by product type and size, converting this into millions of feet of conductor by type, and then use manufacturing standards to convert estimates of conductor requirements into requirements for stranding-machine time. The important point is that the forecasting which is the end product of this process is a forecast of stranding-machine hours.

Businesses tend to make mistakes in both directions in forecasting; they go into insufficient detail, or they become too detailed. The former tendency is illustrated by gross-dollar demand or dollar demand by broad product groups or customer groups. The difficulty with formal forecasts of this type is that they simply do not tell what the demands on the various operations are. For example, a manufacturer of paper products who was having difficulty with production control was found to be limiting his forecasts to forecasts of gross demand by customer class. This had a number of useful purposes for directing sales effort and advertising, but it was totally insufficient in governing purchases of paper stock, since there was no obvious relation between requirements for various grades of paper and sales to various customer groups, and no attempt was made to make this translation.

The second tendency—that of going into too much detail—often follows as a reaction to the difficulties encountered from insufficiently detailed forecasts. The company then goes too far in attempting to detail the forecasts to make them useful to manufacturing, without carefully thinking out what type of detail is needed. For example, the manufacturing department of a company making metal products had over the course of time built up a list of 125 detailed breakdowns of the sales forecast that it wanted. The sales department objected strongly to these breakdowns, maintaining that their forecast of over-all dollar demand was good, the forecast by product group was reasonably good, but the forecasts in detail by various combinations of size, shape, and material were necessarily terrible. This debate led naturally to a good deal of frustration and bickering, with the manufacturing department saying that the sales department's forecasts were no good and the sales department maintaining that manufacturing department demands were unreasonable. Both sides failed to realize that the manufacturing department did not need forecasts by individual products except over a very short span to control finished-stock safety levels, and these could be obtained with adequate reliability by crude statistical devices. But the manufacturing department did need forecasts of demand in terms of activity in major operating centers if it was to have any hope of meeting sales service requirements at reasonable cost.

Explosions

There are, fundamentally, two ways of obtaining forecasts of demand for raw materials, in-process items, or time at operating centers. One way is by straight statistical extrapolation of past parts and material usage or demand for operating time. Some of the techniques applied in this approach are discussed below. This approach is generally simple to set up routinely. It works reasonably well, especially where the general character of end items being sold is not changing, or where there are no cycles in end-product demand which can be forecast. This approach is often used where replenishment of in-process and raw materials is controlled by a simple reorder scheme.

Product explosion is the second way. Where product or product-group forecasts are made as a basis for production planning, these must be exploded, or converted into demand for the various types of manufacturing activity and purchased materials the company wishes to control. Explosion of end-product demand into parts and time requirements is one of the fundamental techniques in production planning and control. It is used not only to convert end-product or product-group forecasts into component-demand forecasts but also to convert actual demand or shipment reports into usage of components, for production control, e.g., in a base-stock control system.

One way to make explosions is to start with a parts and operations list for each end item, showing the type and amounts of materials, parts, and subassemblies which go into a single unit of the item. Operation centers and unit operating times can also be shown. The unit material and time requirements are multiplied by the forecast quantity of the item. The resulting estimates of materials and times required are then posted to summary sheets by component or operating-center number, and the requirements for each material or operating center are totaled to get gross demand implied by the forecast.

When manufacturing operations call for several stages of part, component, and subassembly manufacture, an end-product parts list can show either just the parts and subassemblies used directly and the operations needed to go from these to end product, or the parts and operations list can carry requirements back, breaking subassemblies and components in turn into material and operations to produce them. In the former case, when components directly needed to meet the end-product sales forecast are determined, these requirements must be used with component parts and operations lists to work back another stage. This process has to be repeated until end-item requirements are broken down to purchased material and operating-time requirements. While this step-by-step method calls for more explosion cycles than the other, one-step method, it generally takes fewer computing and posting steps than the one-step method, especially where there is a large joint use of materials, parts, and subassemblies among end items.

Using parts lists to explode seems well adapted to punched-card applications. A punched-card master requirements file is set up containing a deck of cards showing the materials and operations required to make each end item. Each card in the file shows how many of a specified item are needed in a specified end product or how much time in a specified operating center is needed. To compute part and time requirements:

1. A card is punched for each end product, showing the quantity forecast in as much detail by time period as is needed.
2. These cards are used to select corresponding detailed part and time cards from the master file. The forecast quantity cards are collated with the selected part and time cards, and end-product total quantities are transferred. Unit requirements are extended by total forecast quantities.
3. Extended part and time cards are sorted by part and operating-center number and summed to obtain total requirements of each material or operating center.

Another technique, used often in manual systems, is to set up a summary *where-used* sheet. This lists each part, material, or operating center in column headings across the top. Each end-item or end-product group is listed in the row headings. The entries show the quantity of the part, or the time in the center, listed in the column needed to make one unit of the end product shown in the row. In addition, one or more columns may be left for entering forecast quantities by end product. The requirements for any particular part can be obtained by extending the forecast quantities by the unit data shown in the column for the part.

It is important that end products be properly grouped into "families" according to interchangeability of components and common operations. One electrical-products manufacturer, who was faced with an apparently endless array of end products and parts to make them, found that the end products could be classified into a small number of groups within which there was a very high degree of common-parts usage. Setting up proper product families helps in two ways. First, demand for the product family in total may be much easier to forecast than demand for individual products. To the extent components and operations are the same for all members of the product family, a forecast of component demand can be obtained directly from the forecast by product family.

Secondly, proper product families help cut the volume of clerical work in making explosions. It is often possible to set up a series of product groups and subgroups such that some parts are unique to individual products, some parts are interchangeable among all products in a subgroup, some parts are interchangeable among all products in a group, etc. Then all products in one group can be thought of as being a single product in getting requirements of parts common to that group.[2]

SPECIFYING THE FORECAST

Forecast reliability

The question of forecast reliability is one of the greatest sources of misunderstanding and frustration (of both managers and forecasters) in the construction of forecasts. One reason for this is the widespread belief that a forecast, is or should be, a fixed number or schedule—the forecaster's best guess. One study, made in 1947, notes that "in most companies, top management expects the forecaster to make a specific estimate; in others, a range

[2] See James J. Kasney and Charles M. Bristol, Jr., "A Short Cut Tabulating Method of Inventory Control," *Bulletin of the National Association of Cost Accountants*, April, 1956, p. 1010, for a description of use of the product-family concept to cut down the size of the explosion job in one punched-card system.

is acceptable provided it is not too great."[3] General business thinking apparently has not changed greatly since. This is unfortunate, since it reflects a basic misunderstanding of what a forecast is.

A forecast is by nature an evaluation of incomplete evidence indicating what the future may look like. Thus no forecast can be expected to be entirely accurate. There is some evidence that business managers go through three phases of thinking about forecasts. During the first, or "honeymoon," phase, a forecast, particularly if it is based on any moderate amount of impressive statistical data, is viewed as gospel or fundamental truth of some sort. The second phase begins when the fact dawns that forecasts are usually wrong and sometimes considerably off. This brings on a period of disillusionment and confusion probably not too different from that experienced by some people in the early Renaissance period when the fact was brought home to them that the sun might not revolve around the earth, as a literal reading of the Bible might suggest. Finally, the forecast user develops an appreciation of the forecast as an estimate or a guide, tempered by the recognition that the forecast will be in error to some degree and that plans must be made taking the magnitude of possible error into account.

Despite the demand for a single-number forecast, one point is fundamental: a forecast will be in error to some extent no matter how sophisticated the techniques of forecasting may be. The forecast error may be reduced somewhat but it will still remain (at least until an engineering breakthrough is accomplished in the area of crystal-ball manufacture). Therefore a forecast made without an estimate of possible error is incomplete, if not misleading. In production planning and inventory control, one basic function of inventories and production flexibility is to absorb unexpected fluctuations in demand or departures from forecast. *Stock levels and production plans can hardly be set rationally without an estimate of the size of possible forecast error or the range of possible demand which may reasonably be expected.* This is true of both very short-run item forecasts and of longer-run forecasts of demand for facilities and time.

Using an average and estimate of error

Where estimates of forecast reliability are made, the usual method of specifying reliability is probably first to make the best single estimate of demand; then limits are set to bracket this, and these may be established either intuitively or by statistical analysis. The accuracy of past forecasts

[3] G. Clark Thompson, "Forecasting Sales," *Studies in Business Policy*, no. 25, National Industrial Conference Board, Inc., New York, 1947.

may be studied statistically to determine the distribution of error. Another approach is to study the fluctuation statistics of short-run demand to determine, for example, how far demand varies in a particular period about the mean level, or to determine whether variations from one period to the next tend to be self-compensating or independent. A wide variety of techniques may be used for making these analyses, ranging from relatively simple methods to the sophisticated techniques of modern mathematical statistics.[4]

Maximum-minimum demand forecasts

Maximum-minimum demand forecasts are another approach to estimating forecast error. In this approach the sales organization defines the maximum demand under which it is willing to operate without emergencies or customer delays and the minimum demand it can stimulate. This approach does not avoid the inherent difficulties related to forecast uncertainty. The need is still there to define the risk associated with forecast uncertainty and the level of risk that is acceptable. Sometimes, however, the intuitive definition implied by setting maximum-minimum limits is easier to obtain and to understand than the alternate procedure of estimating the statistical distribution of forecast errors and setting probability limits.

A maximum-minimum demand forecast represents a request by the sales organization for a commitment from manufacturing to operate within the forecast limits routinely, with adequate service. By the same token, the forecast limits define the limits beyond which the manufacturing organization is not expected to go without possible delays in service. An example of a maximum-minimum demand forecast obtained statistically is discussed below.

Responsibility for forecast uncertainty

Forecast errors or limits have a direct bearing on operating cost, since, as noted above, the size of the error or range of limits will determine the inventory and/or production flexibility that must be provided. Discussions in business circles, represented, for example, by presentations to business discussion and study groups, indicate that considerable controversy exists as to who should forecast. In most cases the forecasting function appears to be primarily the responsibility of the sales organization, but it is often argued

[4] See, for example, M. J. Moroney, *Facts from Figures*, Penguin Books, Inc., Baltimore, 1954, and Paul G. Hoel, *Introduction to Mathematical Statistics*, John Wiley & Sons, Inc., New York, 1947.

that since the forecast bears so importantly on a number of functions in the company, it should be made by an impartial group outside the influence of the sales organization.

If we distinguish between a demand forecast and an operating plan, there is good reason to support the view that demand forecasting should be a function of the sales organization, provided control can be set up to assess the sales organization with the costs of forecast error. After all, the sales organization has the prime responsibility for generating customer demand and the most direct interest in maintaining customer service. On the one hand, the forecast establishes limits within which customer service should be maintained; on the other hand, the forecast limits determine the cost of providing service in view of the uncertainty which exists.

Planning methods described in following chapters provide a means for measuring the cost of inventories and production fluctuations versus the width of the forecast limits established. Where sales operations can be assessed for these costs, the sales organizations are in direct position to balance costs of service against service requirements which they feel must be maintained. The manufacturing organization is left with the responsibility of supplying customer demand within the basic framework established by the forecast and planning procedures.

In this connection it is important that clear-cut responsibility for making demand forecasts be established for adequate planning and to prevent one part of the organization from "outguessing" another. The authors, for example, have seen cases where the sales organization was not forecasting demand so much as what it felt the manufacturing department could turn out. When the manufacturing department got its hands on this forecast, it was revised to manufacturing's opinion of what sales could sell. There was no clear-cut division of responsibility between forecasting demand, determining to what extent the forecast demand could be serviced, and planning to meet the forecast.

APPROACHES TO FORECASTING

The field of forecasting method has hardly reached the handbook engineering stage. Techniques are highly diverse and depend strongly on the nature of the company, the data-handling facilities and analysis skills available, and particularly on the types of customer and industry information which may exist. In some industries, e.g., in retail gasoline marketing, published records of tax receipts give good information on past industry sales and it is not too difficult, therefore, to obtain good estimates of share of market. Other companies face situations where their products are sold in competition with a number of products from diverse sources which fill the same basic need, or are in industries where information on competitors' sales can be obtained only by rather difficult intelligence. In these companies the possibility of predicting industry sales based on economic indicators and the use of share-of-market estimates based on marketing programs is less promising. The techniques used by business companies range from the collection-of-opinion or judgment estimates to the use of fairly complex mathematical techniques for studying characteristics of past sales and relationships with reported economic series. Many companies have found it desirable to rely on a combination of approaches as a check one against another.

The approaches to forecasting vary widely among companies—partly because satisfactory general methods of forecasting are rare, partly because expediency and available data have a strong influence, and partly because many, if not most, companies fail to recognize how many forecasts they make.[5] Nevertheless, there are general classes of approaches used for making the different general types of demand forecasts which are needed to operate a business. The table on page 99 gives a rough classification.

Forecast techniques for controlling stocks and procurement of individual items depend very much on the number of items controlled and on the type of clerical system. These forecasts have to be made routinely, and thus the technique used must be designed to accommodate the clerical skills and routine computing facilities available. Where the number of items to be forecast is moderate, graphical methods are often valuable. One manufacturer of food products governs all end-product controls from a set of graphs of past demand by item; these graphs are kept in the plant production control office. If the number of items is moderate to large, several hundred to tens of thousands, or if punched-card or internally programed equipment is used to process records, numerical averaging techniques such as those described below are used.

Collective opinion

The collective-opinion approach to forecasting is probably one of the most usual. This may start with an estimate from salesmen or branch sales managers of estimated demand for the coming year or quarter. Branch demand

---

[5] A comprehensive survey of forecasting methods and the uses to which they are put by a variety of heavy chemicals manufacturers is presented in "Business Forecasting: A Special Report," *Chemical and Engineering News*, pp. 124–138, July 12, 1965.

Use	Time span	Characteristics	Techniques

Business planning:
  Product planning
  Research programing
  Capital planning
  Plant location and expansion
	Generally five years or more; sometimes less	Broad outline forecast, often qualitative only	Technical-economic studies; economic and population studies; marketing studies

Intermediate operation planning:
  Capital and cash budgets
  Sales planning
  Production planning, especially in seasonal business
  Setting production and inventory budgets
	Generally six months to two years; at least through one cycle in seasonal business	Used for analysis of alternative operating plans; numerical; not necessarily detailed by item; estimate of reliability needed	Collective opinion; trend analysis; seasonal index analysis; correlation with economic indices; combination techniques

Short-run production control Adjusting production and employment levels to account for departures of total inventory from plan	One to six weeks; span equals lag between decision to adjust operating rates and time output is actually affected	Forecasts of operating activity, not item forecast	Statistical trend extrapolation; explosion of short-term product or product-class forecasts

Forecast of item requirements:
  Placing purchase orders
  Scheduling items into production
  Replenishing warehouse stocks: controlling decisions when and how much to replenish
	Span equals lead time between placing order or scheduling run and receipt or completion. Estimate of error, or maximum demand needed to protect service	Designed for routine use in manual, punched-card, or electronic systems	Explosion of end-product demand; graphical; statistical or numerical techniques

may then be put together and reviewed by district managers; district estimates will be synthesized in turn, until finally an estimate for the company as a whole is obtained. On the other hand, it may start at the home office, with each of several product managers or members of the sales and general executive staff making independent forecasts. A final forecast is built up out of these forecasts by review and discussion. The advantages of this general approach to forecasting are that it is less elaborate and requires less technical skill. It makes direct use of qualitative knowledge that people in the field or home office may have about product developments, advertising programs, and the like; and as the forecast is built up it passes the review of a number of people with various types of specific knowledge who can assess its accuracy. This approach to forecasting is considered by some companies to be particularly useful in building up forecasts by product or customer group.

The fundamental difficulty with this approach is that it is subjective. It requires field personnel to make a balanced independent appraisal of their possibilities which is neither optimistic, in the sense of being a hoped-for goal, nor too pessimistic, in order to make attainment of the forecast easy. This approach to forecasting also takes time, in two senses: a good deal of time can be spent by field and home-office personnel in making up and agreeing on the forecast, and the elapsed time between making initial field forecasts and arriving at an agreed-upon company forecast can run to several months.

A forecast of this type made by active field people may also tend to be too heavily influenced by immediate events. If sales have taken a little short-term dip, the situation for the coming year looks rather dark; if sales have shown some improvement, or if a few good customers have been landed in the recent past, the view for the coming year may be very optimistic indeed.

Finally, the difficulty always exists that where an estimate is arrived at presumably based on collective opinion, the final result may depend far more on the opinions of one or two influential or persuasive individuals than on those of the group from which it was drawn. Despite the difficulties and dangers with this type of forecast, however, it does serve as a useful way of bringing field opinion to bear on forecasting, bringing out the possible effects of new merchandising or advertising programs and broadening the base of participation in the forecasting job.

One major manufacturer of home appliances uses the composite-opinion method exclusively. Sales of this company are seasonal, reaching a peak in April and May, and the planning year, July 1 to June 30, has been established for general forecasts and production planning. Sales forecasts are built up starting with the individual salesman, who is required to submit a formal estimate of unit demand by quarter by model class and class of business. This must be in the hands of the salesman's branch manager by April 15. The branch manager reviews and consolidates the individual salesmen's estimates and submits them in turn to his division manager by April 30. The branch forecasts are then reviewed and consolidated at the division level and are submitted to the general sales manager by May 15. During the period from May 15 to June 1 the division forecasts are consolidated and reviewed by the general sales manager's staff and discussed informally with other company executives, including the controller and heads of merchandising, production-planning, and engineering departments. By June 1 a formal sales forecast by model class and by quarter for the company as a whole is required.

During the first week in June this forecast is reviewed and approved formally by the planning committee, composed of the treasurer, general manager of manufacturing, general sales manager, engineering-department manager, and the controller. The approved forecast is then assigned to the production-planning department, whose job it is to convert the forecast into a plan of manufacturing operations for the coming year. The tentative production plan is used by the controller's department to produce an estimated-income statement and by the treasurer's office to produce a cash budget. The production plan and the cash budget and estimated-income statement are submitted jointly to the planning committee for general review and approval.

Detailed plans by production units and purchasing plans are laid out from an explosion of the general production plan. In addition, division managers are required to submit estimates by the twenty-first of each month covering expected sales in units by product class for the following month. These, together with forecast inventories, are used to set production plans for the forthcoming month.

The company recognizes that this scheme places a burden on the field sales organization right at the peak of the selling period. It feels, however, that in the first place this is primarily a sales-planning function and that successful forecasting depends on close contact with market conditions and merchandising plans. Their most serious concern is with the 3-month lag between initiation of field forecasts and final plans. This has been cut to the feasible minimum, in this company's view; even the 3-month period leaves very little time for working out operating plans based on the forecast.

It may be of interest to note that this company does not admit making short-run forecasts of demand by model number of forecasts of usage of raw materials (except certain common raw materials with long lead times, ordered from the production plan). Field stocks of assembled units, raw materials, and parts are controlled by a reorder-point system, with the reorder points set by warehouse stock control men.

Economic forecasts

The use of professional economists for business forecasting is growing. Wilson Wright notes: "The increased acceptance of production planning has widened the demand for adequate economic forecasting of professional quality, for production can be planned most effectively only when some measure of confidence can be placed in the sales forecasts and other estimates which must be used."[6] The primary function of the economist in business is to assess trends in economic conditions and their influence on

[6] Wilson Wright, *Forecasting for Profit*, John Wiley & Sons, Inc., New York, 1947.

the industry and the company. In this way the economist can properly place the company's outlook in perspective. In some cases the economist's role is limited to broad background studies of this type, while in others he may make use of these results as a basis for detailed forecasts by commodity and customer group. Wright's book gives an excellent description of the point of view and methods of approach which business economists may use.

Combination methods

In most companies a combination of approaches to demand forecasting is used. Some companies rely on economic forecasts for the period 1 to 5 years ahead for product policy and capital planning. Field-opinion forecasts may be used for near-term estimates, with the economic forecast serving as a basis for reviewing and tempering field estimates. Frequently statistical techniques are used to break down field forecasts into finer detail. For example, in one chemical company selling a competitive and highly seasonal consumer product, field estimates of total demand for the year as a whole serve as a starting point. Historical analyses of sales are made, to produce a seasonal index showing the historical percentage of annual sales in each month. Statistical trend analysis is used to arrive at a preliminary estimate of the detailed breakdown by product group. Both of these statistical estimates are reviewed by responsible sales executives to confirm or adjust the detailed estimates based on knowledge of special circumstances or merchandising plans.

Statistical and economic methods may also be used together with field forecasts of demand to provide a cross check. For example, an analysis of the trend in demand, together with fluctuations about the trend line, may be used to obtain a preliminary estimate of demand, with a measure of estimated reliability. Figure 5.3 illustrates a possible trend-line extrapolation forecast. The center line represents the calculated trend of past demand, and the dashed portion is the extrapolation into the future. The two lighter lines above and below the trend line represent "control limits," based on past fluctuations of actual sales from the trend so that, if the trend continues, actual sales would be expected to fall within the limits 99 per cent of the time.

The trend line is one forecast of demand, and the control limits give an estimate of reliability provided the basic conditions determining the trend do not change. In some companies this type of forecast will be compared with a field forecast. If the field forecast falls within the control limits (the circle in Figure 5.3), it is accepted as consistent with the past trend and is adopted. If the field forecast falls outside the control limits (the cross in

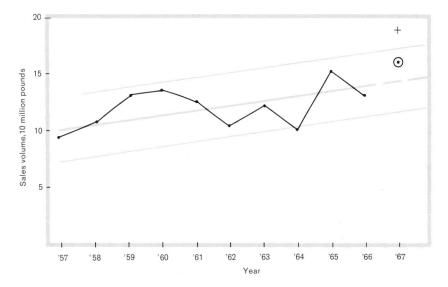

FIGURE 5.3 Trend-line control over field forecast

Figure 5.3), it is questioned. If the departure from trend cannot be justified, the trend control limit nearest the field estimate is accepted as the approved figure.[7]

Statistical and mathematical methods

Statistical methods for forecasting have been given a mixed reception in business, although undoubtedly most forecasters make use of these procedures to some degree. Statistical forecasting methods include *correlation analysis, extrapolation,* and *projection.* Each has its virtues and its limitations and, hence, a particular usefulness in forecasting.

CORRELATION ANALYSIS

Some companies have found it possible to correlate sales in their industry or company with economic indices such as the Federal Reserve Board *Index of Industrial Production,* various estimates of personal income, disposable income, the F. W. Dodge indices of construction contracts awarded, etc.

[7] See, for example, C. Ashley Wright, "Improving the Accuracy of Economic Forecasts," *Proceedings, Modern Statistical Methods for Business and Industry,* Carnegie Institute of Technology, Pittsburgh, April 30–May 1, 1953.

Where an index can be found to which company sales are highly correlated, but with a lag, correlation techniques may be highly useful. If the lag is long enough, the company can use the reported index figures as a basis for forecasting future demand. Various supplies of building materials, for example, have found that their sales tend to lag behind indices of construction contracts awarded by a few months. Where the lag is insufficient for longer-term forecast requirements, correlation with the reported index still leaves the company with the need to predict the index itself. Even so, in the hands of a professional economist such correlations may be very useful. A number of companies have reported approaches to forecasting using correlation with economic indicators.[8] Not only can forecasts be made on the basis of correlation with other events which have already taken place, but they can also be refined by autocorrelation with earlier forecasts. For example, one manufacturer supplying the garment industry found that over the course of several years demand for his product was very stable and closely correlated with disposable income. However, over a period of 6 to 18 months, sales showed violent fluctuations, due apparently to a combination of variations in customers' inventory policies and to periodic waves of optimism or pessimism in the garment trade. The result was that a short-term dip in sales tended to be followed by an offsetting peak as consumer demand forced customers to restore inventory positions. The company forecaster found autocorrelation techniques to provide a useful device for predicting the expected trend in sales in the near future, based on sales levels during the immediately preceding months and the long-term trend determined from extrapolation of disposable-income figures.

EXTRAPOLATION

Linear extrapolation of trends has obvious dangers, since accuracy of the extrapolation depends on conditions holding in the future which have caused the past trend. If anything, the dangers of trend extrapolation have been so belabored that business executives are sometimes excessively shy of trend forecasts. After all, though a trend is only a trend, still it *is* a trend. Trend-extrapolation methods are particularly useful in making short-run forecasts for adjustment of production levels, item control, or for establishing reorder quantities.

Figure 5.4 illustrates the use of extrapolation methods for meeting short-run maximum-demand estimates for stock control.

The *average* trend indicates expected demand of 500,000 pounds in September. The maximum-demand forecast indicates the level that demand

[8] See, for example, G. Clark Thompson, *op. cit.*, pp. 15–20.

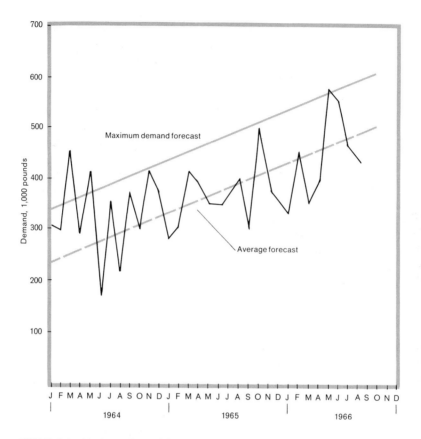

FIGURE 5.4 Maximum-demand forecast by trend extrapolation

might reach, the level the company would like to be able to service without delays in service or emergency measures. The maximum-demand forecast for September is 600,000 pounds. This indicates, if the company is prepared to meet maximum demand, that it can expect to finish September with 100,000 pounds in inventory—maximum less average forecast.

If the product made by the company were a chemical, petroleum, or some similar item for which storage capacity would be definitely limited, a minimum-demand forecast might well be needed. If you sketch in a minimum-demand trend, you can see that it might well be drawn about 100,000 pounds below the average forecast, indicating a minimum expected demand for September of 400,000 pounds. If production rates for September must be fixed, the company will plan to produce to meet a maximum demand of 600,000 pounds but will expect to end the month with an inventory of 100,000 pounds. Since demand may fall as low as 400,000 pounds, the company requires storage capacity of at least 200,000 pounds, the maximum inventory anticipated. Storage capacity must at least equal the difference, maximum- less minimum-demand forecast.

Trend extrapolation is well suited to many types of forecasts required in a production-control system, because this approach is adapted to mechanization or routine clerical procedures. The dangers are minimized where the control system is designed to be responsive to short-run forecast errors in keeping the inventory position in balance. Nevertheless, organization of a production-control system requires careful review of the types of extrapolation forecast to be used, to be sure they are made in a systematic manner suited to the particular needs of the system.

Average demand or usage over some past period is often used as an extrapolation forecast, particularly for controlling stocks of particular items and choosing purchase or manufacturing quantities. When this type of detailed forecast is used, the question arises: Over what period should the average be computed? Using too long a period may give insufficient weight to recent changes in usage. Too short a period may yield an unreliable estimate, giving too much weight to a chance fluctuation. One common method is to set up a procedure for computing an average usage rate based on, say, the preceding month or 6-month period. No general rule for choice of averaging period can be cited; the choice depends on the particular usage characteristics of the items being controlled.

The most straightforward approach for determining an adequate average period is by trial on past usage records. Choose a sample of items to be controlled. Obtain a detailed record of usage over a period of several months to use for trial "forecasts" in which the effectiveness of forecasting over varying periods can be tested by "simulation." For example, the initial month's average usage can be used to "forecast" the first following week, and the "forecast" compared with actual usage. By repeated trial through the time period sampled, statistics of forecast errors can be built up, a sample distribution of errors in estimation of usage rates which would have resulted had a 1-month base period been used. Repeated trials using averaging periods of differing lengths and comparison of the resulting distributions of errors give a basis for picking the most efficient period for the purpose of minimizing the error.

Another approach to extrapolation forecasts is often useful in control systems employing a fixed-order quantity, some of which are described in

Chapters 4 and 6. Under this scheme, the "average" used for estimating reorder quantities is determined as the average rate of usage since the last reorder was placed. The usage or demand rate d is calculated in the following way:

$$d = \frac{Q}{t - t_1}$$

where Q = reorder quantity last used
$\quad t_1$ = date reorder last placed
$\quad t$ = present date

This may be used to recalculate the reorder quantity based on the new usage rate, or at least to see if any adjustment in reorder quantity is justified. The new usage rate may also be used to adjust reorder points.

PROJECTION

Projection attempts to accomplish through refined calculation what extrapolation does geometrically and thereby to obtain a more accurate view of the future. These projection methods comprise a group of versatile and effective methods of forecasting future demand which come under the heading of what economic forecasters refer to as "naïve." By applying this label to projection methods of forecasting, economists mean to suggest that such forecasts are made blindly rather than mindlessly. It is true that forward projection of demand according to a mathematical model based solely on the past pattern of demand fails to reveal the underlying sources of this demand, but it is also true that such mathematical models can provide highly reliable means for short-term forecasting.

In making short-term forecasts, since there is no demand-generating process implied by the mathematical model, it is desirable to adjust the model and its parameters (the numbers that describe the model) as new data become available. This adjustment can be achieved in varying degrees of elaboration, limited usually by the effort one is willing to make in processing the data and in performing the projection computations. Among the simpler methods is the moving-average technique in which the forecast of future demand is taken to be the arithmetic average of the demands during the last n periods beginning with the most recent. As each new period is completed, the oldest of the n periods is replaced by the newest, and future demand is based on this new average. This method is generally adequate for handling forecasts for items whose demand does not change very rapidly.

However, in many cases the amount of uncertainty in future demand is high, and future demand may, in addition, be the result of seasonality and trend as well as assorted random factors. In such cases, projections based on more refined models are needed. It is necessary then to obtain a model of the demand process from a statistically derived fit to previous demand data so that these demand data—and, it is hoped, future demands—may be represented by a mathematical expression. One such projection technique, exponential smoothing, is finding wide acceptance in inventory control applications because it is self-adjusting and because it lends itself to electronic computer applications.

FORECASTS BY EXPONENTIAL SMOOTHING

There is usually good reason to believe that the more recent demand data are more pertinent to the demand-generating process than the older data and that more weight ought to be given to the more recent data in constructing and adjusting the model. There are a variety of methods of time-series analysis which accomplish this. The technique of exponential smoothing, very familiar to the electrical engineer and the servo systems designers, has found wide acceptance and use in forecasting for inventory control. The smoothing operation on past demand data produces an estimate of average or expected usage $\bar{d}$, which can be expressed for an item of reasonably uniform demand over time, as

$$\bar{d}_0 = ad_0 + a(1 - a)d_1 + a(1 - a)^2 d_2 + \ldots + a(1 - a)^n d_n + \ldots$$

where d_0 = actual usage in the time period just ending

d_1 = actual usage in the first preceding time period, etc.

a = ratio of weighting constants, between 0 and 1

The total of the weighting constants $(1 - a)$, $(1 - a)a$, $(1 - a)a^2$, etc., is 1.

There are a number of reasons for using this form of extrapolation for estimating short-term usage rates. One is computational convenience. The expression given above for the current estimate of usage rate, $\bar{d}_0$, can be written as

$$\bar{d}_0 = ad_0 + (1 - a)\bar{d}_1$$

where $\bar{d}_1$ is the estimate made at the end of the first preceding period. This means that to get a new estimate of usage, we take the estimate made a period before, multiply it by a number, $(1 - a)$, less than 1, and add to it usage during the intervening period multiplied by a. This is a convenient formula, particularly for mechanical computation, and it is not difficult to handle in a manual system. It requires keeping only three current numbers: the preceding estimate; the weighting ratio a; and usage in the current period.[9]

Another advantage of this type of estimator is its flexibility. The ratio a can take on any value from 0 up to (but not including) 1. When a is 1, the formula reduces to using the current period's usage rate as a forecast or estimator. When a is chosen very close to 0, this is essentially equivalent to using an arithmetic average over a long period of time as the best estimate of the future usage rate. Intermediate choices for a give forecasts which give more or less emphasis to current usage versus long-run average, depending on whether a is chosen closer to 1 or to 0.

Most patterns of usage or demand have a sizable random element. Often they also show a moderately short-term cyclic pattern. For example, demand may come in waves as customers react in a similar way to news or the business outlook in stocking inventories or letting them run out. If the random element is large, relatively more weight on the long-term average is usually desirable. The appropriate value of the weighting ratio a can best be determined by trial on a sample of actual past demand or usage data.

Here is an example, using the data in Table 5.1. The forecast for January, 1963, has been arbitrarily chosen as 24.0 thousand. Table 5.1 shows the forecasts derived by choosing various values of a in the formulas given before—$a = 0.2$, 0.4, 0.6, and 0.8. For example, using $a = 0.2$, the forecast for February, 1963, is calculated as

$$\text{February forecast} = \overset{\text{January orders}}{(0.2)30.6} + \overset{\text{January forecast}}{(1 - 0.2)(24.0)}$$
$$= 6.12 + 19.2$$
$$= 25.3$$

and for March, 1963,

$$\text{March forecast} = \overset{\text{February orders}}{(0.2)30.0} + \overset{\text{February forecast}}{(1 - 0.2)(25.3)}$$
$$= 6.0 + 20.24$$
$$= 26.2$$

---

[9] For items whose underlying demand pattern is changing with time, i.e., either rising, falling, or cyclic, the smoothing process is more involved. See Robert G. Brown, *Statistical Forecasting for Inventory Control*, McGraw-Hill Book Company, New York, 1959.

TABLE 5.1   Example of exponentially smoothed forecasts

Year	Month	Orders (000)	Forecasts (000)			
			$a = 0.8$	$a = 0.6$	$a = 0.4$	$a = 0.2$
1963	January	30.6	24.0	24.0	24.0	24.0
	February	30.0	29.3	28.0	26.6	25.3
	March	44.6	29.9	29.2	27.9	26.2
	April	30.2	41.7	38.4	34.6	29.9
	May	41.2	32.5	33.5	32.8	30.0
	June	15.0	39.5	38.1	36.2	32.2
	July	36.7	20.0	24.2	27.7	28.8
	August	20.8	33.4	31.7	31.3	30.4
	September	38.1	23.3	25.2	27.1	28.5
	October	29.8	35.1	32.9	31.5	30.4
	November	40.5	30.9	31.0	30.8	30.3
	December	36.8	38.6	36.7	34.7	32.3
1964	January	27.8	37.2	36.8	35.5	33.2
	February	30.5	29.7	31.4	32.4	32.1
	March	40.7	30.3	30.9	31.6	31.8
	April	38.8	38.6	36.8	35.2	33.6
	May	34.8	38.7	38.0	36.6	34.6
	June	35.0	35.6	36.1	35.9	34.6
	July	38.0	35.1	35.4	35.5	34.7
	August	40.2	37.4	44.0	36.5	35.4
	September	29.2	39.6	41.7	38.0	36.4
	October	51.1	31.3	34.2	34.5	35.0
	November	39.3	47.1	44.3	41.1	38.2
	December	35.9	40.9	41.3	40.4	38.4
1965	January	32.5	36.9	38.1	38.6	37.9
	February	45.7	33.4	34.7	28.4	36.8
	March	35.4	43.2	41.3	35.3	38.6
	April	39.8	37.0	37.8	35.3	38.0
	May	56.5	39.2	39.0	37.1	38.4
	June	55.0	53.0	49.5	44.9	42.0
	July	46.5	54.6	52.8	48.9	44.6
	August	44.2	48.1	49.0	47.9	45.0

Figure 5.5 shows a comparison of the errors or differences between the forecast and actual orders in terms of the number of months in which the forecast exceeded actual demand by any stated amount. The forecasts using $a = 0.2$ and 0.8 are compared.

In addition to the forecast of expected demand, a second piece of information is needed from the smoothing process. The error of the forecast is needed in order to make certain decisions concerning the maximum demand likely to be experienced during the period over which the forecast is made. This error estimate is obtained by noting the differences between actual and forecast demands over a period of time. The dates of Table 5.1 show errors in forecast for $a = 0.2$ as tabulated in Table 5.2. To obtain the range of likely outcomes for the forecast for February, 1963, we need the details of the errors made historically in this forecast *and* some assumption (unless verification is possible) of the distribution of the forecasts. It is frequently

FIGURE 5.5 Differences between forecast and actual demand; comparison of two geometrically weighted forecasts

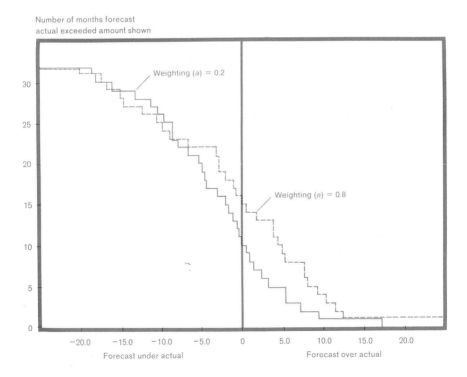

assumed, in the absence of data to the contrary, that demand is normally distributed and that, if the conditions that prevailed for, say, the month of February, 1963, were to hold constant with only the random elements of demand operating to cause variations in this demand, then the monthly demands would distribute themselves in the familiar bell-shaped fashion about a mean value of 25.3 units. The dispersion of this demand about the mean is given by the standard deviation (root mean square value) of the forecast error.

Computation of the standard deviation is tedious, and therefore the mean absolute deviation (MAD) is employed as an excellent approximation. As the name implies, the MAD is the arithmetic average of the forecast errors without regard to their sign. The MAD of a normal distribution is 0.8 times its standard deviation. In the exponential smoothing technique, the MAD estimate is produced in the same manner as the forecast itself. In Table 5.2 an initial value of the forecast error MAD = 5.0 is assumed. Using a value of $a = 0.2$ and the initial values of forecast and MAD previously assumed, we calculate the MAD for February, 1963, as follows:

$$\begin{array}{cc} & \text{January error} \quad \text{January MAD} \\ \text{February MAD} = & (0.2)\ (6.6) + (1 - 0.2)\ (5.3) \\ = & 1.32 \quad\quad + \quad 4.24 \\ = & 5.6 \end{array}$$

and for March, 1963,

$$\begin{array}{cc} & \text{February error} \quad \text{February MAD} \\ \text{March MAD} = & (0.2)\ (4.7) + (1 - 0.2)\ (5.6) \\ = & 0.94 \quad\quad + \quad 4.48 \\ = & 5.4 \end{array}$$

The complete forecast for February, 1963, is for an expected demand of 25.3 units and a MAD of 5.6 units, and for March, 1963, the expected demand is 26.2 units and a MAD of 5.4 units. The importance of the MAD is that it provides us a basis for setting a safety stock to cover demand in excess of expectation. It is important to note that both the forecast and the MAD are for monthly periods. If the lead time over which the forecasts are applied are other than 1 month, it is necessary to scale the expected demand to the corresponding time interval. In the present example, the expected demand would be linear with the time period and the MAD will vary as the square root of the time period. That is to say if we are forecasting for a 2-month interval, the expected demand for 2 months will be double that for 1 month and the MAD will be $\sqrt{2} = 1.41$ times that for 1 month.

TABLE 5.2   Forecast errors

Year	Month	Orders (000)	Forecast ($a = 0.2$)	Absolute error, actual minus forecast	Mean absolute deviation (initial MAD = 5)
1963	January	30.6	24.0	6.6	5.3
	February	30.0	25.3	4.7	5.6
	March	44.6	26.2	18.4	5.4
	April	30.2	29.9	0.3	8.0
	May	41.2	30.0	11.2	6.5
	June	15.0	32.2	17.2	7.4
	July	36.7	28.8	7.9	9.4
	August	20.8	30.4	9.6	9.1
	September	38.1	28.5	9.6	9.2
	October	29.8	30.4	0.6	9.3
	November	40.5	30.3	10.2	7.6
	December	36.8	32.3	4.5	8.1
1964	January	27.8	33.2	5.4	7.4
	February	30.5	32.1	1.7	7.0
	March	40.7	31.8	8.9	5.9
	April	38.8	33.6	5.1	6.5
	May	34.8	34.6	0.2	6.2
	June	35.0	34.6	0.4	5.0
	July	38.0	34.7	3.3	4.1
	August	40.2	35.4	4.8	3.9
	September	29.2	36.4	7.2	4.1
	October	51.1	35.0	16.1	4.7
	November	39.3	38.2	1.1	7.0
	December	35.9	38.4	2.5	5.8
1965	January	32.5	37.9	5.4	5.1
	February	45.7	36.8	8.9	5.2
	March	35.4	38.6	3.2	5.9
	April	39.8	38.0	1.8	5.4
	May	56.5	38.4	18.1	4.7
	June	55.0	42.0	13.0	7.4
	July	46.5	44.6	1.9	8.5
	August	44.2	45.0	0.8	7.2

CONTROL OVER FORECASTS

Setting up procedures for making required forecasts is only the first step. Another part of the forecasting job, and an important one, is establishment of procedures or bases for reviewing forecasts made. Review or control breaks down into two parts: (1) determination whether forecasts are being made according to the procedures established; (2) measurement of the accuracy of forecasts made and determination of causes for major errors, as a basis for improving the quality or effectiveness of the forecasting procedures.

Control over use of procedures is particularly important in the case of short-term forecasts made in branches or factory storerooms for the control of individual items. The forecasting procedure may not be identified as such. It will often take the form of a simple calculating routine to be used in reviewing the size of, say, a reorder quantity. Where mechanical processing methods are used, routine forecasting procedures can be built in as part of the control-system routine.

Control over the quality of forecasts is another matter. All too often no critical examination of forecasts against actual results is made. It is important that a careful record be kept by the forecaster of actual versus forecast demand for each major forecast made for four reasons. In the first place, knowledge of the reliability of forecasts is basic to fixing inventory reserves needed to maintain service in the face of forecast error. Second, knowledge of the range or distribution of forecast errors and of the cost of maintaining inventory to absorb forecast error gives a basis for determining where effort should be concentrated in improving forecasts and how much effort is justified. Third, a record of forecast errors and an examination of the causes of major errors give the forecaster raw material to study in improving forecasting techniques and reliability. Fourth, a continuing record of forecast errors gives the forecaster and others a basis for determining whether there is any systematic bias in the forecast.

Control charts of the type used in control of quality in manufacturing operations are often useful devices for controlling forecast accuracy.[10] A continuing chart of the difference, forecast less actual demand, when maintained for each major forecast, gives an important record for determining the limits of forecast reliability, unexpectedly large forecast errors, and developing trends and biases in the forecast errors.

SUMMARY

Once it is recognized that forecasts are not merely desirable but logically necessary to a control system which is attempting to anticipate customer demand, four basic steps must be taken.

First comes the determination of what forecasts are necessary. What are

[10] R. K. Mueller, *Effective Management through Probability Controls*, Funk & Wagnalls Company, New York, 1950, gives an excellent general introduction to the concepts of probability control charts.

the functions of the control system with respect to each operating center and inventory? How far in advance must inventory build-up or replenishment be planned? What is the unit or quantity being forecast? These determinations must be made from top to bottom in the system—from forecasts for capacity planning through forecasts for level operation in the face of seasonal demand, from forecasts for week-to-week employment planning in operating centers to procedures for keeping item inventories in balance from day to day.

Next comes the question: How? Which forecasts should be made by the economist, if the company has one? Which can be made by statistical analyses of past sales or indicators of business activity? Which ones can best be made from field or executive opinion? Can combinations of techniques be used to give a cross check? Where can simple extrapolation techniques be used for frequently required short-term forecasts, e.g., of item demand or department load? What estimates of forecast reliability can be obtained? Can the idea of maximum-minimum forecasts be used to set limits on the expected range of demand?

Third, there is the question of responsibility. Who will be responsible for making the forecasts? Who will be responsible for the procedures used and resulting accuracy? Will costs of inventories because of forecast inaccuracy be charged to the responsibility of those making the forecast?

Finally, forecasts must be controlled. Can control charts be set up? Can provision be made for periodic, possibly annual, review of routine detailed forecasts? Can charges for forecast errors be used as a basis for control? For example, can the sales department be charged for the difference between a maximum-demand estimate and actual usage, in order to keep their maximum-demand estimates from becoming too conservative (high)?

PROBLEMS AND DISCUSSION TOPICS

1. The monthly demand for four items was recorded as follows:

Month	1	2	3	4	5	6	7	8	9	10	11	12
Item 1.	170	170	170	170	165	170	170	170	170	170	170	170
Item 2.	150	165	180	195	210	225	240	255	270	285	300	315
Item 3.	135	195	170	190	200	140	210	170	170	35	220	220
Item 4.	140	150	160	170	180	190	190	180	170	160	150	140

   a. Plot the monthly demand for each item.
   b. On the basis of the plot, estimate each demand for the thirteenth month; the fourteenth month.
   c. Explain the basis of your estimate.

    d. For which item do you believe your estimate for the thirteenth month is the most certain (in the sense that the percentage difference between actual and forecast demand will be least); for which, the least certain?

2. Which of the four items described in problem 1 will require the highest amount of safety stock; which, the least? Explain, describing the feature of the demand plot that determines the safety stock.
3. In forecasting demand for item 3 in problem 1, the projection method described on page 108 is used, with a weighting ratio $a = 0.1$. This method produces a forecast in the fifth month of 170 units for the sixth month. Continue the monthly forecasts for the seventh to the thirteenth months; tabulate the monthly forecast error (actual demand − forecast).
4. Describe and discuss the information you would like to have in preparing a 2-year forecast for a rubber-footwear manufacturer. What additional information would you need for a 10-year forecast?

BIBLIOGRAPHY

Brown, Robert G.: *Smoothing, Forecasting and Prediction,* Prentice-Hall, Inc., Englewood Cliffs, N.J., 1963.

Brown, Robert G.: *Statistical Forecasting for Inventory Control,* McGraw-Hill Book Company, New York, 1959.

Croxton, F. E., and D. J. Cowden, *Applied General Statistics,* Prentice-Hall, Inc., Englewood Cliffs, N.J., 1955.

Fetter, Robert B., and Winston C. Dalleck: *Decision Models for Inventory Management,* Richard D. Irwin, Inc., Homewood, Ill., 1961.

Fukuda, Y.: "Optimal Policies for the Inventory Problem with Negotiable Lead Time," *Management Science,* vol. 10, no. 4, pp. 690–708, July, 1964.

Hertz, D. B., and K. H. Schaffir: "A Forecasting Method for Management of Seasonal Style-goods Inventories, May, 1959," *Journal of the Operations Research Society of America,* pp. 45–52, January-February, 1960.

Moroney, M. J.: *Facts from Figures,* Penguin Books, Inc., Baltimore, 1954.

Parker, L. L.: "Economical Reorder Quantities and Reorder Points with Uncertain Demand," *Naval Research Logistics Quarterly,* vol. 11, no. 4, pp. 351–358, December, 1964.

Silver, Edward A.: "Bayesian Determination of the Reorder Point of a Slow Moving Item," *Operations Research,* vol. 13, no. 6, pp. 989–997, November-December, 1965.

Silver, Edward A.: "Some Characteristics of a Special Joint-order Inventory Model," *Operations Research,* vol. 13, no. 2, pp. 319–322, March-April, 1965.

Thompson, G. C.: "Forecasting Sales," *Studies in Business Policy,* no. 25, National Industrial Conference Board, Inc., New York, 1947.

Thompson, Howard E.: "Sales Forecasting Errors and Inventory Fluctuations: Random Errors and Random Sales," *Management Science,* vol. 12, no. 5, pp. 448–456, January, 1966.

Wright, Wilson: *Forecasting for Profit,* John Wiley & Sons, Inc., New York, 1947.

6

SYSTEMATIC
CONTROL
OF
INVENTORY

INTEGRATION OF SYSTEMS ELEMENTS

Effective and efficient inventory management requires routine application of the concepts discussed in the preceding chapters. Management must establish operating objectives which can be translated into inventory objectives. The task of inventory management is one of controlling inventory through the selection of the time to order and the quantity to order, taking full account of likely future requirements (demand) and the uncertainties in their estimate, inventory, and ordering or setup costs. The inventory manager must, in short, implement a higher-echelon policy decision in a "best" sense. (The process is necessarily circular since the higher-level policy planning must be made after evaluating alternative policies. For example, a policy which requires inventory to provide a particular level of service should be based on an understanding of the inventory investment which that level of service will require.) Good decisions regarding the timing of replenishment orders and their size require application of the order-quantity and forecast considerations previously described.

The inventory manager facing the task of controlling an inventory of perhaps several thousand different items with a limited management effort must, for practical reasons, systematize his decision-making efforts. He must find the best available solutions to the problems of order quantity and ordering frequency, and he must find a way of applying these solutions in a routine way. Each inventory situation presents its own unique set of considerations and requirements, and it is difficult to prescribe any particular form of system for a given inventory situation without examining that situation in some detail. There are various forms of inventory-control systems, and the choice of a system for a particular application depends on the information available for its operation and the level of performance desired of the inventory.

FIXED ORDER QUANTITY SYSTEMS

Probably the oldest and most common reordering systems use a fixed-order quantity and a variable ordering interval. The inventory can be broken into two independent segments: cycle stock, as discussed in Chapter 4, and safety stock. Under a fixed-order system, the same *quantity* of material is always ordered. The *time* an order is placed is allowed to vary with fluctuations in usage. The workings of the system can be seen in Figure 6.1. An order is placed whenever an amount on hand is just sufficient to meet a "reasonable" maximum demand over the course of a replenishment lead time, as shown in Figure 6.1.

FIGURE 6.1   **Basis for determination of reorder point and safety stocks**

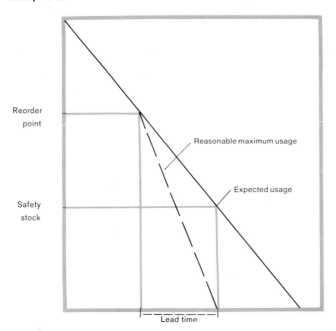

This type of reorder system is a close relation to one of the oldest stock-control systems in common industrial use, the *two-bin* system. In this type of system, commonly used in parts warehouses, for manufacturing floor stocks and in similar circumstances where large numbers of low-value items are controlled, the stock is physically segregated into two bins, hence the name. Stock is drawn from one bin until it is empty. When the first bin is empty, a reorder is placed; thereafter stock is drawn from the second bin; the second bin is stocked at a level believed to be adequate to meet demand during the time required to receive the replenishment stock. The two-bin system is simple to operate and requires a minimum of record keeping.

A system with a fixed-order quantity can be specified by (1) the lead time U between placing and receiving an order; (2) the order size q; (3) the safety stock S; and (4) the expected demand rate d. The expected inventory balance—i.e., if demands were made uniformly at the expected rate d—is shown in Figure 6.1. The inventory balance, averaged over time, is the safety stock S plus half the order size q:

$$I = S + q/2$$

The reorder point (Y in Figure 6.2) is the inventory balance at which a new order is placed. The reorder point is reached when the inventory balance equals expected demand during the lead time plus the safety stock needed to protect against possible excess demand over that expected during the lead time.

However, when the lead time is long relative to the expected time between orders, care is needed in defining the rule governing reordering and the reorder point. If the lead time is 3 months, for example, and the amount purchased at each order is a 1-month supply, this does not mean that it is

FIGURE 6.2 Expected inventory balance, demand uniform at expected rate

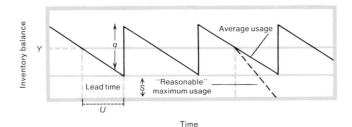

necessary to place a new order when the amount on hand drops to a maximum 3 months' usage. Since an order will be placed, on the average, once a month, there will almost certainly be some orders outstanding all the time which, on being filled, will help replenish the inventory on hand. Thus it is characteristic of replenishment systems that the safety stocks, reorder points, and the like should be based *both on the amount on hand and on order.* Where the lead time is short compared with the usual time between orders, as is assumed in most factory two-bin systems, the amount on hand and the total on hand and on order are in fact equivalent at the time of reordering.

Safety stock in a fixed-order system

The amount of stock currently on hand and on order is the maximum amount that will be available for use during the period in the future up to a time equal to the lead time. If the amount on hand and on order is kept in excess of maximum requirements during a lead time in the future, no problems should be encountered.

The inventory actually on hand at any time is the difference between the total of orders placed up to a lead time previously and the sum of cumulative forecast requirements and cumulative forecast errors to date. A reorder is placed whenever available stock reaches or drops below lead time requirements; that is:

$$\text{Inventory on hand} + \text{orders placed but not received} = \text{forecast demand over the lead time} + \text{safety stock}$$

Since inventory on hand and already on order is the most that will be available for use during the lead time when the new order is being filled, the inventory on hand will reach a minimum at the end of the lead time. If the forecast usage rate is unbiased, the expected inventory on hand at the end of the lead time is the safety stock. This is the expected level of the minimum points. However, the actual minimum balance will fluctuate. The fluctuations in the minimum balance on hand will be just equal to the fluctuations in actual demand during one lead time compared with forecast or average demand. Whenever actual demand exceeds the forecast over a lead time by more than the safety stock, the inventory will run out.

To fix the safety-stock level, therefore, two pieces of information are required: (1) a distribution of differences between forecast and actual demand over a lead time, showing how frequently these differences may be expected to exceed any given size;[1] and (2) an agreement as to how frequently run-outs may be allowed to occur. The size of forecast error which is exceeded only with the allowed frequency can be determined. This is the size of the safety stock required to give the required degree of protection against run-out.

The MAD as described on page 112 provides the first of the two pieces of information needed to fix the safety-stock level. The MAD, as a measure of the dispersion of the demand, provides an estimate of the probability that demand will exceed forecast by any stated amount. It is possible, therefore, to provide a safety stock equivalent to some multiple of the MAD in order to obtain a specified protection against excess demand, that is, against stock-out. The matter of the *kind* of protection desired is taken up in the next section; the concern here is with amount of protection against simple stock-out provided by an amount of safety stock.

It is obvious that the additional amount of protection against stock-out diminishes with additional increments of safety stock. The first unit of stock in excess of expected lead-time demand provides the largest increment of protection against stock-out; the second, a little less, and so on. Similarly, if safety stock for an item is provided in multiples of MAD, the protection against stock-out afforded is as follows:

Multiples of MAD	Probability of Stock-out
0.0	0.50
0.5	0.27
1.0	0.11
1.5	0.03
2.0	0.01
2.5	less than 0.001

Service levels

The key to setting the safety-stock level, however, is the "reasonable" maximum usage during the lead time as shown in Figure 6.1. Each storage unit in the manufacturing-distribution system serves either the demands of

[1] The lead time itself may vary if suppliers are unreliable or if the time an order spends in transit fluctuates. This type of variability should be taken into account, if it is serious, in calculating usage or demand fluctuations during a lead time. This can be most simply decided by comparing the variability of lead time with the variability of demand, expressed in commensurable units, time supply, for example. The total variance (see Glossary) in lead-time demand is the sum of the variance in demand over the expected lead time and the variance in the lead time itself.

customers for finished products or the demands of operating units for materials or both. We would like these demands to be met. The maximum usage against which the inventory protects depends on the nature of short-term fluctuations in the rate of usage or demand and the risk the management is prepared to face in running out of stock. This maximum level is the level of sales or usage beyond which the management is prepared to face the shortages.

Setting a safety stock implies some kind of management decision or judgment with respect to the maximum usage or demand level to be allowed for, the allowable risk of service failure, or the cost of service failure. This must be balanced against inventory cost to determine an appropriate level of safety stock once service failure or the service requirement is defined.

There are a number of ways of defining the service requirement, each appropriate to particular circumstances. *Reliability* of service, the measure of service performance of an inventory, refers to the level of certainty with which the intended *availability* is achieved. An inventory cannot make goods available to a distant user as rapidly as a nearby one; service performance measurements should recognize this fact and should specify performance in terms of this intended standard. The availability standards are usually not stated explicitly by the firm; policy on availability is instead expressed by the decisions made in locating stocking points.

The reliability of service, on the other hand, can be defined in various ways. Something more than the simple directives to the inventory controller to "give good service" and "prevent back orders" is needed. A more operational definition of service reliability is needed in order to provide a meaningful measure of performance and to establish the inventory requirements for providing desired levels of service. The following are some useful standards of service reliability.

Fraction of Order Cycles without Stock-out. Service reliability here is defined as the fraction of replenishment cycles completed without depletion of stock.

$$\text{Reliability} = 1 - \frac{\text{number of stock-outs}}{\text{number of replenishments}}$$

If, for example, in the course of the weekly replenishment of an item, stock had run out five times during the year,

$$\text{Reliability} = 1 - \frac{5}{52} = 1 - 0.096 = 0.904$$

or a 90.4 per cent reliability (service level). This definition may be applied to a single item over a number of replenishment cycles, as in the example above, or to a large number of items in a single cycle. Obviously when a stocking policy based on this form of service is applied to a broad line of items the faster-moving items will show a greater number of stock-outs per period than the slower-moving ones. The firm accordingly can concentrate its expediting energies on these fast-moving items which affect a large volume of sales.

Expected Stock-out Rate. Instead of measuring the number of stock-outs relative to the number of order cycles, we can measure the number of stock-outs in an item per unit of time. This definition is useful when it is desired that all items have the same frequency of stock-out. The performance measure in this case is not a dimensionless reliability of service; it is instead an *un*reliability rate, the number of stock-out occurrences per unit of time.

Fraction of Demand Filled from Stock. This measure of service reliability considers back ordering a unit of a fast-moving item and a unit of a slow-moving item as equally undesirable. To give validity to this concept, back-order volume is expressed in sales value rather than stock units. In employing this measure, it is assumed that the actual volume of unfilled demand is known. If back orders are logged and shipped when stock becomes available, then the unfilled demand can be measured. In many inventory situations it is difficult to measure demand and to measure the sales which are lost.

Fraction of Orders Shipped Complete. A firm occasionally must place a premium on shipment of complete orders. In those cases where the costs of filling an order are high and not strongly dependent on either the quantity ordered or the number of items ordered, it is of interest to ship complete orders. This measure of service reliability is dimensionally the same as the fraction of demand filled from stock but generally will be numerically lower.

Fraction of Time out of Stock. This measure is usually numerically equivalent to the fraction of demand filled from stock. Over the long term, if 95 per cent of demand is available from stock, the items are in stock 95 per cent of the time.

Fraction of Line Items Filled. In wholesale or retail distribution, there is frequently less importance attached to the available quantity of the items ordered than to the fact that some quantity is available at all. In such cases service reliability is measured in terms of the fraction of lines in a multiline order filled from stock.

All these definitions are related one to another, basically because they are all closely related to the probability distribution of sales, i.e., to the expected pattern of sales about the average. The choice of an appropriate safety stock in any particular two-bin or similar reordering system depends both on the definition of an appropriate measure of service or risk and on the selection of a level of risk which seems appropriate in view of costs of carrying inventory and the costs, losses, and inconveniences of being out of stock.

Three general problems arise in the application of one or another of these measures of service. First, given that the appropriate definition can be arrived at, it is not at all easy to arrive at an objective measure of what the level of service ought to be, say, by balancing costs. Sometimes, however, it is possible to help operating management arrive at some judgment with respect to good service level by showing the relation—graphically or in tabular form—between service level and inventory requirements, as discussed above.

For example, Figure 6.3 shows, for a hypothetical example, the number of weeks in which the demand for switches may be expected to equal or

FIGURE 6.3 Cumulative distribution of weekly demand

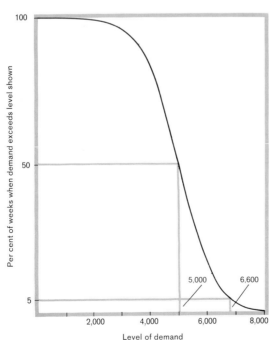

Per cent of weeks when demand exceeds level shown

Level of demand

exceed any specified level. If it takes Brown & Brown, Inc., a week to replenish its stocks and the management wishes to keep the risk of running out of stock at a point where it will expect to be out of stock only once every 20 times, i.e., 5 per cent of the times the stock approaches depletion, then it will have to schedule the stock replenishment when the inventory of switches on hand drops to 6,600 units. In this case the expected or average weekly usage is 5,000 switches. Thus the safety stock maintained is 6,600 (inventory on hand when reordering—reasonable maximum sales during a lead time) minus 5,000 (average or expected sales during a lead time), equaling 1,600 switches.

However, if the management were willing to accept a 10 per cent risk, i.e., a 10 per cent chance that stock will run out before a replenishment is received, about 6,200 units would be needed on hand when a reorder is placed, giving a safety stock of 1,200 units. Carrying the extra 400 units to reduce the risk from 10 to 5 per cent implies that this reduction is at least worth the annual carrying cost of the extra units in inventory.

The cost of service failure, on the other hand, is real but far from explicit. It rarely, if ever, appears on the accounting records of the company except hidden in extra sales or manufacturing costs, and it is characteristically very hard to define. The choice by management of any desired inventory or service-risk level implies a cost attributed intuitively or indirectly to service failure. Determining the relation between the appropriate inventory level and service cost gives the management an indication of what it is in fact assuming as a service cost, as a means for determining whether this assumption is anywhere near realistic.

For example, one often hears the policy flatly stated: "Back orders are intolerable." This type of absolute statement can be converted into a quantitative statement by use of devices of the type shown in Figure 6.4. Figure 6.4 shows the facts which might be displayed for the management of a hypothetical company to help it decide on a customer-service policy. To get a 90 per cent level of customer service (i.e., to fill 90 per cent of orders immediately), a little over 3 weeks' stock must be carried—an investment of $67,000 with an annual carrying cost of $13,500. Filling another 5 per cent of orders immediately (increasing the service level to 95 per cent) would mean about 2 days' more stock, with an additional annual cost of $1,300. Filling an other 4 per cent (a 99 per cent service level) would cost an extra $2,700 per year. At each point the management can decide whether the extra cost is justified by the improved service. This illustrates a management device for comparing policies on service and inventories for consistency and rationality.

A second difficulty in defining a measure of service precisely is that in the

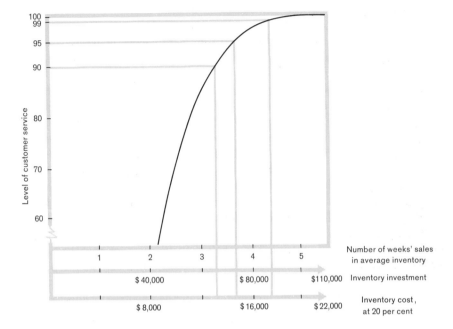

FIGURE 6.4 Representative relation between inventory and service level

short run service experience may depart widely from the expected service level, especially where a high level of service has been specified. Since operations must be conducted in the short run, it may be necessary to set the service level a good deal higher than is desired in the long run in order to have reasonable assurance of attaining the desired level in the short run.

A third problem is technical—the problem of working out, in a particular case with a particular frequency distribution of quantities demanded and specified definition of service, the relation between the level of service and the safety stock, especially where an analytic expression is sought. However, the first two problems noted tend to lessen the desirability or benefit of precision in statement here. It is possible, of course, that not only will the sales rate be subject to random variations, but the delivery or replenishment time of an order will also vary. In this case, a minimum inventory must be established with reference to the probability that sales will exceed given levels before an order is received, i.e., with reference to the joint distribution of sales and delivery times.

The experience of many companies suggests that a useful statement of service requirements has two elements. To put it first very loosely, any "normal" demand should be met within a "reasonable" time. To define "normal" and "reasonable" more closely, we must distinguish between customer demand and operating unit or internal demand. What a customer considers to be a reasonable time depends very much on the product and on trade practice. A housewife going to a store for a dozen eggs expects immediate service, and if one store is out of eggs, she will go to another. The purchaser of a railroad locomotive, on the other hand, expects to wait a number of months for delivery. For any one product, however, there is a time, determined by custom, within which a customer can expect service—the service time. For internal demand, the service time is governed by economy. If the service time in supplying a stock point is too long, the inventory at the stock point will have to be large to meet demand on it. If the service time is too short, this may mean uneconomical processing or large inventories of raw materials or parts feeding into the operation producing the item.

"Normal" demand is also ambiguous. It suggests, however, that the operating management chooses limits of demand within which they would like the system to operate routinely, but it is willing to face the need to take emergency action if demand falls outside the established limits. The uncertainties in customer demand are usually such, and affect demand for parts and raw materials in such a way, that whatever limits are chosen as the limits of normal demand, there is always some risk that the actual demand will fall outside these limits. If the limits are wide, this risk is small. The system will cope routinely with almost any circumstance, but inventories, which depend directly on the width of these limits, must be large. If the limits are narrow, inventories for routine operation will be low, but the system will frequently be in a state of emergency.

This way of specifying the service requirement is useful, often because operating executives find it easier to define a service policy in terms of "reasonable" service and "normal" demand levels than to agree on and understand a service policy based, say, on a 5 per cent chance of run-out on each reorder. On the other hand, this type of statement of service policy or requirements can be directly interpreted in terms of inventory and operating requirements. For example, the policy might be stated: Immediate delivery on all business up to 30,000 units per month. This policy in fact defines the maximum reasonable demand for the coverage, 30,000 units per month. If the lead time in supplying the item to stock were one month and the expected number of items ordered were about 20,000 per month, the safety stock carried would be 30,000 minus 20,000, or 10,000 units. The frequency with which "emergencies" will arise is the same as the frequency with which run-outs will occur, and this depends on the distribution of actual demand about the forecast or expected rate over a lead time.

Relation between safety stock and order size

To a first approximation, in reorder systems of the constant order size type, the order size is determined by the cost of ordering, inventory carrying costs, and the mean sales rate, as discussed in Chapter 4; and the safety stock is determined by the lead time and the usage forecast reliability. The resulting inventory is made up of two components

$$I = S + q/2$$

independently arrived at.[2] The interaction among frequency of reorder, the size of reorder, and safety stocks is often ignored, as being unimportant, in setting up even fairly sophisticated inventory-control schemes. This is frequently and justifiably done to simplify inventory control, particularly methods for adjusting reorder quantities and safety stocks to changing costs and sales.

However, analysis will show that the safety stock, reorder quantity, reorder level, and the like, are not entirely independent under the fixed order size system. Where the order size is fixed, the minimum stock fixes the risk to be borne each time the inventory approaches the reorder point. The size of the amount ordered, however, determines the frequency of exposure to risk. The bigger the order placed, the less frequently will the inventory be exposed to run-out; thus, with a fixed safety level, the risk will be lower or the level of service will be higher. Therefore the risk of depletion will vary inversely with the size of the order quantity for a fixed safety stock.

The precise way the required safety stock depends on order quantity and the lead time is related directly to the average level of protection desired (or frequency of run-out permitted) and the distribution of actual demand about the expected level over a lead time. For example, if a run-out on the average of once every 4 years is permitted, and the order quantity equals an average of 1 month's usage, then a safety stock is needed to bring the chance of run-out on each reorder down to 2 per cent. On the other hand, if the order quantity will last 3 months on the average, since the number of exposures is reduced, the risk of run-out on each reorder can be increased to 6 per cent, cutting the safety-stock requirements. Whitin[3] discusses the form of this interaction under certain specific assumptions about the form of the distribution of actual demand, and Parker describes a method of incorporating order size into the safety-stock calculation.[4]

[2] See p. 119.
[3] T. M. Whitin, *The Theory of Inventory Management*, Princeton University Press, Princeton, N.J., 1953, p. 56 ff.
[4] L. L. Parker, "Economical Reorder Quantities and Reorder Points with Uncertain Demand," *Naval Research Logistics Quarterly*, vol. 11, no. 4, pp. 351–358, December, 1964.

In many practical cases, the most economical relationship between re-order point and order quantity can be worked out numerically or graphically as follows:

1. Choose a series of possible order quantities.
2. Divide each into the average usage rate, to obtain the average number of orders per year.
3. Multiply the number of orders by the cost of making an order, to obtain the annual ordering costs under each assumed order quantity.
4. Multiply one-half the order quantities by the annual unit carrying cost, to obtain the annual carrying cost of cycle stock under each assumed order quantity.
5. Divide the allowed annual frequency of run-out by the number of orders per year, to obtain the allowed risk of run-out on each order for each assumed order quantity.
6. From the observed or calculated distribution of demand about the average or expected level, determine the safety stock required, to obtain the allowed risk of run-out for each assumed order quantity.
7. Multiply the required safety stock corresponding to each assumed order quantity by the annual unit inventory carrying cost, to obtain safety-stock carrying costs.
8. Add the reordering costs (point 3), cycle-inventory costs (point 4), and safety-stock costs (point 7) corresponding to each assumed order quantity. Make a graph of total annual cost versus order quantity, similar to Figure 4.2 (page 57), and choose the order quantity with lowest indicated total costs.

DEFINITION OF COMPONENTS IN A FIXED-ORDER SYSTEM

Where a system of the fixed-order type is used for maintaining in-process inventories, it is important that the demand for components be carefully analyzed in order that the definition of items held in inventory be consistent with the assumptions upon which the system is based. Such a system assumes a homogeneous demand. Where the demand for a given component is a mixed stream arising from two different sources with different characteristics, attempts to control this component by the use of a single inventory and reorder system may lead to excessive inventory and reordering costs. For example, where a component is used both for a standard item produced in relatively large runs and for special items produced on an occasional basis, the combined demand for the component is likely to be heterogeneous, made up of orders arising at random for a small number of components of special items together with more regularly placed orders for large quantities of the component for standard product assembly runs.

FIXED-INTERVAL SYSTEMS

The use of a fixed-reorder cycle with variable order quantities is a major alternative open to the use of a fixed-order system, where uncertainty forces departure from the pattern of uniform order quantities placed at regular intervals. Periodic reordering systems are popular and are frequently used, particularly where some type of book inventory control is employed, and where it is convenient to examine inventory stocks on a fixed time cycle, for example, in warehouse control or in systems where orders are placed mechanically. Continuous review of inventory balances, such as is required in fixed-quantity systems, may be awkward and extremely expensive; as an alternative, inventory balances on individual items will be periodically reviewed, for example, daily, weekly, or monthly.

A variety of rules or procedures can be used, but the basic idea underlying all of them is the same; namely, look at stocks on a fixed frequency, e.g., once a month, and place a replenishment order based on the amount used or demanded since the last review, as shown in Figure 6.5. The problem is that many of these superficially very similar ways of handling a fixed-reorder system may have hidden traps. A typical difficulty is instability in reordering habits and inventory levels caused by "over-compensation," i.e., by attempting to outguess the market or usage rates and to assume that high

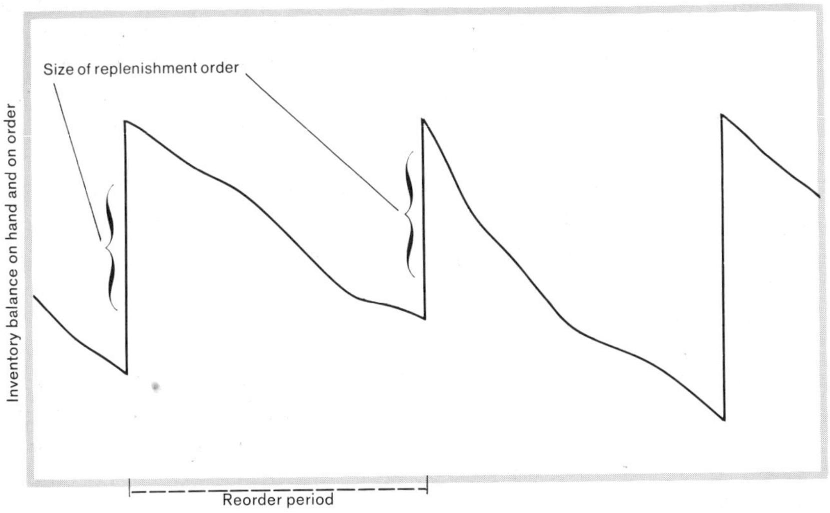

FIGURE 6.5 Inventory balances under a fixed-period replenishment system

or low usage or demand at one point, due possibly to purely random causes, indicates an established trend which must be anticipated. Lack of care in selecting the review period or the order-replenishment rule can lead to instability in inventory balances or excess requirements of safety stock to preserve customer service.

To take a simple but not uncommon example, suppose the inventory of an item is reviewed monthly. If the expected or average usage were 20 units per month but in some months it jumped to 30 units, the production controller might anticipate a continuing usage rate of 30 units monthly. He might therefore place an order not only to replenish the 30 units withdrawn but also to build up the inventory by another 10 units to meet the expected higher-usage trend, a total order of 40 units. This will be all right if in fact the trend exists. However, demand fluctuations frequently are random; during the next period, demand might total only 15 units. Now, since 10 extra units were ordered in the previous period, only 5 need be ordered to replenish stocks to meet the average usage rate. Variations in demand from 30 to 15 units per month lead to monthly production orders varying from 40 to 5 units. The value of good demand forecasts is evident.

One industrial-abrasives manufacturer found himself in a characteristic state of being out of stock or having too much stock, even though his inventory-control procedures were, superficially at least, soundly conceived. The procedures worked as follows: Each week the production-scheduling clerk examined the ledger card on each item, and each month he placed a replenishment order on the factory based on the existing finished stock on hand in the warehouse, and a projection for the coming 2-month period, based on a lead time of 6 weeks, of the change in the rate of sales during the past 2-month period. When inventories were below normal or standard, production was increased to make up the difference plus anticipated shortage if the high sales rate continued. The opposite was done if inventories were high. The manufacturer blamed the instability of his market and the perversity of his customers for the difficulties he faced in controlling inventory when in fact the seemingly logical reorder rule he had developed made his production rate overreact to essentially chance fluctuations in demand, to the point where production fluctuations were greater than demand fluctuations.

Concepts of servo theory

The techniques and concepts of servo theory have been found particularly useful in studying the design of efficient fixed-period systems. Servo theory is a body of concepts and mathematical methods which has been developed during the past three decades, originally by electrical engineers, to assist in the analysis and design of automatically or remotely controlled systems. Some concepts of servo theory which are important in inventory control are feedback, lags or reaction times, the type of control, and the notion of stability.

Feedback is basically the use of information on what already has happened in the controlled system to control the system in the future. Most control systems make use of feedback. Servo theory provides an explicit basis for analysis of the efficiency with which feedback information is used. Lags, or reaction times, refer to the time it takes for a command from the control system to take effect. These likewise can have important influences on the efficiency of the system. For example, where the lags are long because of physical characteristics, too tight control may lead to unnecessary fluctuations; or where lags are long because of design characteristics of the control system, the analysis can indicate the cost of these lags in terms of production fluctuations or inventory requirements. Stability is the tendency of a system to return to some "normal" or desired state in the face of shocks imposed from the outside. The type of control system—e.g., whether the system responds to accumulated change (integral control) or to the current rate of change (differential control)—may be very important.

We are constantly required to use control systems of one sort or another in dealing with people and in using things around us. In one sense, a good administrator must have a well-organized, built-in control system, to respond properly to his organization's actual performance, in contrast with his plans for it, so that he can issue considered instructions to stimulate correction without being excessively rigid or upsetting. As another example, it is extremely uncomfortable and can be dangerous to drive an automobile which has little or no play in its steering wheel and which responds too rapidly to small adjustments of the wheel. It is clear, on the other hand, that an automobile would be not only dangerous but quite useless if the steering mechanism had full play and exerted no control over the car's direction.

Experience and trial and error have enabled automobile mechanics to develop a "feel" for the right amount of play to allow in a car's steering mechanism. But some other kinds of systems are less easy to analyze solely through experience and are much more difficult and expensive to correct. Servo theory gives a means for analyzing the behavior of control systems and showing the effect, explicitly, of the concepts described above.

An inventory-control system, though not a mechanical device, is a control system and consequently is subject to the same ills as mechanical servos. Studies of industrial inventory management problems have rather frequently shown that existing inventory-control methods in industry often violate sound control concepts. The economy of the company is maintained, in the face of instability and inefficiency in the inventory-control system, only because of constant attention and the exercise of overriding common sense, and the use of expediting and other emergency measures outside the routine of the system. A control system that works only when there are no problems —nothing needing control—is no control system at all.

Applications of servo techniques to fixed-interval systems

Discrete variable servo techniques can be applied to the analysis of inventory control and reorder rules of the fixed-reorder cycle type.[5] These techniques can be used to design automatic reorder rules and to show that the resulting rule is efficient for the conditions stated, in the sense that it produces the smallest average fluctuation in the inventory balance relative to any sequence of fluctuations in demand compared with forecast.

Under the following assumptions:

1. That the reorder system operates on a fixed-order interval
2. That the lead time, defined as the time required to receive an order for replenishment of stocks after it is placed, is fixed
3. That customer orders are shipped as soon as possible

an efficient and stable reorder rule can be designed in the following simple form:

1. A forecast or estimate of the amount to be demanded is made for a period ahead equal to the delivery lead time plus one reorder cycle.
2. An order is placed to bring the total inventory on hand and on order up to the total demand forecast for the lead time plus cycle time ahead, plus a standard allowance for safety stock.

The simplicity of the rule suggests its usefulness in minimizing costs of stock replenishment in warehouse operations or raw-materials procurement.

The operation of the reorder rule, and the required inventory balances, depend on certain given or imposed conditions:

1. The order-replenishment lead time
2. The forecast usage or demand rate
3. The distribution of demand-forecast errors

[5] See H. J. Vassian, "Application of Discrete Variable Servo Theory to Inventory Control," *Journal of the Operations Research Society of America*, vol. 3, no. 3, pp. 272–282, August, 1955, and J. Forrester, *Industrial Dynamics*, The M.I.T. Press, Cambridge, Mass., 1961.

and certain controllable conditions or elements:

1. The length of the reorder cycle, i.e., how frequently the inventory is checked
2. The allowable risk of back order or run-out (where the risk of run-out may be specified or defined in any of the ways discussed earlier in this chapter)

Establishing a reorder rule makes it necessary to balance certain costs, including investment requirements, the allowable risk of run-out or the run-out cost, and the clerical costs associated with operating the system. The investment cost will usually be a function of the average inventory size, and the clerical costs a function of the reorder cycle. For example, usually the investment cost of inventories is directly proportional to the average inventory balance, and usually the controllable clerical cost changes directly in proportion to the frequency of reorder, i.e., in inverse proportion to the length of the reorder cycle. Given any specified relation or dependence of operating or investment costs on average inventory, specified back-order or run-out risk and length of reorder cycle, it is possible to choose the reorder cycle and risk level to minimize total cost. This, of course, need not be done analytically. Use of graphical methods will permit one to arrive relatively quickly at the specification of controllable items which will minimize the over-all cost of operating the system once the dependence of cost components on the controllable items and average inventory has been determined.

As noted above, the replenishment order placed each period is designed to cover the total-demand forecast for the lead time plus cycle time ahead, plus an allowance for safety stock; i.e., to cover the total maximum demand anticipated over the lead time plus cycle time ahead. Call this the "target" inventory. The inventory balance on hand and on order will reach a minimum just before the end of a reorder cycle, before a new order is placed, and a maximum (equal to the target level) just after a new order is placed. The average inventory on hand and on order, therefore, will be the target level less half the average usage during a reorder cycle.

The average inventory on hand and on order can be viewed as composed of three elements:

1. The *safety stock*, the average level of minimum balances on hand. The safety stock is designed to absorb fluctuations in the minimum balances, as under a fixed-order system. In a fixed-period system the amount of stock on hand at the minimum points will fluctuate by the same amount as the differences between actual and expected demand over the period of a lead time plus cycle time. Thus the required safety stock can be

determined from an analysis of these fluctuations together with a specified risk of run-out.

2. The *cycle stock,* equal to half the average quantity ordered, i.e., half the average usage during one cycle.

3. The *stock on order but undelivered,* which will equal the average usage during the lead time.

Therefore the target inventory can be built up from the safety stock plus the average demand during one cycle (twice the cycle stock) plus the average amount undelivered (average demand over the lead time).

RELATED REORDER SYSTEMS

Modifications of the simplest fixed-interval reorder system or compromises between the fixed-interval system and the fixed-quantity rules are possible and often useful, not only as practical operating systems, but also as models for the examination of certain inventory-systems characteristics.

(s, S) system

The class of system used to review inventory stocks on a periodic basis replenishes these stocks only when stocks on hand and on order have fallen to or below a specified level. When this happens, an order is placed to bring the amount of stock on hand and on order up to a specified maximum level. The frequency of review and the minimum and maximum inventory points can be determined by methods similar to those described earlier in this book. This system of control is particularly useful where the cost of making a review and the cost of placing an order are separate and significant. This class of systems has been named the (s, S) system. This system and many of its variations are widely described in the literature.[6] The ordering rule for an (s, S) system is very simply stated: If fewer than s[7] units are available (on hand plus on order) order enough to bring stock up to a level S; otherwise, do not order. In application to a fixed-interval system, the rules operate as follows:

[6] Cf. K. Arrow, T. Harris, and J. Marshak, "Optimal Inventory Policy," *Econometrica,* vol. 19, no. 3, July, 1951; K. Arrow, S. Karlin, and H. Scarf, *Studies in the Mathematical Theory of Inventory and Production,* Stanford University Press, Stanford, Calif., 1958, chaps. 8–10, 14, 15; H. Greenberg, "Stock Level Distributions for (s, S) Inventory Problems," *Naval Research Logistics Quarterly,* vol. 11, no. 4, pp. 343–350, December, 1964.
[7] Not to be confused with the demand rate s in Chap. 4.

1. Choose two inventory levels S and s, S larger than s.
2. At each review period, compare the available inventory I with S and s.
3. If I lies between S and s, place no order.

If I is at or below the level s, place an order for an amount equal to $S - I$.

This system is obviously controlled by three variables:

1. The maximum available inventory S
2. The reorder point s
3. The length of review period or interval between reviews

This compares with two controllable elements in the systems described above—the time between reviews and target inventory under the fixed-period system, or the reorder quantity and reorder point in the fixed-order or two-bin system. Choice of the three controllable elements to minimize total cost depends on considerations very similar to those mentioned under the other systems.

The reorder point s must be chosen large enough so that whenever the inventory on hand and on order is greater than s, the system is protected from run-out to the desired degree over a period equal to the lead time plus review period. Just as in the case of the fixed-reorder system, the reorder point s represents two components: expected or average demand over the lead time plus review period, plus a reserve against unexpected fluctuations in demand over this period. The reserve component will tend to increase if the review period is made longer, since the uncertainty in total usage will tend to be greater.

The average inventory on hand will equal the safety stock (the reserve against demand fluctuations over a lead time plus review period) plus one-half the average quantity ordered. Since the safety stock, and the cost of carrying it, and the annual clerical costs of reviewing stock levels all depend on the length of the review period, the length of the review period should be chosen to minimize the total of these. Then, fixing the length of the review period sets the reorder point s.

The difference between the maximum-inventory level S and the reorder point s fixes the minimum order that will be placed. The average order placed will be somewhat larger than this; the actual order placed will vary from time to time, and the size of actual orders will depend in detail on the characteristics of demand. As an approximation, the average order placed will equal the difference $S - s$, plus one-half the usage or demand during a review cycle.

The desired average-order size can be calculated using the formula given in Chapter 4:

$$x = \sqrt{\frac{2Ad}{i}}$$

where x = average quantity to be obtained on each order
A = cost of placing or getting an order
d = annual demand
i = annual cost of holding one unit in stock

Then, using the approximation given above, the average order size x will be

$$x = \sqrt{\frac{2Ad}{i}} \cong S - s + Vd$$

where V = length of one review period
Vd = average or expected usage during a period

Thus the maximum-inventory level S can be calculated from the formula

$$S = \sqrt{\frac{2Ad}{i}} - s + \frac{Vd}{2}$$

This scheme for choosing the maximum-inventory level S, the reorder point s, and the review period length V is of course approximate. Arrow, Harris and Marshak[8] discuss the problems of finding an exact solution by analytical means. Basically the difficulty arises from the fact that inventories and actions taken in one period are not independent of other periods. The inventory balance at the beginning of a period is a result of past demand and past replenishment actions. Actions taken during the period influence future inventory balances and costs.

Alternative replenishment flow patterns

Figure 6.6 illustrates schematically some of the variations in the flow of products and parts typical of many manufacturing operations. These operations are usually characterized by a wide line of finished products put together from a large variety of parts or subassemblies. The parts or subassemblies may each go into a number of finished items. Customers may also order parts and subassemblies separately, or these may be used in making one or a few specially ordered products.

Some of the variations in Figure 6.6 include (designated by numbers in parentheses):

[8] *Loc. cit.*

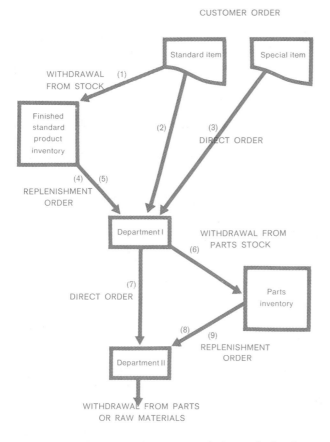

FIGURE 6.6 Alternative order-routing methods, standard and special items

Methods of handling customer orders for standard items:
1. The order is filled from finished inventory.
2. The item ordered is made up on demand in Department I.

Handling customer orders for special items:
3. The item is made up on demand in Department I.

Replenishing finished stocks:
4. Finished stocks are reordered unit by unit as units are shipped to customers.
5. Finished stocks are reordered in economical-run quantities from Department I.

Obtaining required parts in Department I:

6. The parts are drawn from a parts inventory for either an individual customer order or for manufacturing stock for finished inventory.
7. Requirements for a run in Department I are ordered directly from Department II.

Replenishing parts inventory:

8. Parts are replenished by ordering an economical-run quantity in Department II.
9. Parts are replenished by ordering unit by unit as units are withdrawn by Department I.

These individual alternatives are found in many plants. Of course, the number of departments and stocks is generally much greater and the flow of parts more complex. However, the essential characteristics of inventory-control and reordering systems employing these alternates can be seen more easily from the simplified scheme of Figure 6.6. Some common inventory-control and reordering systems made up of combinations of these include the following:

1. Perhaps the most common system is one in which finished-stock and parts inventories are kept, and each is controlled separately, using a fixed order size system. Customer orders for standard items are filled from finished stock. When the stock is depleted to a reorder point, an order is placed on Department I to make replenishments. Department I in turn draws down on parts stocks, and when these are drawn down to a reorder point, a replenishment order is placed on Department II.

   Orders for special items are placed directly on Department I. Parts are drawn from the parts stock (excluding, of course, special parts ordered from the parts-fabricating department directly).

   This arrangement requires: (*a*) inventories of finished-stock items sufficient to meet maximum demand during a lead time in Department I (essentially, the inventory on hand of finished items equaling, on the average, the safety stock to cover the Department I lead time, plus one-half a reorder quantity); and (*b*) inventories of components on hand and on order sufficient to meet maximum demand during the Department II lead time (again, inventories on hand equaling the safety stock covering the lead time, plus one-half the reorder quantity, on the average). This can mean rather substantial inventories of components due to the uncertainty concerning *when* the demand from Department I will fall.

2. A frequently useful system based on a form of order "explosion" avoids some of this difficulty. Under this system, customer orders for stock items

are filled from finished stock. Replenishment orders for stock items are "exploded," or converted into orders for components which are then filled directly, e.g., in Department II. When the components are ready, the final work in Department I is completed. The standing inventory of components to meet Department I requirements as they occur is eliminated, at the cost of increasing the finished-item lead time and consequently the required safety stock. However, where the components are numerous and individually would be produced in large quantities, the saving in component inventories may be sizable. A smaller inventory of components to meet special-item needs may be carried or not.

The base-stock system

The systems for replenishing inventories described above characteristically leave the control of any inventory at the stock point. Any information sent back to the supplying operation is in the form of an order for replenishment. For example, in systems of the two-bin type, the information about usage or demand is held at the stock point; the only information transmitted back is an order to produce or ship the predetermined order quantity. In systems of the fixed-period type, an order is placed each period for a replenishment quantity.

When this type of control system is viewed as an information system, the flow of information follows the pattern shown in Figure 6.7. A customer order is placed on stock point 1 and is filled from stock. Depending on the replenishment rule used, at an appropriate time stock point 1 places a replenishment order on operation 1. Operation 1 in turn orders parts or materials needed, e.g., from stock point 2, to fill the replenishment order. Stock point 2 in turn eventually places a replenishment order on operation 2 when appropriate, and so on. Operation 2, in short, reacts solely to replenishment orders from stock point 2.

This type of information flow is simple and straightforward, but it has one important disadvantage. Customer orders, one unit or a few units, may arrive frequently. Replenishment orders to successive operations back in the chain will tend to become progressively larger and less frequent. This has the characteristic of increasing the variability in demand on stock points, such as from operation 2 on stock point 3, and correspondingly increasing the requirements for reserve stocks to prevent run-out. The control at each stock point and the operation supplying it is, in short, able to "see" only as far as the next operation ahead.

Another type of information flow different from Figure 6.7 might be visualized. This is shown schematically in Figure 6.8. In this system, when-

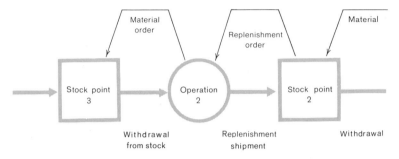

FIGURE 6.7   Pattern of information flow, two-bin system

ever an order is received from a customer for an item, the facts of the order are reported back to each operation processing the item or a part for it. From time to time, then, the operation will process a quantity of the item or part and feed this to the stock point following. The actual replenishment of each stock point may be on an economical-run or batch basis or on a fixed-period basis, or on some combination. The essential point is that each operation in the system works against actual customer demand rather than against demand generated by secondary stock points.

This scheme keeps the uncertainty inherent in demand for finished stocks from multiplying into uncertainty about the timing of need for large quantities of component items, with corresponding growth in component-inventory needs. This becomes particularly valuable in circumstances where a wide line of finished items (several thousand or tens of thousands) is assembled in a large variety of ways from a moderate (a few thousand) number of components. The demand for individual finished items may be very erratic, and consequently the replenishment orders for individual finished

FIGURE 6.8   Pattern of information flow, base-stock system

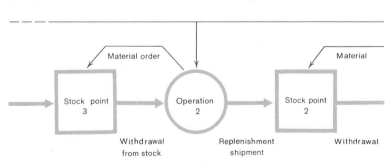

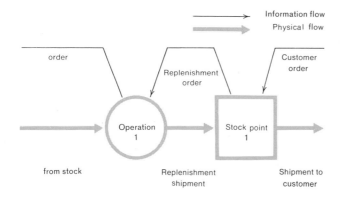

items may be irregularly and unpredictably spaced. If component-parts stocks are controlled based on direct usage, i.e., requirements to fill production orders for finished items as they occur, the demand for components may appear to be in large individual quantities irregularly timed, and therefore component-inventory levels may need to be high. Where tried, however, it has been found that if finished-item demand is exploded into components and the demand for individual components represented by finished-stock movement is totaled over all finished items containing the component, many control benefits can result. The demand for components represented by finished-stock movement is usually more stable, and more forecastable, than if component demand is looked on as simply demand by the next manufacturing stage. The component-inventory controls can then be set up to keep the total available quantity of the component between manufacture and finished stock—separate or assembled—constant.

This is done by setting up a base-stock level at each stock point sufficient to cover (a) maximum demand for the item, as represented by customer

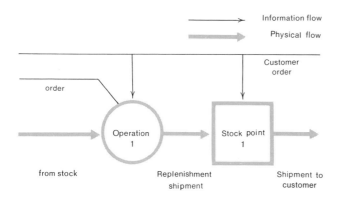

orders, during the lead time for the supplying operation, plus (*b*) the amount of a standard or minimum run or order of the item.[9] Reported demand—from explosion of customer orders—represents a commitment for replenishment and is subtracted from the inventory balance on hand and on order. When the difference between the base-stock level and the balance on hand and on order reaches the standard or minimum-order quantity, a new run is started or a new order is placed. This restores the balance on hand or on order to the base-stock level.

It is not necessary that *each* customer order be reported back through the system. Orders may be compiled and reported through the system periodically. This is particularly true where a large number of operations is affected, and the number of finished items is sizable. Orders of all types may be assembled for, say, a week at a time and converted or exploded into demand on individual operations at one time. When customer demand is reported periodically, the base-stock level at each point must be set up to cover maximum customer demand during the supplying-operation lead time *plus* the interval between reports of demand.

For example, a branch warehouse may report customer demand by item each week to the factory shipping department. When reported customer demand shows that the inventory on hand at the branch or in transit has been depleted below the warehouse base-stock level by the amount of an economical shipment, a new shipment is made, to bring stocks up to the base-stock level. Reported demand from all branch warehouses would be consolidated weekly by item for control of, e.g., final assembly. When reported demand for any item since its last run has accumulated to an economical manufacturing quantity, a new run of the item is made to feed factory finished stock. Likewise, the reported demand from all branch warehouses can be broken down into demand for parts, subassemblies, intermediate products, or raw materials, and supplies of these items replenished in the same way.

[9] To provide immediate service. See pp. 145–146 for the effect of allowable delays in filling orders.

Operation 3
lead time:
3 weeks

Operation 2
processing time:
1 week

FIGURE 6.9   Flow of materials through stock and processing points

How is the base-stock level affected by the time allowed for filling an order and the lead time in obtaining an item? To see this, let us break down the lead time into two parts: first, the service time between placing a requisition on a stock point and getting the material; and, second, the time to process the material. For example, with reference to Figure 6.8, the lead time in filling a customer order would be made up of, first, the interval between receipt of the order and the time the item is on hand at stock point 1 (customer-service time) and, second, the time needed to deliver the order to the customer. The lead time for operation 1 in supplying stock point 1 would be made up, first, of the interval between placing an order for material on stock point 2 and the time the material is ready for use (operation 1 service time) and, second, of the processing time at operation 1.

If customer orders are to be filled from stock immediately—i.e., if the customer-service time is to be zero—the base stock at stock point 1 must be equal to maximum customer demand during the lead time for operation 1 plus any economical- or standard-run quantity.

If the base stock at stock point 2 is large enough—i.e., at least equal to maximum demand for the item carried during the operation 2 lead time—the operation 1 service time will be zero, and the operation 1 lead time will be simply the operation 1 processing time. On the other hand, if no base stock is set up at stock point 2, the operation 1 service time will equal the operation 2 lead time. Then, the operation 1 lead time will equal the operation 2 lead time plus the operation 1 processing time. If customer orders are to be filled immediately, the base stock at stock point 1 must be larger, to cover the longer operation 1 lead time.

To make this more concrete, let us use a numerical example. Suppose we are controlling stocks in the process shown in Figure 6.9. We are faced with the following requirements:

1. We would like to fill customer orders on demand, i.e., keep the customer-service time at zero.
2. The operation 1 processing time is 1 week.

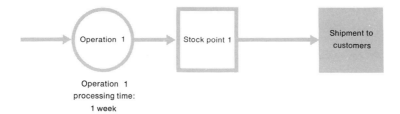

Operation 1
processing time:
1 week

3. The operation 2 processing time is 1 week.
4. Stock point 3 contains a purchased item; the procurement lead time is 3 weeks.

For simplicity, suppose we want to make or purchase the items at each stage one at a time. If the items were to be made in batches, the next following base stock would be increased by the amount of one run or order. Here are two of the various alternatives we have:

1. *a.* Set a base-stock level at stock point 3 equal to 3 weeks' maximum customer demand, converted into purchased-item usage. This will make the operation 2 service time zero and thus the operation 2 lead time will be 1 week.
   b. Set a base-stock level at stock point 2 equal to 1 week's maximum customer demand, converted to in-process item usage. This will keep the operation 1 service time at zero and the operation 1 lead time 1 week.
   c. Set a base-stock level at stock point 1 equal to 1 week's maximum customer demand. This will give immediate service to customer orders, as required.
2. *a.* Set the base-stock level at stock point 3 as before, 1. *a.*
   b. Set the base-stock level at stock point 2 at zero. This will mean the operation 1 service time will equal the operation 2 processing time, 1 week, and the operation 1 lead time will be $1 + 1 = 2$ weeks.
   c. The base-stock level at stock point 1 must now be set equal to 2 weeks' maximum customer demand to provide immediate service to customer orders.

The second alternative eliminates an intermediate inventory, with a corresponding increase in the lead time to replenish the finished inventory and a corresponding increase in finished-inventory requirements. Since inventory tends to build up in value and become more specialized in later stages, it is generally desirable to set adequate base-stock levels at raw and in-process stages, to minimize service times and thus cut base-stock levels needed later.

In many job-shop, or special-order, businesses, it is not necessary or sometimes not even possible to forecast end-product demand in detail. Delays in filling customer orders are permissible. In these circumstances the base-stock level for end products can be set equal to maximum customer demand over the supplying-operation lead time *less* the allowed customer-service time. If the customer-service time is greater than the processing time of the supplying operation, the service time for this operation can be increased until its lead time equals allowed customer-service time. This in turn permits a cut in the next earlier base-stock level.

In summary, if a delay in filling customer orders is allowed, one can move back through the operation, subtracting processing times from the allowed customer-service time. The base-stock level can be set equal to zero at all points up to the point where total processing time equals the allowed service time. From this point back, base-stock levels would be set to keep service times down to zero.[10]

To illustrate the effect of allowable customer delays using the example of Figure 6.9, suppose the allowable customer-service time were 8 working days (with 5 working days per week). Since the allowed customer-service time is greater than operation 1 processing time, the base stock at stock point 1 can be set at zero.

The operation 1 lead time can equal 8 days. Since 1 week (or 5 days) will be taken up in processing, the operation 1 service time can be $8 - 5 = 3$ days. This means that if the operation 2 lead time is held to 1 week or 5 days (the processing time), by having adequate stocks at stock point 3, the base stock at stock point 2 can be set at 5 days (operation 2 processing time) less 3 days (allowed service time at operation 1), or 2 days' maximum demand. This means that the base-stock level at stock point 3 must be set equal to 3 weeks, in order that the operation 2 lead time can be held to 1 week.

A forecast of maximum demand is needed at each point, covering the period indicated by the required base-stock level. For example, in the last illustration, no forecast is needed at stock point 1, since a zero base-stock level is permitted; a forecast of maximum demand over 2 days is needed to set the quantity for the base stock at stock point 2; and a forecast of 3 weeks' maximum demand is needed to set the base-stock level at stock point 3. Thus an allowed delay in customer service can be used to cut the base-stock levels and forecast spans required in later inventory points. On the other hand, the base-stock levels set at each point, and thus the forecast spans used, together with the processing times at each operation, determine how low customer-service delay can be made.

The main points of a base-stock system are:

1. Reporting customer demand is separated from actual replenishment runs or shipments. In this way demand can be reported frequently to control operations, but runs or shipments can be made in economical lots.
2. Each operation works against customer demand, to maintain a constant supply of each item in the system, except only for fluctuations due to processing in lots, i.e., cycle stock.

---

[10] This assumes, again, that items are made unit by unit. Where items are made in batches, the base-stock level must be increased by the size of a batch.

3. A base stock is established at each stock point adequate to meet *customer* demand and demand fluctuations, translated into demand for the particular item stocked, over the lead time for the operation supplying the stock point plus the interval between reports of demand, less the allowed service delay at the next following operation.
4. Replenishment of a stock point is initiated by the supplying operation on the basis of reported customer demand, rather than by the stock point itself through a replenishment order.

There are many variations for handling order explosions in a base-stock system, but they all operate on the same basic principle. In a mechanized system, e.g., a punched-card system, a master file may be maintained which shows component or part numbers going into each finished-product number. The master deck can then be used to generate component orders on the basis of finished-product orders. Order explosion methods can be readily incorporated into digital-computer programs where equipment of this type is used for production control. They can also be adapted to manual systems, through the use of edge-punched cards, duplicating master sets, and the like.

COMPARISON OF METHODS FOR HANDLING UNCERTAINTY

The methods described above are superficially somewhat different and serve best under different circumstances. The basic element common to them is uncertainty in requirements. Each in its own way is designed to handle uncertainty. The optimum reorder quantity (expected reorder quantity at optimum interval V in the fixed-cycle case) is approximated in each case by

$$q = \sqrt{\frac{2Ad}{i}}$$

However, the average inventory will, in general, be somewhat larger in the fixed-cycle system, since it must be set to protect over a lead time plus cycle time, $U + V$, compared with a lead time only. Where sales errors or fluctuations are independent of one another in time,[11] the safety stock under the fixed-cycle system would be bigger than under the fixed-order system by a factor of

$$\sqrt{1 + V/U}$$

where U is the lead time and V the cycle time, the time between reorders.

[11] For example, under the Poisson hypothesis.

Either approach to handling uncertain demand on inventory—using a fixed order size and letting the timing of orders vary, or placing orders at fixed times but in varying amounts—serves the same basic functions. The inventories carried under either system serve as lot-size stocks to permit economical shipments and as fluctuation stocks to absorb variations in demand. Similar costs determine the choice of stocks under each. Whether to choose one type or another depends on detailed study of the item, the nature of control needed, and the source of supply.

The fixed order size system—the two-bin and similar systems—serves well wherever some type of continuous monitoring of the inventory is possible, either because the physical stock is seen and readily checked when an item is used or because a perpetual inventory record of some type is maintained. It tends to yield less close control over stocks. It is often found particularly useful in managing inventories of low unit value items purchased infrequently in large quantities compared with usage rates. This type of scheme serves best where the item is, for example, purchased outside, represents a minor part of the supply point's total output, or is otherwise obtained from a source whose schedule is not tightly linked to the particular item or inventory in question. Floor stocks represent a good example of its use, where a large supply of inexpensive parts—nuts and bolts—is put out directly available to production workers without requisitions, and where a replenishment supply is purchased whenever the floor indicates that the supply on hand has hit the reorder point.

A periodic system is useful where tighter, more frequent control is needed because of item value. It is useful also where a large number of items is to be ordered jointly, as when a warehouse orders many items from one factory. This, of course, permits each item to be shipped in smaller lots more frequently while still getting freight advantages on large total shipments. Since the safety stocks needed vary directly with the length of the period between orders, the system is less well suited to circumstances where the cost of ordering and low unit value of the item would suggest infrequent large orders. The regularity of reorder is an important advantage where the item represents an important portion of the supplying plant's output.

The intermediate systems suggested can, of course, be designed to incorporate the better control and cost features of either "pure" scheme in particular circumstances.

The inventory levels, reorder points, reorder quantities, ordering frequencies, rates of production adjustment, and other controlled parameters can and must be kept under control under any of the systems described. Two types of control are needed. First, policies and costs may change, and inventory procedures should change with them. This is not too difficult to achieve where the influences of these costs and policies are explicitly identified. It is generally desirable to provide for routine periodic review of costs for revision.

Second, usage rates and fluctuation characteristics may change. These changes must be recognized, distinguished from chance fluctuations, and adjustments must be made. A number of techniques work here too. Control-chart procedures, like simple quality-control methods, may be used to spot "significant" shifts in usage characteristics (usage rate, fluctuation, order size or frequency, etc.). Sometimes usage rates and other usage characteristics are checked at each review or each time a reorder point is crossed. These schemes are easily incorporated in the programs of data-handling systems used for inventory control. They are often used in manual systems, but care is needed to be sure that they are not simplified to the point of danger. (If the experience period is too short, the usage estimates may fluctuate unnecessarily and cause corresponding inventory fluctuations.)

UNCERTAINTY IN PRODUCTION CYCLING

Methods for calculating the length of run of each of several products made in series on the same equipment are described in Chapter 4, for the circumstances where the usage rates of each product are known.[12] Usually, however, usage rates are not known and constant; demand for individual items and for all items in total will fluctuate from day to day. Under these circumstances, it is not possible to set a production schedule for cycling equipment among products and calmly live with it, except at the cost of substantial inventories to protect each item. It is generally much more satisfactory and economical to set up a total inventory sufficient to provide for cyclic fluctuations in stocks of individual items plus protection against fluctuations in total demand for all products than it is to monitor the actual production operation to keep the inventory balanced among individual products.

This can be approached in the following way. Ideally, the inventory of any one item will vary from zero, just at the beginning of a run, to some maximum, just at the end. The maximum inventory will depend on the normal run length of the item compared with other items made in the cycle. In fact, it can be shown, under the assumptions made in Chapter 4, that the ratio a_j of the maximum inventory of an individual product to the total inventory of all products (measured in commensurable units, such as production hours) is

[12] Chap. 4, pp. 67–72.

$$a_j = \frac{2s_i(1 - s_i/p_i)}{\sum_j s_i(1 - s_i/p_i)}$$

where, as in Chapter 4,

s_j = usage or sales rate for each of the individual products
p_j = production rate for each of the products

These ratios a_j can be computed and used to monitor the cycling of products in the following way. Production of an individual item is continued until one of the following conditions results:

1. The inventory of some other item runs out.
2. The inventory of the item being run builds up to a proportion a_j of the total inventory on hand.

At this point the production operation is shifted to the item that has run out or, if there is none, to the item with the lowest ratio of inventory on hand to usage. That item is then run according to the rules 1 and 2 above. While fluctuations in demand affect the total cycle inventory level, this device helps distribute the effect of these fluctuations among all products.

It is of course necessary to protect against runs of demand for individual products during the course of a cycle. In effect, in production cycling problems, the longer the run on each product, the longer one must wait for a rerun of that product; therefore a larger safety stock must be maintained as protection. Shorter, more frequent runs give greater flexibility and shorter waiting periods between runs, and thus lower safety-inventory requirements. The increase in safety requirements with increasing cycle length will usually lie between an increase proportional to the square root of the cycle length and an increase proportional to the cycle length itself, depending on the nature of autocorrelation in item sales.

The extra stock needed can have a serious effect on cycle-length calculations and costs. For example, a chemical company arrived at production-run cycles, for a set of five products going through the same equipment, on the basis of only setup costs and cycle inventories—e.g., lot-size inventories— ignoring the interaction between cycle length and safety stocks. On this basis it was found that an over-all product cycle of approximately 20 days, or 1 production month, appeared optimum, allowing 4 days per product, on the average. However, a research team investigating this process discovered that the uncertainty during the long lead times introduced by the long production cycle was so great that the over-all product cycle could in fact be economically cut back to less than 10 days. Doubling setup costs would be more than offset by savings in inventory and storage costs resulting from a reduction in the needed safety stocks.

Figure 6.10 illustrates the cost characteristics found to exist. The three dashed lines show separately the annual costs of change-overs, carrying cycle stocks, and carrying safety stocks, compared with the length of the individual production cycle. Adding together only the first two costs leads to the lower of the solid lines. This is at a minimum when the production cycle is 20 days long, indicating an apparent annual cost of $40,000. However, if *all* costs are included, the total annual cost on a 20-day cycle is $95,000. When all costs are included, costs are minimum when the cycle is 10 days long, only $70,000, a saving of $25,000 annually on these products.

MULTIPLE-ITEM ORDERS—JOINT REPLENISHMENT

Sometimes, when an economical order is calculated, the controlling order cost may apply to the gross-order size which can be split among a number of items. For example, a field warehouse may obtain a large number of items from a single source. It may be desirable to have any shipment from the

FIGURE 6.10 Influence of safety stocks on choice of an optimum cycle length

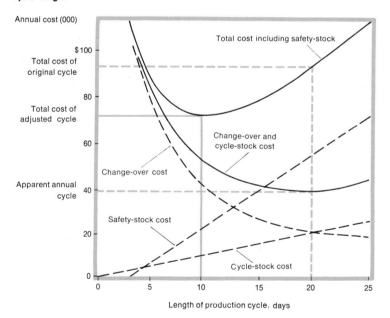

source to the warehouse equal an economical size, such as a carload, in total, but the mix of items in the order may not affect the cost of making the shipment measurable. Frequently, a distributor may wish to order a group of items supplied by a single vendor not all of which he needs at the present. He may order some items early from the vendor in order to take advantage of a variety of forms of discount offered, to reduce total order costs in those cases where the cost of an additional line on an order is less than the cost of a one-line order, or to meet a vendor constraint such as minimum order size.

Sometimes in manufacturing operations the cost of setting up a process may indicate the size of a total run or batch of an item, but the run can be split among a number of individual package sizes, etc. For example, in textile manufacture, it may be desirable to dye or print a large quantity of cloth which can be put up in a number of different-width bolts. In chemical manufacture, process economics or physical requirements may dictate the total size of a batch made, but this batch can be put up in a number of different container sizes.

In cases of this type, the economical order-quantity concept can be used to determine the size of the total run or batch. Procedures can then be set up to determine (1) when to make a batch and (2) how to balance the batch or shipment among individual items. These procedures must meet the following requirements:

1. A batch, run, or shipment must be started, to be completed before any individual item runs out.
2. The sum of the amounts of the individual items made or shipped must equal the total desired economical batch or order.
3. The quantity made or shipped should be balanced among individual items to delay need for the next run or shipment as long as possible.

An approach that can be used follows these lines:

1. A reorder point is set on each individual end item, e.g., each package size. This is set in the usual way, to cover maximum demand or to give the desired service protection on the individual item over the procurement lead time.
2. A new run or shipment is made whenever the inventory on hand or in process of an individual item reaches a reorder point.
3. The new run or shipment is distributed among the individual items as follows:

Let I_i = inventory on hand or in process of one item, the ith item

p_i = reorder point, the ith item

s_i = expected usage rate, the ith item

Q_i = amount of the run or shipment given over to the ith item
Q = total run or shipment size
I = total inventory, all items
P = total of the individual reorder points
S = total of the individual usage rates

Note that the quantities Q, I, P, and S must all be in common units. Then the amount of any individual product shipped would be

$$Q_i = s_i \left(\frac{Q + I - P}{S} \right) - I_i + p_i$$

This will result in an inventory on hand or in process which will be balanced among all items in the following sense: The expected time before the inventory of an item reaches a reorder point will be the same for all items. This will put off the need for a new run or shipment as long as possible.

To illustrate how this procedure works, suppose a chemical product is put up in three package sizes: 6-ounce, 25-ounce, and 2-quart. Table 6.1 shows the inventory position by item for the three package sizes. The

TABLE 6.1   Batch size: 4,000 gallons

	Item						Total
	6-oz		25-oz		2-qt		
	1 doz = .5625 gal		1 doz = 2.344 gal		1 doz = 6.00 gal		
	Doz	Gal	Doz	Gal	Doz	Gal	Gal
Usage/Week	100	56.25	250	586.00	150	900.00	1,542.25
Reorder point	200	112.50	350	820.40	250	1,500.00	2,432.90
Date	Balance		Balance		Balance		
6/1	400		490		375		
6/2	390		420		360		
6/3	375		390		340		
6/4	320	180.00	340	796.96	300	1,800.00	2,776.96

final column shows the total position. Under each package size is shown (1) the estimated weekly usage, (2) the reorder point, and (3) the daily inventory balance on hand or in process (these might be shown separately in practice). The usage rates and reorder points are shown both in dozens (the normal customer ordering unit) and in gallons (the standard unit used to allocate a batch). The economical batch size has been determined to be 4,000 gallons.

The inventory balance for the 25-ounce pack has dropped below the reorder point of 350 dozen on June 4. The first step, then, is to extend the inventory balances in dozens by the appropriate gallons per dozen (shown at the top of each item column) to obtain the total inventory on hand or in process, 2,776.96 gallons. (The calculations are carried out to several decimal places for convenience in balancing.)

From Table 6.1 we can calculate the ratio $\dfrac{Q + I - P}{S}$:

Q, total amount of a batch $\quad = 4{,}000$ gallons
I, total inventory $\quad = 2{,}776.96$ gallons
P, total of reorder points, gallons $= 2{,}432.90$ gallons
S, total usage, gallons $\quad = 1{,}542.25$ gallons/week

$$\frac{Q + I - P}{S} = \frac{4{,}000.00 + 2{,}776.96 - 2{,}432.90}{1{,}542.25}$$
$$= 2.8167$$

The individual orders can now be calculated, from the formula

$$Q_i = 2.8167 s_i - I_i + p_i$$

as follows:

Item	2.8167 × Weekly usage	−	Inventory	+	Reorder point	=	Order Dozen	Gallon
6-oz	281.67	−	320	+	200	= 161.67	90.94
25-oz	704.18	−	340	+	350	= 714.18	1,674.03
2-qt	422.51	−	300	+	250	= 372.51	2,235.03
								4,000.00

Rounding off to the nearest dozen would give the following order:

Item	Dozen	Gallon
6-oz	163	91.69
25-oz	714	1,673.16
2-qt	373	2,238.00
		4,002.85

The inventories on hand or in process would then be:

Item	Dozen	Gallon
6-oz	483	271.69
25-oz	1054	2,470.12
2-qt	673	4,038.00

and these new balances can be entered on the inventory balance record.

This procedure requires a calculation which can be done in a straightforward way from data on the inventory record. Where balances of individual items are maintained on separate cards or records, a notation can be made on each record of the items to be ordered with it. In a mechanical system, using punched-card or internally programed equipment, product codes designed to identify common-source groups are helpful in selecting the records for items to be ordered in conjunction.

This type of procedure can be employed in balancing replenishment shipments to a field stock point (where weight or volume may be used as the common measure). It can also be used where a single item is stocked for convenience in a number of different locations such as branch locations or departments, where transshipment from one location to another is not feasible but where there is a cost or price advantage in placing a single order to replenish all locations. It can be incorporated in any of the types of reorder systems described earlier.

CLASSIFICATION OF ITEMS IN INVENTORY

Close examination of a large number of multi-item inventories has revealed a useful statistical regularity in the distribution of the demand rates of the items in an inventory. It has been observed that item demand rates follow a *lognormal* distribution;[13] the logarithms of the item demands are normally distributed; that is, they fall into the well-known bell-shaped normal distribution pattern. Consequently, most items have relatively low demand and a few high demand; proportionately few items account for the major part of

[13] R. G. Brown, *Statistical Forecasting for Inventory Control,* McGraw-Hill Book Company, New York, 1959, and J. Aitchison and J. A. C. Brown, *The Lognormal Distribution,* Cambridge University Press, New York, 1957.

total demand. This observation is useful in several regards. It assists in identifying the amount of investment represented by the different portions of
inventory and it aids in classifying the inventoried items according to their
demand rates so that each group may be provided with an appropriate form
of control. In addition, the fact that item demand is lognormally distributed
makes possible the analytical calculation of inventory investment.

One frequently hears a rule of thumb quoted such as: 20 per cent of the
items in inventory account for 80 per cent of the dollar demand. This rule of
thumb is approximately true, but the stated percentages will vary depending on the kind of inventory. Inventories of consumer goods will typically
show a lesser concentration in the top items than will an inventory of industrial items. This concentration is depicted in Figure 6.11.

The dispersion in demand rates suggests that high-volume items should
be handled differently from low-volume items. One approach is to segment
stock into what is called an ABC classification:

Class A: The top 5 to 10 per cent of items, which accounts for the highest
          dollar inventory investment

**FIGURE 6.11   Relation between percentage of items
and percentage of demand**

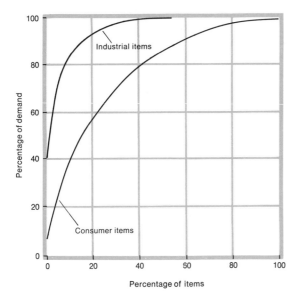

Class B: The middle 20 to 30 per cent of items, which accounts for a moderate share of the investment

Class C: The large remaining group of stock-keeping items, which accounts for a small fraction of total investments

An objective of such classification is to separate out the third group which is large in number and which may potentially require a large amount of record keeping and attention but which is relatively unimportant from the point of view of keeping inventory investment at reasonable levels. These items are characteristically low unit value items with low usage rates. Some companies try to set safety stocks at very high levels to be very sure that stocks of these items will not run out. The inconvenience and expense of expediting receipt or manufacture of these items or of holding up production in the event of a stock-out makes it well worth while to hold large safety stocks.

On the other hand, companies using this type of classification system will sometimes set relatively low safety-stock levels for the first group of items, which constitute a large proportion of the total inventory investment. The inventory investment required to eliminate stock-outs and the need for expediting would be relatively large; therefore these companies rely on frequent review of inventory levels of these items, close watch of progress of replenishment orders, and prompt attention for expediting where necessary. It is worth while to spend the money for detailed control and expediting of these items to keep from running out of stock while still reducing the need for large safety inventories.

In general, it is possible to spend more on cost elements that are relatively fixed, independent of volume, to handle high-volume items or to improve service of high-volume items, and it is possible to spend more *per unit* to reduce fixed costs or improve service on low-volume items. For example, high-volume items may be carried in more local warehouses to improve service availability, at low transportation cost, while low-volume items may be held centrally and shipped by air freight to cut inventory requirements while maintaining service.

As a related example, high reliability of service can be gained by having large local inventories. However, the turnover of the last increment of inventory is very low (even though the physical items may move in and out of stock) in the sense that the high inventory is designed so that the last element of stock is very rarely required. An alternative to high inventory is to set a somewhat lower conventional level of service reliability, but to reinforce it by routine use of a secondary high-speed (even though more costly) replenishment system on the few occasions when stocks approach run-out.

The cost of occasional high-speed replenishment may be on the average less than the cost of maintaining larger inventories the year around.

COMPUTER-BASED INVENTORY-CONTROL SYSTEMS

Inventory management has been described as a task in control-systems operations. Decisions regarding the timing and quantities of replenishment orders are made according to rules derived from statements of management policy and observations of demand rates and costs. In day-to-day operations, the inventory manager monitors the status of his inventory and makes routine application of these decision rules to order replenishment. For an inventory of, say, a few dozen SKU's, the procedures of data collection and transmission, stock-status review, demand forecasting, and ordering can frequently be reduced to simple, routine procedures and calculations which can be handled manually or with simple computational aids such as nomographs, tables, and desk calculations; many of the advantages of carefully derived decision rules can thus be obtained.

In many instances, however, inventories will contain many thousand items. In the distribution industries—food and drug wholesaling, in particular —single stocking points of 20,000 items are common and there are many that contain upwards of 100,000 items. Manual control of inventories of 20,000 items does not permit full application of refined decision rules and a compromise must be struck between precision of control and the manual effort required to provide such control. Review is less frequent, forecasts are simple projections or estimates, and order quantities are based on rules of thumb such as time supply. In effect, a larger inventory is carried (to provide a specified level of service) as an economic alternative to the added costs of tighter control of inventory.

The advent of the stored-program computer has shifted this point of economic balance a great distance in the direction of tighter control of inventories. It is now possible to apply even the most sophisticated decision rules to the control of multithousand-item inventories by incorporating inventory records (withdrawals and receipts) into the data-processing system of a firm equipped with the modest-capacity computers now being offered by business-machine manufacturers. Such computers can maintain inventory records as part of the normal flow of business transactional data. The decision rules can be programed and stored for use by the computer which can then make the routine reordering decisions. Packaged programs for forecasting, order quantity, and a number of inventory analysis routines are being offered by some equipment manufacturers to retail, distribution, and manufacturing firms using their equipment.

PROBLEMS

1. The service level to be provided by an inventory is a matter to be re-solved by statements of company policy. However, service can be defined and measured in a variety of ways. All such measurements and definitions express the extent to which inventory covers the uncertainty in the fore-cast. A measure of service commonly employed is the fraction of demand immediately filled. List at least four alternative measures and identify inventories for which they may be particularly applicable.

2. In a fixed-quantity inventory system, the order quantity is computed in accordance with the ordering rules described in Chapter 4. If the firm decides that its capital costs have risen, what is the effect on the probability of stock-out on each order cycle and on the fraction of de-mand filled immediately?

3. In a fixed-interval system, the inventory levels just before and just after replenishment for six replenishment periods are as follows:

Period	1	2	3	4	5	6
Just-before units	80	20	60	$-50*$	30	10
Just-after units	220	260	210	230	240	200

*50 units back order at time of fourth replenishment.

    a. What is the average cycle stock?
    b. What is the average safety stock?
    c. What is the average inventory?
    d. What is the per cent service during these six periods in fraction of demands immediately filled?

4. A distributor who handles the local sale of a broad line of a certain manufacturer's products is restricted to ordering not oftener than once a month. The manufacturer will not ship less than a certain dollar quantity and will not sell to the distributor unless the full line is stocked. The de-mand for these items is erratic and highly variable; some items move in large volume, others move very slowly. What costs should the distributor consider in developing ordering rules in ordering from this supplier?

BIBLIOGRAPHY

Arrow, Kenneth J., Samuel Karlin, and Herbert Scarf: *Studies in the Mathematical Theory of Inventory and Production,* Stanford University Press, Stanford, Calif., 1958.

Balintfy, Joseph L.: "On a Basic Class of Multi-item Inventory Problems," *Management Science,* vol. 10, no. 2, pp. 287–297, January, 1964.

Beckmann, M.: "An Inventory Model for Arbitrary Interval and Quantity Distribution of Demand," *Management Science,* vol. 8, no. 1, pp. 35–57, October, 1961.

Bowman, Edward H., and Robert B. Fetter, *Analysis for Production Management,* Richard D. Irwin, Homewood, Ill., 1961.

Feeney, G. J., and C. C. Sherbrooke: "The (S–1, s) Inventory Policy under Compound Poisson Demand," *Management Science,* vol. 12, no. 5, January, 1966.

Forrester, Jay W.: *Industrial Dynamics,* The M.I.T. Press, Cambridge, Mass., 1961.

Freeman, R. J.: "S, s Inventory Policy with Variable Delivery Time," *Management Science,* vol. 3, no. 4, pp. 431–434, July, 1957.

Gaver, D. P., Jr.: "On the Base-stock Inventory Control, October, 1958," *Journal of the Operations Research Society of America,* pp. 689–703, November-December, 1959.

Greenberg, Harold: "Stock Level Descriptions for (s, S) Inventory Problems," *Naval Research Logistics Quarterly,* vol. 11, no. 4, pp. 343–350, December, 1964.

Hunt, Joseph A.: "Balancing Accuracy and Simplicity in Determining Reorder Points," *Management Science,* vol. 12, no. 4, pp. B–94–103, December, 1965.

Pinkham, Roger: "An Approach to Linear Inventory-Production Rules," *Operations Research,* vol. 6, no. 2, pp. 185–189, March-April, 1958.

Prichard, James E., and Robert H. Eagle: *Modern Inventory Management,* John Wiley & Sons, Inc., New York, 1965.

Schild, A.: "On Inventory, Production and Employment Scheduling, May, 1958," *Management Science,* pp. 157–168, January, 1959.

Veinott, A. F., and H. M. Wagner: "Computing Optimal (s, S) Inventory Policies," *Management Science,* vol. 11, no. 5, March, 1965.

Winters, Peter R.: "Multiple Triggers and Lot Sizes," *Operations Research,* vol. 9, no. 5, pp. 621–634, September-October, 1961.

7

PRODUCTION-
PLANNING
METHODS

SCOPE OF PRODUCTION PLANNING

Allocation of production resources

Production planning is the process of deciding on the resources the firm will require for its future manufacturing operations and of allocating these resources to produce the desired product in the required amounts at the least total cost.

Production planning therefore involves setting the limits or levels of manufacturing operations in the future. Arriving at a production plan requires that business management make a number of important decisions. Some of these include deciding what the general size of the labor force will be during the period planned, and if hiring campaigns or layoffs are necessary, when these will be; setting plant and equipment capacities where these are flexible; and setting the desired or objective levels for inventory control. Production planning sets the framework within which detailed schedules and inventory-control schemes must operate.

Production planning is specifically concerned with the future, with layout of production operations to meet future anticipated sales with facilities which in some cases may not even yet exist. The plan may cover a few months or several years. Typically, in a well-designed control system, production plans may be drawn simultaneously and in possibly different degrees of detail for varying periods in the future. For example:

1. Plans covering the next several months or year may be used to set labor budgets and inventory goals.
2. Plans covering, say, 5 years may be used to govern capital-equipment budgeting for increased capacity.
3. Plans covering, say, 5 to 15 years may be used to govern plant construction and product development.

Production plans are designed to fix some or all of the characteristics of manufacturing and distribution operations that are assumed given in more detailed planning or control.

Thus the objective of production planning is to arrive at statements about the general characteristics—the framework—of manufacturing operations during the period planned. This framework should be designed to meet recognized company goals—filling customers' requirements to the extent they can be foreseen, meeting obligations to employees and the community for stable operations, and minimizing total costs. The costs in this case include facility and capital costs, including such costs as equipment capacity and inventory costs, costs of labor turnover, and costs of setting up multishift operations.

Uses of production planning

Production-planning methods have two important uses that need to be distinguished. One is direct planning, i.e., drawing up production plans to be followed, subject to costs that have been estimated and policies that have been agreed on, with respect to finances, customer service, and labor stability. These plans can be used to decide where extra capacity is needed and to set manufacturing operations.

The other important function of these planning techniques is to give business management guides for use in setting the basic policies themselves. Business management often must make judgments about qualitative factors they find difficult to weigh. One method of helping to make these judgments is to lay out plans under alternative assumptions about policy decisions, to make clear the impact on capacity and labor requirements, customer service, and financial needs, of alternative decisions in judgment areas.

For example, when forecasts of future demand are subject to error, as they usually are, it may not be easy to decide how far to go in building plant and inventories to meet demands. Showing the plant and inventory requirements and costs under alternative decisions and the possible final outcomes will not eliminate the risk or the need for decision, but it may help management arrive at a sound judgment, knowing the potential gains and losses associated with alternative decisions. Production-planning methods can also help direct research and engineering effort to bottlenecks or critical manufacturing areas where modes and improvements might yield substantial payoffs in manufacturing economy.

PLANNING TO MEET SEASONAL DEMAND

Anticipation stocks are carried to meet planned or expected increases in demand rates. Such stocks are built to buffer production rates and capacities from the effects of seasonal demand or surges in demand due to promotional efforts, and to support sales over periods of planned shutdown such as for plant vacation or maintenance shutdown. This buffering was identified as one of the major inventory functions in Chapter 2. The approach to the control of all forms of anticipation stocks is identical to that which applies to seasonally fluctuating sales. The following discussion of planning for seasonal demand is intended to treat all forms of anticipation stocks.

Seasonal demand patterns result in new types of planning problems. It is useful, perhaps, to think of two types of seasonal problems:

1. The "crash," or short peak-season, problems which arise, for example, in the toy industry before Christmas or in certain fashion clothing lines at various times during the year.
2. More conventional seasonal problems arising in industries where sales show a pronounced seasonal swing, but where these may be of less relative importance or where the peak season may extend over several weeks or months. Examples include demand for automobiles, many kinds of building materials, some kinds of cosmetics, and some types of home appliances.

In crash-type problems, the effects of uncertainty tend to be concentrated in the critical high-demand period, often when little can be done to correct for discrepancies between forecast and actual demand that materialize. The kind of seasonal problem where uncertainty is less important arises in industries which are stable but whose demand patterns are subject to external seasonal influences. The basic yearly pattern of demand may be quite predictable and the over-all volume may be reasonably well estimated. There may be a small error, e.g., only a few per cent, in estimating either the total volume or the size of the peak.

Problems of this latter sort resolve into three questions:

1. *Maintenance of safety stocks.* It is necessary to adjust the forecast of expected demand to allow for safety stocks to protect against forecast errors. Examples of an original and adjusted, or maximum-demand, fore-

cast are shown in Figure 7.1. In most businesses the risks and costs of back orders so outweigh inventory cost that substantial protection in the form of safety stocks is justified. These safety stocks must be large enough so that stocks can be restored after a sudden unexpected sales spurt by a smooth and moderate adjustment in production rate, but small enough so that the amount of inventory carried after the season is not excessive.

2. *Setting the production rate.* A production plan or pattern must be laid out to meet the adjusted forecast. Once the adjusted demand forecast or forecast plus safety stock has been obtained, the next task is to plan the production rate or draw in the production curve, shown in Figure 7.1. The difference between forecast and production plan will result in a planned inventory as illustrated. The total costs of inventory and production de-

FIGURE 7.1   Product with seasonal demand, cumulative-demand forecast

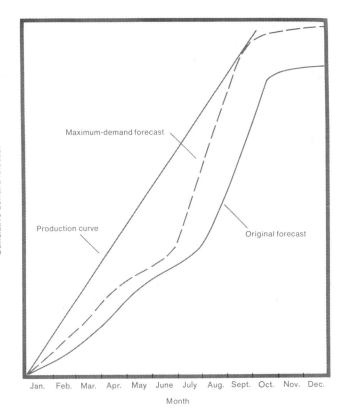

Cumulative-demand forecast

Maximum-demand forecast

Production curve

Original forecast

Jan.   Feb.   Mar.   Apr.   May   June   July   Aug.   Sept.   Oct.   Nov.   Dec.

Month

pend on the form of the production curve, and characteristically the object is to choose this curve or production plan to minimize the expected total of these costs. The techniques for achieving the solution to the second, or planning, question may range from complex computing techniques for solving sizable problems stated as linear programs to very simple graphical techniques—a chart of cumulative-sales forecast plus safety stock, and a straightedge.

3. *Short-term adjustment.* The production plan must be controlled or adjusted to keep it aligned with the demand forecast, as actual experience modifies the forecast and/or results in depleted or excessive inventory compared with plan. Control methods are discussed in Chapter 8.

Planning procedures

DEMAND FORECASTS AND THE PLANNING HORIZON

A demand forecast may represent an anticipated level of demand or a pattern of demand. The opportunity to take advantage of seasonal inventories in planning production requires a more detailed forecast of demand than a mere knowledge or estimate of the level or average rate of demand. If seasonal or other cycles can be predicted, production can be planned to take advantage of the predicted pattern of demand. Thus an important question in determining the approach to planning problems is the degree to which demand cycles such as seasonal variations in demand can be predicted.

Principles governing forecasting method and responsibility are discussed in Chapter 5. Some of the principles bearing directly on seasonal planning problems, however, bear repetition. In the first place, the forecast must be in sufficient detail and over a sufficient span to permit the plan to be drawn. Seasonal plans may be thought of as employment or operating schedules rather than as detailed specifications of precisely which items would be made at a particular time. While it may be necessary to forecast by items or groups of items in order to build up the demand forecast, the objective is to forecast demand on operating units or pools in terms of man-hours, machine hours, or some other appropriate measure of activity. The demand forecast should ultimately be constituted in these terms.

Where demand exhibits cyclical characteristics, it is rarely, if ever, necessary to forecast more than one full cycle in advance.[1] The important point, however, is to recognize and define the planning cycle appropriately. Too

---

[1] See F. Modigliani and F. E. Hohn, "Production Planning over Time and the Nature of the Expectation and Planning Horizon," *Econometrica,* vol. 23, no. 1, January, 1955.

frequently, plans are worked out on the basis of calendar-year forecasts when the planning cycle should run from, say, September to September. The beginning of the planning cycle should characteristically be the point after the peak-demand period when the demand rate first falls below the average for the cycle—the point where inventories characteristically reach minimum.

SPECIFICATION OF PRODUCTION REQUIREMENTS

A forecast of the expected pattern of customer demand is not in itself an adequate basis for production planning. The demand forecast must be converted into a specification of production requirements. At least three types of adjustments must be made:

1. To put the forecast of demand on a calendar consistent with production operations
2. To allow for possible errors in the forecast
3. To account for inventories in storage points serving later operating stages (later manufacturing operations, in transit, or in branch distribution points)

Demand forecasts are characteristically quoted as a schedule of anticipated demand, for each, say, month covered, or alternatively as a statement of cumulative expected demand by the end of each week, month, or quarter. (It is assumed that this forecast has been converted into a measure of production for the operation being planned.) This must be adjusted to be consistent with available production days, which of course are not uniform in each period. For example, Table 7.1 illustrates a schedule of available production days. Suppose a forecast of demand on a packaging operation has been made, as shown in Table 7.2. Then the demand forecast can be con-

TABLE 7.1 Schedule of available production days

| Month | Production days | | Month | Production days | |
	Mo	Cum.		Mo	Cum.
January	22	22	July	12*	137
February	19	41	August	22	159
March	21	62	September	20	179
April	21	83	October	23	202
May	22	105	November	19	221
June	20	125	December	21	242

* Two-week vacation shutdown in July.

TABLE 7.2   Forecast of demand—packing-line hours

Month	Demand in line hours		Month	Demand in line hours	
	Mo	Cum.		Mo	Cum.
January	275	275	July	310	1,960
February	260	535	August	320	2,280
March	265	800	September	330	2,610
April	275	1,075	October	350	2,960
May	280	1,355	November	340	3,300
June	295	1,650	December	300	3,600

verted to the production-time scale by direct comparison of the cumulative entries in Tables 7.1 and 7.2. For example, the tables show that demand equal to 1,075 line hours is expected during the first 83 days of the production year (end of April), or 1,960 hours are expected in the first 137 days of the production year. The comparison-cumulative expected demand during the production year is shown in Figure 7.2.

The next type of adjustment required is an allowance for necessary operating inventories in the manufacturing and distribution system. These include, for example, stocks in transit. If the transit time averages 2 weeks from factory warehouse to branch points, then stock equal to 2 weeks' sales will be in transit. The material must be produced at least 2 weeks in advance to allow time for transportation. Where inventories are built up between later operations or in field stock points to allow for economical shipment, to protect against short-term demand fluctuations, to permit subsequent production operations to respond smoothly to demand fluctuations,[2] or even to allow more uniform rates of operation at subsequent stages in the face of seasonal demand fluctuations, these must all be allowed for.

For example, suppose in the instance cited above that 2 weeks (10 production days) must be allowed for packing and transport to field branches, that branches in total carry an average of 300 line hours in safety and cycle stocks (to protect against short-term sales fluctuations and to allow replenishment shipments of reasonable size), and it is planned that the factory warehouse carries 250 line hours, to allow economical runs of individual items (products and package sizes) and to permit smooth adjustment to short-run sales fluctuations.[3] Then required cumulative production must stay ahead of expected demand at any time by at least 550 line hours plus 10 production days.

[2] See Chap. 8.
[3] See Chaps. 4 and 8 for methods for determining the size of these stocks.

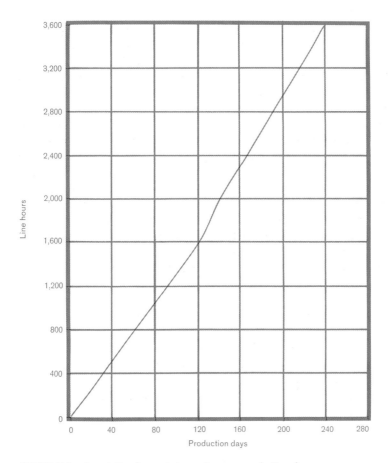

FIGURE 7.2 Cumulative forecast demand versus production days

One further adjustment is necessary. As pointed out in Chapter 5, no forecast can be assumed to be accurate; in fact, the opposite must be assumed. Expecting a forecast to be in error in some degree is not a reflection on the forecaster but a recognition that a forecast is a measure of *expectation;* no degree of sophistication in forecasting has yet been demonstrated which will eliminate uncertainty, and thus error. As noted in Chapter 5, a forecast only of expected demand versus time is incomplete without a specification of the range and likelihood of possible departures of actual from expected demand.

The significance of this point as it affects responsibility for forecasting and the costs which forecasting errors generate is discussed elsewhere. It is sufficient here to note that any longer-range production plan, e.g., a plan for meeting seasonally fluctuating demand, requires (1) a forecast of expected demand and (2) a recognition and estimate of possible errors in the forecast during the period. These two can then be converted by various devices into an estimate of production requirements to give an adequate guarantee of meeting actual conditions as these develop.

There is no satisfactory general way for taking account of expected forecast error to adjust the demand forecast as a basis for production planning. The adjustment to be made is not difficult in principle, but the numbers or values going into the adjustment are hard to estimate with any great accuracy. The adjustment to be made is one of increasing or cutting the quantities shown in the demand forecast until the risks and costs of carrying inventory versus running out of stock are in balance. The difficulty comes in estimating the cost of run-out and estimating the likelihood of an error of any magnitude. It is thus usually necessary to choose the adjustment method that is most expedient in view of information available and the characteristics of the people who must make the necessary policy or operating decisions.

This note of resignation, however, should not be interpreted as implying that arbitrary, unsystematic "judgment" adjustments are to be tolerated. The adjustments will depend ultimately on judgment, but the method should be sufficiently systematic to assign responsibility for judgments, to make clear the influence of governing policies in case these are changed, and to permit review of results to improve the quality of basic data and judgments as experience builds up.

One approach is to attempt an explicit balance of the costs and risks of inventory versus stock run-out. The cost of carrying a unit of inventory per unit time is usually reasonably determinable. The cost of having an extra unit in inventory at any one time depends not only on the cost per unit time but also on the sales rate—the time a unit must be held before it can be sold. In advance of the main selling season the cost is fairly low; the inventory can be liquidated during heavy sales. However, when the inventory is large enough or when the time is near enough to the end of peak sales, the risk or cost of inventory is considerably increased, especially if there is any likelihood that the inventory will have to be carried over or liquidated in the period of slack sales. Thus the two elements which influence inventory cost are the cost of holding a unit of inventory per unit time and the approximate sales rate which influences how long the item must be held.

The cost of running out of stock is usually much less easy to obtain, but frequently a satisfactory estimate can be obtained. This cost, too, may depend on the time in the cycle. In some industries the cost early in the cycle, when sales are low, is merely the clerical cost of rehandling the order to fill

it later. This is true, for example, where off-season sales are largely convenience orders placed by dealers in anticipation of later sales. Sometimes the
cost of run-outs can be equated to the gross contribution to overhead and
profit on demand diverted elsewhere. Sometimes this is a minimum and must
be increased to take some account of possible loss of customers. In some
cases the cost of run-outs can be equated to the cost of emergency action
to avoid them, such as emergency overtime, special subcontracting, etc.
Fortunately, in most cases a reasonable adjustment to the forecast can be
arrived at if only approximate estimates or ranges for these costs can be
established.

How can these costs be used to arrive at an adjustment? The essential
procedure is to plan extra inventory up to a point where the cost of carrying
the next unit in stock times the expected time it will remain in stock just
equals or offsets the risk that this unit will be needed to avoid back orders
or run-out times the saving if a back order is avoided. Approximate formulas
or graphs for making this determination can be worked out. An example is
given in Appendix C.

Another approach is to use the maximum-demand concept outlined in
Chapter 5 and noted earlier in this chapter. Under this concept the sales
organization provides a cumulative forecast of the maximum they reasonably
expect to sell rather than an estimate of what they think most likely. This
approach does not avoid the issue, but it does restate it. Sometimes it is
easier to obtain a forecast of what production operations must be prepared
to meet. The problems, need for control, and methods of arriving at this type
of forecast are discussed in Chapter 5. Such a forecast must be an estimate
of maximum *reasonable* demand, not a blue-sky estimate of what might
happen if this turned into the best of all possible worlds, but an estimate of
demand below which orders should be filled routinely and service maintained but above which emergency action, including possible delay in filling
orders, may be tolerated.

Returning to the examples of Tables 7.1 and 7.2, let us suppose the sales
department has agreed to a maximum-demand forecast 10 per cent above
the cumulative expected demand. This is shown in Figure 7.3 as a dashed
line above the original estimate. To determine production requirements,
transit and other inventory requirements must be added to these. These were
10 days' sales in transit plus 550 line hours in inventories at the factory and
in the field. When these are added to the maximum-demand forecast, the
production-requirements schedule results, as shown by the upper line in
Figure 7.3. The production requirements define what the production plan
must be laid out to meet.

Once the adjusted demand forecast, or original forecast plus safety stock,
has been obtained, the task is to plan the production rate or draw in the

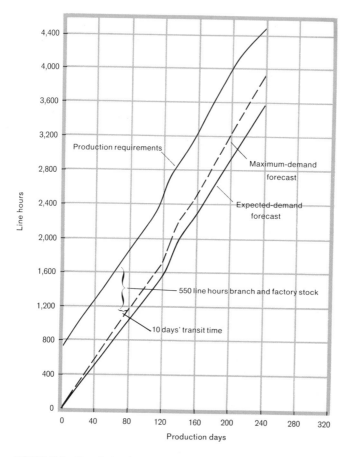

FIGURE 7.3 Cumulative forecast of expected and maximum demand, cumulative production requirements

production curve corresponding to cumulative production requirements in Figure 7.3 that will minimize the total of production and inventory costs. A number of techniques have feen found useful for doing this job.

Setting the production rate

GRAPHICAL TECHNIQUES

Where the problem of planning production against forecast seasonal demand is not made too complicated by a variety of items, processes, and stages, graphical or arithmetic techniques can be used. They offer the great advantage of being relatively simple to use and easy to understand. For example:

Suppose a company has a forecast at the beginning of the year which calls for requirements as outlined in Table 7.3. The first column shows expected demand month by month; the second column shows accumulated expected demand; the third column shows reserves for inventories required for various purposes; the fourth column shows the total amount that must be produced by the end of each month, allowing for an opening stock of 3,500 units; and the last column shows the number of production days available.

The cumulative requirements, after subtracting opening stock, are shown in Figure 7.4. The company might decide to produce at an average annual rate of 100,000 units, the production plan shown as a straight line in Figure 7.4. This plan would produce just enough inventory at the end-of-year peak to meet requirements. The month-end seasonal inventories (equal to the difference between the production plan and the cumulative production requirements) are shown in Table 7.4. They average 9,600 units, plus 3,400 units as safety or other reserve stock, giving a total average inventory of 13,000 units. If the annual inventory carrying cost were $45 per unit, the seasonal anticipation stocks would be costing about $430,000 per year.

Various alternatives might be tried to reduce this cost. For example, operations might be run at the rate of 250 units per day during the low

TABLE 7.3 Forecast of sales and safety stocks needed
(In units)

Month	Expected demand	Cumulative demand forecast	Required inventories	Cumulative production requirements*	Cumulative production days
January	6,000	6,000	3,000	5,500	22
February	4,000	10,000	2,500	9,000	41
March	3,000	13,000	2,100	11,600	62
April	4,000	17,000	2,500	16,000	83
May	6,000	23,000	3,000	22,500	105
June	9,000	32,000	3,500	32,000	125
July	11,000	43,000	4,000	43,500	137
August	12,000	55,000	4,200	55,700	159
September	13,000	68,000	4,400	68,900	179
October	12,000	80,000	4,200	80,700	202
November	11,000	91,000	4,000	91,500	221
December	9,000	100,000	3,500	100,000	242

*After allowances for opening stock of 3,500.

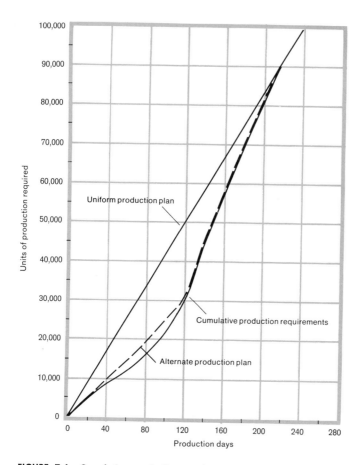

FIGURE 7.4 Cumulative production requirements and alternate production plans

months of the year, building up to a peak rate of over 950 units per day in September. This plan, shown by the dashed-line segments in Figure 7.4, would result in substantially lower anticipation stocks. The average inventory would be 4,450 units, with 3,400 units safety stock, or 1,140 units seasonal anticipation stock. At $45 per unit the cost of seasonal stock under this plan would be only $51,500 per year, a saving in inventory cost of over $375,000 per year.

This, of course, is not all net saving, since it is gained at the cost of adding and laying off the equivalent of some 700 units of daily production capacity. If the company involved were, say, a chemical plant operating well

TABLE 7.4   Monthly ending seasonal inventory

Month	Units	Month	Units
January	3,590	July	13,110
February	7,940	August	10,000
March	14,020	September	5,070
April	18,300	October	2,770
May	20,890	November	240
June	19,650	December	0

Average seasonal anticipation inventory	9,600
Average reserve	3,400
Average total inventory	13,000

under capacity and the variation from 250 to 950 units of production a day could be managed by adding and then laying off some 100 semiskilled men, the saving in inventory cost, equivalent to $4,000 per man hired and released, might well justify the change.[4] On the other hand, if the change in operating levels meant adding and laying off some 1,000 to 1,500 employees of various skills, the inventory saving might fall short of offsetting the hiring, training, and layoff costs, not to speak of its effect on community relations. Under these circumstances the change might not be worth while.

This alternative production plan, of course, calls for substantially increased plant capacity—nearly 60 per cent more—for the same average through-put. If the capacity were not available and had to be added, or if it would be gained at the cost of overtime or second-shift premiums or additional equipment installations, the simple cost calculation just outlined would have to be extended to include these extra costs and investments (not a difficult task if the procedures are well laid out).

By making similar trial calculations under other operating patterns, one can reasonably quickly get a picture of the influence of the operating pattern on cost and can arrive at a pattern which comes close to giving the minimum over-all cost. This plan then represents the basis for procurement, employment, and inventory control during the coming months until new forecasts call for an adjustment.

The operating plan summarized in Table 7.5 is essentially a minimum-cost plan, under the conditions that (a) annual inventory holding costs are $45 per unit, (b) the cost of hiring and training an employee is $225 (typical of many industries), and (c) a change of 40 units in the daily

---

[4] Where company employment policy restricts freedom to make a change of this magnitude, the indicated saving is a measure of the cost of the policy.

rate of output requires employment or release of 100 men. The cost of seasonal inventory equals 2,275 units (average seasonal anticipation stocks) at $45 per unit, or about $102,000. The plan calls for varying the production rate from a low of 250 units per day to a maximum of 550 units, a change of 300 units; this requires hiring and training 750 new employees at a cost of $225,000. (If the hiring and subsequent layoff of 750 employees is considered an undesirable employment variation, the solution must be sought within whatever are set as the feasible or tolerable levels.)

Thus, under the plan in Table 7.5 the total of seasonal anticipation inventory stocks and hiring and training costs is $327,000. This represents a net saving of over $100,000 per year compared with the uniform production plan in Figure 7.4. If the same cost factors are used to evaluate the two extremes described above, one calling for a production rate varying from a low of 250 units to a high of 950 units, the other being the uniform plan in Figure 7.4, the total cost of these plans is roughly the same, $430,000 to $450,000 annually.

A number of devices can be used to help work out the seasonal plan graphically. Frequently, for example, the production level can take on only discrete values; i.e., production must operate on a 0-, 1-, 2-, or 3-shift basis. This tends to be true particularly of assembly or product line operations,

TABLE 7.5   Minimum total cost plan

Month	Monthly production plan (units)	End-of-month seasonal inventory (units)
January	5,500	0
February	4,750	1,250
March	5,250	3,900
April	5,250	4,750
May	7,450	5,700
June	11,000	7,200
July	6,600	2,300
August	12,100	2,200
September	11,000	0
October	11,800	0
November	10,800	0
December	8,500	0

Average seasonal anticipation stock	2,275
Average safety reserve	3,400
Average monthly inventory	5,675

especially where overtime on a planned basis is not allowed by policy. Some production planners have found it useful to lay these alternatives out on a plastic sheet. The scale on the plastic sheet is the same as that on the planning graph. Lines are cut through the sheet representing cumulative production or output versus time for each of several levels of operation. The slopes of the lines cut in the sheet are the effective rates of output. Then the plastic sheet and cumulative production requirements graph can be used together to lay out alternative production plans for test. A number of other devices and methods have been used successfully to meet the same objectives.[5]

Graphical methods usually do not allow one to arrive directly at a minimum-cost plan that takes into account the various inventory, hiring and layoff, and overtime penalties which may exist. It is necessary to work out and cost two or three alternative plans to find one that is close to optimum, as in the example cited above. This is frequently necessary in any case, in order that management can weigh differences in tangible cost against intangible differences which may exist.

LINEAR-PROGRAMING METHODS

Various mathematical programing methods[6] have been used for production planning in the face of seasonal production requirements. Linear programing has been found useful both as a routine planning procedure and as an investigative tool to determine how important seasonal inventories were, and how critical different cost elements were, in determining optimum plans. In one instance, for example, the management had been concerned about whether seasonal inventories should be built up or production rates be adjusted in the face of seasonal sales. Linear-programing methods were used to show that over a wide range of costs for inventory and changing production levels the operation could safely be planned at a uniform rate in the face of seasonal sales. Principal attention could be devoted to other aspects of the problem.

The use of linear programing in production planning is based on certain assumptions which may appear on first inspection to be rather rigid:

1. Production requirements are assumed known and exact. This, of course, is rarely true, but the requirements schedule does represent the best estimate, including an allowance for demand-forecast error.

[5] See, for example, J. E. Cotter, "Production Planning by Business Days," *Mill and Factory*, October, 1953.
[6] See E. H. Bowman and R. B. Fetter, *Analysis for Production Management*, Richard D. Irwin, Inc., Homewood, Ill., 1961, and R. Howard, "Dynamic Programming," *Management Science*, vol. 12, no. 5, pp. 317–348, January, 1966.

2. Cost functions or relationships are assumed to be linear; i.e., cost relations are assumed to consist of fixed elements plus elements which vary directly in proportion to the variables specified in the plan—amount of overtime, amount of inventory, etc.

Devices for avoiding the dangers implicit in the first assumption have been noted in connection with converting the demand forecast into a schedule of production requirements. The seriousness of the second assumption depends entirely on the particular problem. However, in production-planning problems, costs are usually known only approximately, and to the extent that they are known they can usually be approximated by linear relation or combinations of linear relations.

A technical discussion of the linear-programing problem can be found in a number of excellent references.[7]

The application of linear programing to production planning can be illustrated by the example of production in a single operation to meet a specified set of production requirements. The production requirements specify quantities of product to be available in each of several time periods (days, weeks, or months) in the future. Limits on production can be expressed as the maximum quantities of product that can be produced in regular and overtime operation in each of the time intervals to be planned. The final restriction is that the production requirements must be met; the total of opening inventory plus accumulated production planned must equal or exceed accumulated expected sales at every point in the period. The objective is to construct the plan which minimizes the total cost of production and storage where the costs considered are the added unit cost incurred in overtime operation and the unit inventory carrying charge.

To solve this problem, a tabular array may be set up, like Table 7.6. The production requirements stated in Table 7.3 have been used for illustration. It is assumed that the cost of holding an item in inventory 1 year is $45, i.e., $3.75 per month; that up to 450 units per day may be produced on regular time; and that maximum additional output of 90 units per day may be obtained on overtime, at an extra cost of $10 per unit.

The cost figures shown in the tabular array represent the excess of cost of producing in the periods represented by the column headings for use or sale in the period represented by the row. For example, the excess cost of producing in January on regular time for use in January is zero; the cost of

[7] See, for example, A. Charnes and W. W. Cooper, *Management Models and Industrial Applications of Linear Programming*, vols. I and II, John Wiley & Sons, Inc., New York, 1961, and G. B. Dantzig, *Linear Programming and Extensions*, Princeton University Press, Princeton, N.J., 1963.

producing on regular time in February for use in April is 2 months' carrying charge, or $7.50. The figures in the "Capacity" row in the column headings are figures representing restrictions on regular and overtime production. The figures in the column at the extreme left represent the production requirements period by period. The table is completed as follows:

The first row of the table opposite "Available" in the first period (January) is copied directly from the "Capacity" row in the heading just above. The cost figures on the next row below are scanned to locate the lowest (in this case under "Regular" production in January). In the third row is entered that type of production to be planned. This figure is the lesser of the "Required" or "Available"—in this case 5,500 units, since the "Required" figure is smaller. If the "Required" figure were greater than the "Available," the "Available" amount would have been entered as planned; then the column with the next lowest cost would have been chosen and the balance of "Required" entered as planned if less than the "Available" figure. This procedure would be continued until production equal to the "Required" figure had been planned. In the first period (January), the only alternative would have been overtime production at a cost per unit of $10. Note that requirements for one period can never be met from "Available" in a later period; this reflects the requirement that planned inventories cannot be negative.

When the "Planned" row for the first period is completed so that the total of planned figures equals the "Required," the "Available" row for the second period (February) is completed. This is obtained by subtracting the "Planned" from "Available" row in January, entering the difference as available in February. These figures represent production capacity as yet unassigned. The "Planned" row for period 2 (February) can be completed in the same manner as for period 1, and this procedure is continued until the table has been completed, as shown in Table 7.6. The production plan for each period can then be obtained by adding up the "Planned" figures in each column. The planned seasonal inventory can be obtained by subtracting the "Required" figure for each period from the column total "Planned" for the corresponding period, which when added to the required inventory (Table 7.3) gives the total inventory planned, period by period.

This general procedure involving only inspection and simple additions and subtractions is also quite well suited to punched or edge-punched card use. For example, a deck of punched cards might be made out in the general form shown on page 182. Each card represents one unit of available capacity. The total number of cards equals the total capacity of all types for the time which is being planned. Each card shows the period with which it is associated, the type of production it represents, and (as illustrated) a

TABLE 7.6 Determination of production plan

Month required	Amount required	Type of production	January Reg.	January O.T.	February Reg.	February O.T.	March Reg.	March O.T.	April Reg.	April O.T.	May Reg.	May O.T.
		Capacity	9,900	1,980	8,550	1,710	9,450	1,890	9,450	1,890	9,900	1,980
January	5,500	Available	9,900	1,980								
		Cost	0	10								
		Plan	5,500									
February	3,500	Available	4,400	1,980	8,550	1,710						
		Cost	3.75	13.75	0	10						
		Plan			3,500							
March	2,600	Available	4,400	1,980	5,050	1,710	9,450	1,890				
		Cost	7.50	17.50	3.75	13.75	0	10				
		Plan					2,600					
April	4,400	Available	4,400	1,980	5,050	1,710	6,850	1,890	9,450	1,890		
		Cost	11.25	21.25	7.50	17.50	3.75	13.75	0	10		
		Plan							4,400			
May	6,500	Available	4,400	1,980	5,050	1,710	6,850	1,890	5,050	1,890	9,900	1,980
		Cost	15.00	25.00	11.25	21.25	7.50	17.50	3.75	13.75	0	10
		Plan									6,500	
June	9,500	Available	4,400	1,980	5,050	1,710	6,850	1,890	5,050	1,890	3,400	1,980
		Cost	18.75	28.75	15.00	25.00	11.25	21.25	7.50	17.50	3.75	13.75
		Plan									500	
July	11,500	Available	4,400	1,980	5,050	1,710	6,850	1,890	5,050	1,890	2,900	1,980
		Cost	22.50	32.50	18.75	28.75	15.00	25.00	11.25	21.25	7.50	17.50
		Plan							2,120		2,900	
August	12,200	Available	4,400	1,980	5,050	1,710	6,850	1,890	2,930	1,890	0	1,980
		Cost	26.25	36.25	22.50	32.50	18.75	28.75	15.00	25.00	11.25	21.25
		Plan							320		0	
September	13,200	Available	4,400	1,980	5,050	1,710	6,850	1,890	2,610	1,890	0	1,980
		Cost	30.00	40.00	26.25	36.25	22.50	32.50	18.75	28.75	15.00	25.00
		Plan							2,400		0	
October	11,800	Available	4,400	1,980	5,050	1,710	6,850	1,890	210	1,890	0	1,980
		Cost	33.75	43.75	30.00	40.00	26.25	36.25	22.50	32.50	18.75	28.75
		Plan										
November	10,800	Available	4,400	1,980	5,050	1,710	6,850	1,890	210	1,890	0	1,980
		Cost	37.50	47.50	33.75	43.75	30.00	40.00	26.25	36.25	22.50	32.50
		Plan										
December	8,500	Available	4,400	1,980	5,050	1,710	6,850	1,890	210	1,890	0	1,980
		Cost	41.25	51.25	37.50	47.50	33.75	43.75	30.00	40.00	26.25	36.25
		Plan										
Total Production Plan Regular Overtime			5,500	0	3,500	0	2,600	0	9,240	0	9,900	0

	June		July		August		September		October		November		December		Total
	Reg.	O.T.	Reg.	O.T.	Reg.	O.T.	Reg.	O.T.	Reg.	O.T.	Reg.	O.T.	Reg.	O.T.	
	9,000	1,800	5,400	1,080	9,900	1,980	9,000	1,800	10,350	2,170	8,550	1,710	9,450	1,890	
	9,000 0 9,000	1,800 10													
	0 3.75 0	1,800 13.75	5,400 0 5,400	1,080 10 1,080											
	0 7.50 0	1,800 17.50	0 3.75 0	0 13.75	9,900 0 9,900	1,980 10 1,980									
	0 11.25 0	1,800 21.25	0 7.50 0	0 17.50	0 3.75 0	0 13.75	9,000 0 9,000	1,800 10 1,800							
	0 15.00	1,800 25.00	0 11.25	0 21.25	0 7.50 0	0 17.50	0 3.75 0	0 13.75	10,350 0 10,350	2,170 10 1,450					
	0 18.75	1,800 28.75	0 15.00	0 25.00	0 11.25 0	0 21.25	0 7.50 0	0 17.50	0 3.75 0	720 13.75 540	8,550 0 8,550	1,710 10 1,710			
	0 22.50	1,800 32.50	0 18.75	0 28.75	0 15.00	0 25.00	0 11.25	0 21.25	0 7.50	180 17.50	0 3.75	0 13.75	9,450 0 8,500	1,890 10	
	9,000	0	5,400	1,080	9,900	1,980	9,000	1,800	10,350	1,990	8,550	1,710	8,500	0	91,440 8,560 100,000

Mo	Type of product	Cost for use in month i											
		1	2	3	4	5	6	7	8	9	10	11	12
1	1*	0	3.75	7.50	11.25	15.00	18.75	22.50	26.25	30.00	33.75	37.50	41.25

* 1 = regular production
  2 = overtime production

series of fields giving the cost of the production represented by the card for use in any subsequent months. The same card field is used for any usage month on all cards. Where the usage field is for a month *prior* to the month with which the card is associated, a very large number (e.g., a series of 9's) is punched in that field.

This deck of cards can then be sorted into increasing order based on the entries in the field representing period 1. The first cards in order are then selected, the number selected equaling the number of units of production required in the first period. The remaining cards are re-sorted in increasing order of cost in the field for period 2, and a number equal to period 2 requirements is selected. This process is continued until requirements for all months are satisfied. The selected cards can then be by month and type of production to obtain the production plans.

This type of scheme illustrates the sort of computing technique that can be designed for handling production-planning problems by linear-programing means. There are various general computing techniques for solving linear-programing problems.[8] These frequently require substantial computing capacity to handle sizable problems and are not well suited to many practical production-planning problems. For one reason, it is sometimes difficult for the industrial planner making routine use of these methods to obtain an intuitive grasp of their nature. For another, usually some special scheme can be constructed to take advantage of the particular form of any given problem.

Linear programing has been found useful in circumstances where the problem is complicated, for instance, by one or more of the following conditions:

1. Several product lines using the same facilities or staff
2. Possibilities of planned use of overtime to meet peak needs

[8] See, for example, A. Charnes and W. W. Cooper, *op. cit.*

3. Need for considering extra-shift premiums
4. Several stages in manufacturing, with seasonal storage possibilities between
5. A number of alternate plants, with different cost and employment situations, to meet demand
6. Joint planning of plant operations and of the assignment of branch warehouses to the plant

When the seasonal planning problem is attacked as a linear-programing problem, the objective is to minimize the total of costs incurred in carrying inventories forward in slack periods to meet future sales peaks, changing the production level to meet sales requirements, or resorting to overtime. The objective has to be reached within the limitations imposed by (a) capacity restrictions on the amount which can be produced at normal or overtime rates in any month; (b) the requirement that inventories in each line or product be planned large enough to meet sales requirements; and, possibly, (c) the amount of variation that can be tolerated in the planned production rate. Illustrations of production-planning problems formulated in linear-programing terms can be found in technical literature on the subject.[9]

Controlling production

Once the production plan has been made, it and the sales forecast dictate a sequence of planned inventory balances. However, as sales experience accumulates, actual stocks will fall below or exceed the planned balances. The minimum inventory balance or safety stock which has been (or should have been) set up will absorb the immediate effects of departures of actual sales from forecast, but it will be necessary to keep adjusting production plans *periodically* to bring inventories into line. The size of the needed safety stock depends on the way production adjustments are made.

Two types of adjustments to the plan may be made. Periodically the cumulative forecast for the remainder of the planned cycle may be adjusted as sales expectations change, or, as the end of the cycle approaches, the forecast may be extended to cover the next planning cycle. Either the basic forecast or the maximum-demand forecast may be changed. In this case, the

[9] See A. Charnes, W. W. Cooper, and Donald Farr and Staff, "Linear Programming and Profit Preference Scheduling for a Manufacturing Firm," *Journal of the Operations Research Society of America*, vol. 1, no. 3, pp. 114–129, May, 1953; J. F. Magee, in *Notes on Summer Course in Operations Research*, Massachusetts Institute of Technology, Cambridge, Mass., June 16–July 3, 1953; see also E. H. Bowman and R. B. Fetter, *op. cit.*

plan can be redrawn, taking into account the existing inventories. Between revisions in the forecast (which may be made quarterly or even less frequently) short-term adjustments in the production level may be made, based on the discrepancy between existing and planned inventories. Methods for making these adjustments are discussed in Chapter 8.

SPECIAL DEMAND SITUATIONS

Planning for special products

Most businesses supply a variety of products, made up of some items which are carried in stock to be sold off the shelf and other items which are made up as demanded by customers. It is worth while to distinguish between standard and special items and between stock and nonstock items. Standard items are those which the company considers part of its normal line of products. These may be carried in stock to fill customer demand, or they may be made up individually on customer order. Special items are those which are made directly to customer specifications. They may, and normally do, include many standard components; they may also include unique components.

The ability to plan production ahead in a business with a large component of nonstock and special orders depends primarily on the ability to forecast. Special orders, by their very nature, are essentially impossible to forecast specifically in most businesses. Beyond this, nonstock items are usually put in the nonstock category because ability to forecast demand for them is too limited to support the risk of inventory obsolescence. On the face of it, then, planning on special orders in a business with a large special or nonstock component would seem to be impossible.

Fortunately, it is frequently possible to forecast demand for a class of products including demand for special items in that class, even though the individual items cannot be forecast. Proper organization of product classes and the use of statistical averages to convert or explode product-class demand into demand for raw materials, standard components, and time requirements in operating centers, provide a basis for converting product-class forecasts into the kinds of forecasts needed for future production planning.

Where demand is seasonal but still consists to a sizable degree of special or nonstock orders, there is no opportunity to put the finished product into inventory in advance of the seasonal peak. Explosion of demand into time for final assembly or other finishing operations, and use of subassemblies or components, however, makes it possible to plan stock production to allow adequate time in final operations for special or nonstock items during the sales peak, and makes it possible to build up seasonal inventories of components to level operations in departments manufacturing parts and components.

To illustrate the principle, let us suppose we are planning the operations of a plant making a line of stock and special-order products in two operating centers, component processing and finishing. A forecast of demand, separately for stock items and special-order items, has been made and converted into a table of production requirements on the finishing center (see Table 7.7).

Let us assume that it has been decided to plan for uniform production through the year.[10] This means that we must plan the operating level at 121,000 units ÷ 242 production days, or 500 units per day. This gives a production plan as shown in Table 7.8.

The cumulative production plan is shown in the second column. From this is subtracted the allowance for the forecast production requirements for special orders, since these cannot be produced to inventory. The remainder is the cumulative production plan for stock items. The cumulative production requirements for stock items subtracted from the cumulative production plan for these items gives the planned seasonal inventory of stock items,

[10] The procedures that follow depend not on this assumption but on the assumption that some total-production plan is established to meet the total cumulative requirements shown in Table 7.7, by methods described earlier in the chapter.

TABLE 7.7   Demand forecast converted to production requirements*

| Month | Cumulative production days | Stock items, cumulative | Special items | | Total cumulative requirements |
			Monthly	Cumulative	
January	22	5,500	1,100	1,100	6,600
February	41	9,000	700	1,800	10,800
March	62	11,600	400	2,200	13,800
April	83	16,000	1,000	3,200	19,200
May	105	22,500	1,800	5,000	27,500
June	125	32,000	1,900	6,900	38,900
July	137	43,500	2,000	8,900	52,400
August	159	55,700	2,300	11,200	66,900
September	179	68,900	3,500	14,700	83,600
October	202	80,700	2,300	17,000	97,700
November	221	91,500	2,000	19,000	110,500
December	242	100,000	2,000	21,000	121,000

* Obtained from the demand forecast as described above (p. 167 ff.) with allowance, for example, for stock-inventory requirements.

TABLE 7.8 Production plan—finishing center

Month	Cumulative production days	Cumulative total production plan	Cumulative allowance special-order items	Cumulative production plan stock items	Cumulative production requirements stock items	Planned seasonal inventory stock items
January	22	11,000	1,100	9,900	5,500	4,400
February	41	20,500	1,800	18,700	9,000	9,700
March	62	31,000	2,200	28,800	11,600	17,200
April	83	41,500	3,200	38,300	16,000	22,300
May	105	52,500	5,000	47,500	22,500	25,000
June	125	62,500	6,900	55,600	32,000	23,600
July	137	68,500	8,900	59,600	43,500	16,100
August	159	79,500	11,200	68,300	55,700	12,600
September	179	89,500	14,700	74,800	68,900	5,900
October	202	101,000	17,000	84,000	80,700	3,300
November	221	110,500	19,000	91,500	91,500	0
December	242	121,000	21,000	100,000	100,000	0

shown in the last column. This inventory plus the allowance for fluctuation and transit stocks gives the total inventory plan.

Note that in this example, as in others, it is essential to reduce production requirements for individual products or product groups to a common unit. This may be machine hours, man-hours, pounds, or whatever is an appropriate measure of the operating level of the department or center being planned.

The production plan for component processing can be determined in a similar way, starting with the production plans for stock items and special-order items. These plans, when exploded into requirements for component processing, stock components, and special components separately, give the "demand" for stock and special components.[11] An allowance for processing and transit time between component processing and finishing must be added to these to obtain the production requirements for stock and special items. A component-processing plan can then be constructed in the same way as that for finishing. The allowance for processing special components on de-

[11] The explosion of stock demand into requirements for stock-component production may be done directly from product or product-family engineering parts lists, or average explosion factors may be obtained statistically by analysis of a sample of product demand. Explosion factors for special items must normally be obtained statistically.

mand must be subtracted in each month to obtain the plan for stock-component production, including any seasonal build-up of stock-component inventories.

Fundamentally, then, where nonstock or special items are important, the problem in production planning is to set operating levels high enough to allow time for processing the anticipated nonstock orders. The slack time, if not used in the manufacture of nonstock items, must then be taken up by the manufacture of stock items to inventory. The planning methods discussed above can be used to decide how much material to put into inventory and to determine the rate of production needed through the sales peak for the items planned for inventory, the stock items, with time reserved under the plan each month to process that month's anticipated nonstock demand. Operating and inventory levels can be controlled in the face of actual demand fluctuations about forecast by the techniques described in Chapter 8.

Where the business is totally special-order business, such as engineering service, equipment manufacture, and the like, service times in filling demand tend to be long, capacity adjustments tend to be somewhat slow and difficult to make, and demand is somewhat unpredictable.

Here again, the concept of statistical or average explosion of end-product demand into demand for time and materials can be useful. Planning must be done in the light of a forecast of future gross demand, which may be nothing more than an extrapolation of current demand rates. This can be converted into demand for time and materials—if necessary, using the current mix of time and material usage as a basis for this explosion. This conversion sets a preliminary budget or estimate of requirements to meet demand. Normally, if the level and mix of demand were just as forecast, the backlog of demand in each operating center or department would be about equal to the backlog in any other. The size of the backlog for demands of time, department by department, can thus be used like inventory as a control number. As the backlog builds up beyond plan in any particular area, production operations must be increased; whenever the backlog is depleted below plan, production operating levels must be cut. The procedure for use of backlog in controlling operating levels is analogous to that discussed in Chapter 8 where inventories are employed.

Planning for crash demand

The crash type of problem is frequently encountered in industries where sales are made over a short period of time relative to the production lead time. The risks essentially are those of not having enough to fill demand and thus losing profit or being forced to go to extraordinary measures to buy or produce to fill demand, or of having too much on hand with resulting sizable write-off and obsolescence loss, or expensive storage until the next selling season. The crash question basically is one of deciding how much to have on hand when the main selling season opens.

The answer to the crash question is basically to have enough on hand so that one can expect, on the average, to break even on the last unit produced; i.e., enough is carried so that on the last unit the expected risk of loss due to inability to fill demand equals the expected cost of obsolescence or of carrying the unit through to the next season. The principle involved can be illustrated by a simple example.

A newsboy has, on the average, 10 customers a night who are willing to buy papers costing 5 cents each. The newsboy makes a profit of 3 cents on each paper he sells but loses 1 cent on each paper he takes out but fails to sell. Let us suppose that he has kept records and that 40 per cent of the time he can sell at least 10 papers and 20 per cent of the time he can sell at least 12 papers.

If the newsboy does not know how many papers he will actually sell in any given day but every day takes out 10 papers, he has a 40 per cent chance of selling all the papers and making 3 cents and a 60 per cent chance of not selling all the papers and losing 1 cent on each paper not sold. His net expected profit on the 10th paper is 0.03×40 per cent $- 0.01×60 per cent, or $0.006. On the other hand, if he takes 12 papers every night, he can expect a profit, on the average, on the 12th paper of only 20 per cent $\times $0.03, or $0.006; and 80 per cent of the time he can expect to lose $0.01, an expected loss of $0.008, giving a net expected loss on the 12th paper of $0.002 per day. It would not, then, be worth his while to take out 12 papers; he would probably make the greatest profit by taking 11, as he would do slightly better than break even, on the average, on the 11th paper.

The newsboy problem is, after all, not so different from many business problems. Certainly from the newsboy's point of view the papers he buys which he may not sell represent a lot of money and a sizable risk of his capital. Indeed, perhaps the most important difference between the newsboy and businessmen in other situations is that the newsboy has to make this decision very frequently and therefore has more of a chance to build up experience on which to base intuitive judgments; i.e., he has less need for careful calculation or formal statistical methods to wring out of past experience the information which is of value.

Some common business situations which can be approached in the same general manner as the newsboy case include:

Retail merchants, particularly large-volume or chain-store operators, often must make commitments to buy seasonal style items such as spring dresses, bathing suits, or winter coats well in advance of the selling season. At the time a merchant picks styles and makes commitments he may have little information on what styles his customers will take. He may be able to predict over-all volume fairly well, but he may have trouble with individual styles and colors. If he buys too many of a particular type of item, he faces serious obsolescence losses through write-offs when the season is over. If he orders too few, he must either supplement his purchases during the season at high cost or lose profit on the sale along with his customers' good will.

Manufacturers of highly seasonal goods, such as Christmas candy, many types of toys, automotive antifreeze, and, in some cases, heating oil, face a similar problem; they must have enough on hand to meet demand, but not so much that the end-of-season write-offs or the costs of carrying inventory until the next season eat up profits excessively. When sales are uncertain, as they often are in these lines, the best the manufacturer can do is arrive at a balance between the risks, which minimizes his over-all chances of loss.

Hotels, airlines, and railroads face a similar problem in booking reservations. If they book customers just up to the point where reservations equal available space, last-minute cancellations or no-shows may mean unused space and lost profit. On the other hand, nothing loses a customer's business faster than to deny him space in the face of a confirmed reservation.

Manufacturers of complex equipment, such as automobiles, aircraft and components, and industrial machinery, have to decide, when they stop production on a model, how many spare parts to make to fill future needs. Too large a supply of parts may mean eventual write-off, but too small a supply will mean expensive special runs at a later time to fill customers' legitimate needs. In a case of this type, the effect of the decision lasts a long time compared with the newsboy problem, but in principle the nature of the problem and the decision are very similar.

Manufacturers or merchants running special deals or sales with perhaps specially labeled packages, combination packages, or insertions have to balance the risk of stock run-out, with lost profit opportunities or special reruns, against the expense of product obsolescence or repackaging.

AN EXAMPLE

Consider, for example, a cosmetics manufacturer who wants to make up a special Christmas package in a holiday wrapping containing three normally separate items at a combined price. The company has tried a number of deals of this type in the past, and on the whole they have been highly profitable. However, individually they have been unpredictable; some have been very successful, and some that seemed excellent on paper turned out to be failures.

The market-research manager makes a volume prediction on the specialty item each holiday season; on the average, his estimates come fairly close, but rarely are they on the nose. About half the time they are too high, and half the time too low. In fact, 25 per cent of the time company experience has shown his estimate to be 20 per cent or more on the high side, and just as frequently he misses as badly in the other direction. About 10 per cent of the time he is as much as 40 per cent off in each direction, and occasionally he makes a serious error and actual sales are 75 per cent or more off from the estimate. The company is doing everything it can to improve these estimates, but it is dealing with a very unpredictable type of merchandise. In the meantime the management has to decide how much to make up for the coming Christmas deal.

Cost estimates indicate that if a package is not sold, the items can be repackaged at an extra cost of about $1 per package. If demand exceeds the original run, the extra cost of a special rerun plus emergency shipments to field stocks is estimated to be $1.75 per package. As indicated in Appendix C, the plan with least expected cost would be to plan initially so that the chance that total demand will be covered by the initial run equals the ratio

$$\frac{\text{Special make-up cost}}{\text{Special make-up cost} + \text{repackaging loss}}$$

In other words, the company should make enough so that the chance that total sales will be covered by the initial run equals $1.75 \div (\$1.00 + \$1.75)$, or 64 per cent. With the company's past experience on forecasting success, this means about a 10 per cent overstock; i.e., the initial run should exceed estimated needs by about 10 per cent.

This will not eliminate all the difficulties by any means. There is still nearly a 40 per cent chance that the company will have to make some additional high-cost stock, and there is also a good chance that it will have unsold goods on hand after the holiday. However, this initial decision is about the best the company can do with its present forecasting and manufacturing methods to get the right balance between the two risks and thus minimize the over-all cost.

This is an illustration of a rule of fairly general applicability: Where there is an extra unit cost L, to the extent sales exceed the preseason established quantity, and a unit loss P, to the extent sales fall below the established quantity, then this quantity can be determined as follows:

1. Compute the ratio $L/(L + P)$.
2. Pick the opening or preestablished quantity at the level where the chance of sales being below is $L/(L + P)$ and the chance that sales will exceed this point is $1 - L/(L + P)$.

There is no clear dividing line between crash problems of the type described above and the less severe problems of seasonal sales described earlier. In fact, there are often cases which lie somewhere between, where some information about sales is obtainable from the current campaign to be employed in adjusting production levels. The circumstances of the crash-type problem set in once there is less than a lead time available through the end of the main selling period. Beyond this point further sales information does one no good, at least in the current selling season.

EXERCISES

1. A garden-products manufacturer, selling to a national market, produces a line of seeds, fertilizers, and chemicals. The fertilizers and chemicals are all processed at a single facility, which must produce these products to meet the twice-a-year shipping peaks. The monthly shipping patterns (in units of production-line hours) anticipated for the coming year are as follows:

Shipments, Production-hours

October	1,500
November	2,700
December	3,920
January	4,150
February	3,800
March	3,000
April	2,750
May	2,800
June	3,800
July	4,380
August	3,850
September	1,620

Inventory policy in the firm aims at an average monthly inventory equal to 50 per cent of shipments or 1,200 product hours, whichever is greater. Inventory at the beginning of the planning year stands at 1,350 production hours.

   a. Tabulate the cumulative production requirements for the fertilizer and chemical line.

   b. Calculate the average inventory.

   c. Plot the production requirements and determine, graphically, the production rate required to maintain level production operations over the coming year, to meet cumulative production requirements. What inventories do level production operations result in and how do these compare with the above-stated inventory aims?

2. Construct several variations on the above plan to bring inventories more in line with company inventory policy. Note the changes in production rates required and list them.

BIBLIOGRAPHY

Balas, Egon: "Solution of Large-scale Transportation Problems through Aggregation," *Operations Research,* vol. 13, no. 1, pp. 82–93, January-February, 1965.

Bierman, H. R., L. E. Fouraker, and R. K. Jaedicke: *Quantitative Analysis for Business Decisions,* Richard D. Irwin, Inc., Homewood, Ill., 1961.

Carr, Charles R., and Charles W. Howe: *Introduction to Quantitative Decision Procedures in Management and Economics,* McGraw-Hill Book Company, New York, 1964.

Dantzig, George B.: *Linear Programming and Extensions,* Princeton University Press, Princeton, N.J., 1963.

Dean, B. V., M. W. Sasieni, and S. K. Gupta: *Mathematics for Modern Management,* John Wiley & Sons, Inc., New York, 1963.

Fulkerson, D. R.: "Flow Networks and Combinatorial Operations Research," *American Mathematical Monthly,* vol. 73, no. 2, pp. 115–138, February, 1966.

Hoffman, A. J., and W. Jacobs: "Smooth Patterns of Production," *Management Science,* vol. 1, no. 1, pp. 86–91, October, 1954.

Johnson, S. M.: "Sequential Production Planning over Time at Minimum Cost," *Management Science,* vol. 3, no. 4, pp. 435–437, July, 1957.

8

CONTROL
OF
PRODUCTION
LEVELS

PROBLEMS IN PRODUCTION CONTROL

Control objectives

Control, in the sense in which the term is used here, means the adjustment of operations to conform to plans. As noted earlier, a principal source of difficulty in the management of production is the uncertainty of future requirements. The fundamental function of production control is the timely issuance of orders to the production facility for replenishment stocks in response to short-term fluctuations in demand. Safety stocks of the type described in Chapter 6 give short-term protection against sales or demand uncertainty. For example, they protect individual products over the period required for delivery of an order or between inventory reviews. The effectiveness of control, however, depends on the ability of the control system to restore these safety stocks in case of depletion.

If total demand varies and stocks are being restored from production operations, the ability to restore stocks depends on the ability of the production facilities to react to chance fluctuations in demand. In order to get low inventories, the process must have fast reactions properly controlled or, equivalently, in some cases, large "capacity." If reactions are slow or limited, then inventories must be large. Inventory, in effect, serves another type of protective function, namely, protection of production rate or capacity from the stresses of demand fluctuation.

Considerations in production control

Problems resulting from demand fluctuation arise in a variety of types of manufacturing organizations. For example, changes in the through-put rate of chemical-processing equipment may be slow and difficult or expensive. The output level of an assembly-line operation may depend on the number of stations that are manned or on the number of shifts working. Some time may be required to effect changes in the production rate, by, say, changing the number of stations manned at each point along the line. The production output of job-shop operation may likewise be influenced by the rate at which new workers can be hired and trained, or the cost of making changes in the manning level by bringing in new untrained workers or laying off people.

Simultaneous control of production rates and inventories requires a clear-cut control system with well-specified rules of operation. Sometimes a company will devote great effort to "inventory control" setting "economical" reorder levels, fixing safety stocks or reorder points, etc., without clearly taking the effect of production fluctuations into account. The management calmly assumes that the replenishment orders the system generates will give production operations a reasonable load. A system which might be reasonably efficient for controlling inventories of purchased items may be inefficient where production and inventories are under single management.

Examples of unstable control systems

A RATIONAL METHOD FOR GETTING INTO DIFFICULTY

The system used by the Manger Manufacturing Company is similar to that found in many companies, and many of these companies suffer to some degree the problems the Manger Manufacturing Company faced. The company makes a moderately wide line of builders' hardware. The great bulk of orders are for immediate delivery, and prompt service on customer orders is an important sales point. The company endeavored to give immediate service on stock items, accounting for 75 per cent of its volume. To help achieve this end at moderate cost, the company installed a new inventory-control system with the following elements:

1. An "economic" reorder lot was set for each stock group, taking into account manufacturing setup costs and storage costs.
2. The "normal" manufacturing lead time for each stock group was determined, and "normal" reorder points were set to protect against sales fluctuations while reorders were in process.

The system was designed to work as follows: Orders were entered as received against perpetual inventory records kept for each stock item. Whenever the uncommitted stock on hand or on order fell below the reorder point, the order clerk would issue a manufacturing order for the "economic" quantity.

The company recognized that manufacturing conditions would change from time to time and would be reflected in changed lead times, and that safety stocks and reorder points should be adjusted accordingly. Therefore the production loading section would check each manufacturing order for machine availability; if the order could not be scheduled for completion within the "normal" lead time, the order clerk would be notified of the new completion date. The order clerk in turn would adjust the reorder points for all items in the same stock group to account for the new lead time. The rule of thumb was worked out that the percentage increase in reorder point would be 80 per cent of the percentage increase in lead time. For example, if the lead time for an item in some group were reported to be doubled, i.e., increased by 100 per cent, the reorder points for all items in the group would be increased by 80 per cent. As the lead time was reduced to or below "normal," group reorder points would be restored to normal as well. By this means the company planned to gain the advantage of economic reorder lots with the added feature of realistic reorder points kept in adjustment with current production capabilities.

The company found in practice that moderate fluctuations in demand caused severe fluctuations in production, accompanied by sizable fluctuations is finished stocks. Despite the "inventory control," the company shifted back and forth from an excess stock to an out-of-stock position.

Here are some of the reasons for the company's difficulties:

1. An economic reorder system will not buffer production operations from sales fluctuations. Inventories set up under such a system serve only to permit economical runs on each item.
2. The system violated fundamental principles of control. There was no slack—in fact, there was just the opposite. The system operated like an erratic, nervous driver in heavy traffic who tries to escape one threatening emergency by throwing his wheel in the opposite direction, immediately plunging into another. A chance short-term increase in demand would occasionally cause stocks of a series of items to hit reorder points and trigger production orders. These might cause a temporary overload in a few production operations, causing the production loading section to report extended completion or lead times. The order clerk would then raise the reorder points on the affected product groups. In some cases,

the reorder points would be raised above existing stock levels, causing an immediate rash of reorders for such items. In other cases, reorder points would be brought close to existing stocks and reorders would result in a short time. These reorders would compound production loading difficulties further, causing further increases in lead time and another round of reorders.

As reorders piled up, production units would attempt to catch up by going to overtime work or hiring and training new employees, both costly expedients. Finally, as the production departments built up to meet the flood of work, the loading section would be able to report return to normal lead times and reorder points would be cut to "normal." Now, however, since orders in process were based on high reorder points, stocks on hand and on order would tend to be well above the new—"normal"—reorder points. Demand would be filled for a while from these stocks, and the flow of reorders to production departments would tend to dry up. The production departments would find themselves manned for high activity but running out of work to do.

The scheme of adjusting reorder points amplified normal demand fluctuations; it overcompensated for sales fluctuations and caused production and inventory fluctuations even greater than variations in sales.

THE "30-DAY SALES" RULE

Some companies try to maintain over-all inventory control in the face of sales fluctuations by laying down the dictum that inventory in total shall equal, for example, 30 days' sales. (The number of days, whether 15, 30, or 60, is not important as far as general operating characteristics are concerned.) This scheme, though apparently harmless, can be particularly vicious where sales are subject to short-term cyclical swings, i.e., where the length of a particular cycle is roughly from three to six times the lag in building up or cutting back production. As sales build up and inventories are depleted, the production organization fights not only to restore inventories to their former level but to build them up to the new level indicated by the "30-day" rule and the new sales rate. Then as production operations begin to catch up, sales fall. Production must be cut back below the falling sales rate to work off excess stocks and bring inventories into line with the lower sales rate. Though stemming from the sound objective of keeping inventory investment under control in the face of sales fluctuations, arbitrary rules of this type can cause serious and unnecessary disruptions in the stability of production operations.

Sometimes, of course, such a rule or policy may be interpreted only as a "target," or goal, in which case its effectiveness as a control is at best limited, since it gives essentially no guidance concerning what to do today in view of today's sales, stocks, and production levels.

ELEMENTS OF A SOUND CONTROL PLAN

Steps in control-systems design

A sound production-control system depends on:

1. A forecast of demand, expressed in units of production capacity. Methods for getting such a forecast are discussed in Chapter 5.
2. A production plan or preliminary budget which establishes the inventory and production budget. Methods for obtaining the preliminary budget are discussed in Chapter 7.
3. A control procedure for deciding how fast to restore inventories to budget levels when errors in the demand forecast cause inventories to exceed or fall below budget. Some methods for designing a procedure of this type are described below.

A first requirement is to get a measure of production or demand that is useful and can be applied to production, inventories, and demand equally well. Production, inventories, and demand—especially the latter two—are frequently quoted in physical units such as ounces, dozens, carloads, etc., and sometimes in dollars sold. On the other hand, a company's business can be thought of as selling time of its employees and time of use of its physical assets. The finished product demanded by a customer, or the finished or processed item in stock, is a block of processing time plus raw materials in more or less permanent form. Production-control decisions are answers to questions about how much time to make available and how to use it in view of customer demand for time and the time "stored" in inventory.

How does this bear on the question of a measure of demand? It means, first, that production control is concerned with the availability and use of common—interchangeable—pools of machine and/or employee time. Second, product forecasts, actual demand, and inventories must be convertible into amounts of time of each of the common production pools.

For example, many consumer packaged and bottled goods are produced on mechanized blending and packaging lines. This equipment is readily shifted from one product or package to another, and the same employees are required, whatever the particular item. Sometimes two or more lines may be set up in parallel, but employees can be shifted from one line to another without retraining. In cases like this there is no point in forecasting demand for each item in detail for purposes of controlling the line operation. What is needed is a forecast and control of the hours of line operation in total, to plan the proper number of shifts and arrange for appropriate employees. If the right amount of employee and line time is planned, decisions on what product to make can be reached day to day to keep stocks balanced as actual demand materializes.

Many companies, particularly those supplying industrial customers with items like meters, tools, small-volume chemicals, motors, or equipment, have a different problem. They supply a wide range—often many thousands—of items. Manufacture of different groups of items will call for distinctly different routings through the plant, and each routing may require a number of processing and assembly steps. However, different routings may call for use of common equipment or people, e.g., a particular machining center.

Despite apparent differences between the two cases, the control principles are the same. In the second case, products should be grouped for forecasting purposes so that within each group all products go through the same pools of interchangeable employees and machines, as far as possible. The forecast demand for product groups can then be exploded[1] into forecast demand for individual production pools. The available time in the several production pools can then be controlled by methods such as those described below.

Cost factors

Control of production operations in a particular center amounts to deciding how fast production time should be changed to account for differences between times needed to meet forecast and actual demand. Determining how fast production operations should respond to sales fluctuations and to what extent these fluctuations should be absorbed by means of inventory depends on a balance of costs—the costs of warehousing and cash investment in inventory, as opposed to the costs of changing production rates or building in excess capacity in the production system. In some cases the production rate may be changed by changing the level at which the plant is manned, thus incurring hiring, training, and firing costs. In other cases, flexibility in production rates may be obtainable only by the device of building and manning facilities with excess capacity. In these cases, the cost of production capacity includes the capital cost of excess facilities and the cost of unused labor. A third element of cost, sometimes important, is the actual cost of making out schedules, which depends on the frequency with which

[1] See Chap. 5 for a discussion of the explosion method.

these are made and the degree of precision required. The degree of production flexibility to be built into the control system also depends on the speed of reaction of production which is physically possible, e.g., the time needed to train new employees.

OPERATING WITH A PRODUCTION-CONTROL RULE

Periodic-reorder rule

The periodic-reorder rule described in Chapter 6 could be used as a production-control rule. Under this rule, the warehouse would place an order in each period equal to anticipated requirements over the lead time plus the reorder period, less the amount on order, plus the amount by which desired inventory on hand and on order exceeds actual. This rule was set up on the assumption that there is no cost of changing the size of order from period to period.

How would this work as a production-control procedure? First, a preliminary production budget is drawn up based on the demand forecast, as discussed in Chapter 7. The preliminary production budget or plan takes the place of anticipated requirements, and the "reorder amount" specifies the production or employment level for the coming period. Fluctuations in demand from period to period are passed on to production to their full extent; production will fluctuate around the preliminary budget by the same amount demand fluctuates around the forecast. Inventories will fluctuate about desired levels to the extent of differences between actual and forecast demand over the period of the lead time plus one review interval. Thus the desired or planned inventories must be set high enough to account for differences between the production budget and demand forecast *plus* inventory fluctuations.

PACKAGING-LINE ILLUSTRATION

For example, suppose we are setting up a scheme to control the operating hours of a packaging line. The demand forecast for the coming 13 weeks (expressed in hours of line operation) is shown in Table 8.1. A comparison of actual and forecast demand, week by week, for the previous year, has given results shown in Figures 8.1 and 8.2. Demand in a given week might vary ±18 hours from forecast, and over 2 weeks might vary ±25 hours from forecast.

Production is to be adjusted weekly, and because of the required work

TABLE 8.1   Thirteen-week demand forecast, hours of production per week

Week	Forecast demand (hours of production)	Week	Forecast demand (hours of production)
1	21.0	8	36.5
2	24.5	9	42.5
3	24.5	10	52.0
4	28.0	11	54.5
5	28.0	12	45.5
6	31.5	13	35.0
7	31.5		
		Total 13 weeks	455.0

notice to employees, it takes 1 week for a decision to change production levels to become effective. Thus the sum of the lead time and review interval equals 2 weeks. Inventory fluctuations, as noted above, will equal fluctuations between actual and forecast demand over this interval. Since these fluctuations can run up to ±25 hours over a 2-week span, planned inventories cannot be less than the equivalent of 25 hours of production.

Let us suppose that there were the equivalent of 38 hours in inventory. Then production requirements over the period would be 455 hours (demand) + 25 hours (minimum planned inventory) − 38 hours (on hand), or 442 hours, 34 hours per week. Check will show that a uniform planned rate of 34 hours per week will meet the forecast. In fact, Table 8.2 summarizes the cumulative forecast demand, planned production, and planned

FIGURE 8.1   Excess of actual over forecast demand by week

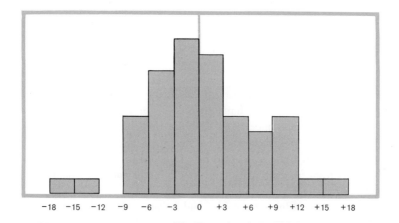

| −18 | −15 | −12 | −9 | −6 | −3 | 0 | +3 | +6 | +9 | +12 | +15 | +18 |

TABLE 8.2 Thirteen-week operating plan

Week	Cumulative forecast + demand	Planned weekly production	Planned cumulative production + inventory	Planned inventory
Opening stock	——	——	38.0	
1	21.0	34.0	72.0	51.0
2	45.5	34.0	106.0	60.5
3	70.0	34.0	140.0	70.0
4	98.0	34.0	174.0	76.0
5	126.0	34.0	208.0	82.0
6	157.5	34.0	242.0	84.5
7	189.0	34.0	276.0	87.0
8	225.5	34.0	310.0	84.5
9	268.0	34.0	344.0	76.0
10	320.0	34.0	378.0	58.0
11	374.5	34.0	412.0	37.5
12	420.0	34.0	446.0	26.0
13	455.0	34.0	480.0	25.0

inventories which might be arrived at. Note that this plan is in terms of production hours, not physical product units. One or a dozen products might be represented, although in the latter case additional cycle inventory would be allowed, as determined by methods of Chapter 4.

Since 1 week's notice to employees is required, production for the first

FIGURE 8.2 Excess of actual over forecast demand, 2-week periods

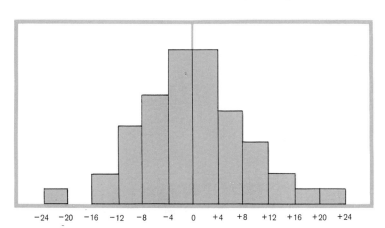

2 weeks is fixed by the original plan. However, at the end of the first week, the first review period, we have a chance to adjust the production rate. Suppose demand during the first week was equivalent to only 17 hours, 4 hours less than the 21 forecast. Then if production were on plan, the end-of-week inventory would be equivalent to 55 hours. Now the control rule takes over:

Production level, week 3 = preliminary budget for the week being planned (34.0 hours)
+ the amount by which originally budgeted production during the intervening period (week 2) exceeds scheduled amount
(34.0 − 34.0 = 0)
+ the amount by which budgeted inventory on hand exceeds actual
(51.0 hours − 55.0 hours = −4.0 hours)
= 34.0 − 4.0 = 30.0 hours

The production level planned for the third week then would be 30.0 hours; the full difference between forecast and actual sales in the first week was taken up by an adjustment in production in the third week.

This may at first glance seem like a roundabout way of arriving at a simple answer: Increase or decrease production in the week being planned by the amount actual sales exceeded or fell below forecast sales in the week just completed. There are two reasons for doing this. First, actual production may not always match the level set; but if it does, any differences will be reflected in the inventory compared with plan and thus taken up in future adjustments to the production plan. Second, some of the modifications to this basic rule will make use of partial inventory adjustments to help level production.

Table 8.3 illustrates actual demand which might be experienced over the 13-week period and the production levels and inventory balances that would have resulted from application of the control rule. Note that differences between the original production plan and production set week by week match differences between forecast and actual sales, with a 2-week delay. Differences between planned and actual inventory balances are equal to the sum of differences between forecast and actual demand for the 2 preceding weeks.

Control systems with proportional response

This production rule has one clear and serious difficulty as a basis for controlling production: It passes back to production the full period-to-period

TABLE 8.3 Comparison of planned and actual demand, production, and inventories

Week	Demand			Production			Ending inventory		
	Forecast	Actual	(F − A)	Plan	Actual	(P − A)	Plan	Actual	(P − A)
Opening stock	....	....	......	....	....	......	38.0	38.0	
1	21.0	17.0	−4.0	34.0	34.0	......	51.0	55.0	4.0
2	24.5	29.3	4.8	34.0	34.0	......	60.5	59.7	−.8
3	24.5	21.5	−3.0	34.0	30.0	−4.0	70.0	68.2	−1.8
4	28.0	30.4	2.4	34.0	38.8	4.8	76.0	76.6	.6
5	28.0	24.4	−3.6	34.0	31.0	−3.0	82.0	83.2	1.2
6	31.5	32.7	1.2	34.0	36.4	2.4	84.5	86.9	2.4
7	31.5	43.5	12.0	34.0	30.4	−3.6	87.0	73.8	−13.2
8	36.5	47.9	11.4	34.0	35.2	1.2	84.0	60.6	−23.4
9	42.5	46.1	3.6	34.0	46.0	12.0	76.0	61.0	−15.0
10	52.0	47.5	−4.5	34.0	45.4	11.4	58.0	58.9	.9
11	54.5	37.1	−17.4	34.0	37.6	3.6	37.5	59.4	21.9
12	45.5	55.7	10.2	34.0	29.5	−4.5	26.0	33.2	7.2
13	35.0	29.6	−5.4	34.0	16.6	−17.4	25.0	20.2	−4.8

fluctuation in demand about the forecast. If this rule were used directly to control production, the fluctuations from one period to the next in the production rate might be uneconomical. In many circumstances it is desirable to make greater use of inventories to even out changes in production rates.

One frequently useful method is to adjust the production rate by some fixed fraction of the discrepancy between planned and actual stock on hand or scheduled. Using symbolic notation to clarify this concept, let

T = lead time, the lag in making a change in production rate effective (1 week in the preceding example)

P_{T+1} = the production level being determined

$P_1, P_2, \ldots$ up to P_T = production levels already set for intervening weeks

$P_1^*, P_2^*, \ldots$ up to P_T^*, P_{T+1}^* = the production budgets set under the preliminary plan

I_0 = inventory actually on hand at present

I_0^* = inventory planned to be on hand at present

Then the control rule described above can be written in symbolic or mathematical form as

$$P_{T+1} = P_{T+1}^* + P_1^* + P_2^* + \cdots + P_T^* - P_1 - P_2 - \cdots - P_T + I_0^* - I_0$$

or

$$P_{T+1} = P_{T+1}^* + [P_1^* + P_2^* + \cdots + P_T^* - P_1 - P_2 - \cdots - P_T + I_0^* - I_0]$$

Comparison will show that this symbolic statement of the production-control rule is equivalent to the verbal statement given before. The first term is the preliminary production plan for the period in question. The quantity in brackets is the correction to restore stocks due to deviations between forecast and actual demand. It is the amount by which stocks on hand or planned under the preliminary budget exceed or fall below actual stocks on hand or planned. If the preliminary plan called for more stocks than actually on hand or planned, the correction term will increase production for the period being planned just enough to overcome the discrepancy, and vice versa. If demand from the present to the end of the period currently being planned coincides with forecast, then by the end of the period being planned, actual inventory will be in line with the preliminary budget.

However, suppose we change the rule, as mentioned above, to adjust the production rate by only some fraction of the discrepancy between planned and actual stock on hand or scheduled. If k represents the fraction used (k being some number between 0.0 and 1.0), the control rule would be changed to

$$P_{T+1} = P_{T+1}^* + k[P_1^* + P_2^* + \cdots + P_T^* - P_1 - P_2 - \cdots - P_T + I_0^* - I_0]$$

When the control number or fraction k is set equal to 1.0, we have the same rule as before. If the control number were set equal to 0, the correction term would be eliminated, and production would follow the preliminary plan regardless of demand. In such a case, of course, planned inventories would necessarily have to be huge to maintain service. In general, the larger the value of k—the closer to 1.0—used, the more responsive is the control system to forecast errors: Production-level fluctuations are larger and inventory requirements are reduced. This type of control method keeps production levels close to preliminary plan but allows them to fluctuate above or below to take up deviations in planned versus actual stocks.

In some circumstances another type of rule may be useful. One scheme allows for modifying the production rate based on departures of inventory from plan. The modification is based on the existing rate rather than on the preliminary plan. The production level for the period being planned is given by:

1. The level to be in effect during the preceding period (already planned)
2. Plus a fraction of the difference between desired and expected inventory at the end of the period being planned *if* the preceding rate is continued.

It is helpful to express this rule in symbolic form to show how it works. If we use the same notation as before,

P_{T+1} = the production level $T + 1$ periods away, to be set
P_T = the production level T periods away, already set
I_0 = the inventory now on hand
I_0^* = the inventory that we had planned to have on hand now

the inventory discrepancy at the end of the period being planned will be equal to the discrepancy that now exists, $I_0^* - I_0$, plus any further discrepancy that may build up from now until the end of the period being planned. The way to get an estimate of further discrepancy is to expect that total sales during the interval will match the forecast, in which case any additional discrepancy will be due to differences between the preliminary and final planned production levels:

$$P_1^* + P_2^* + P_3^* + \cdots + P_T^* + P_{T+1}^* - P_1 - P_2 - P_3 - \cdots - P_T - P_T$$

The last term in the difference represents the fact that the tentative plan is to make P_{T+1} equal to P_T, i.e., to plan production to continue at the preceding rate. The total discrepancy will be

$$P_1^* + P_2^* + \cdots + P_T^* + P_{T+1}^* - P_1 - P_2 - \cdots - P_T - P_T + I_0^* - I_0$$

Then the production level for the period being planned will be

$$P_{T+1} = P_T + k[P_1^* + P_2^* + \cdots + P_T^* + P_{T+1}^* \\ - P_1 - P_2 - \cdots - P_T - P_T + I_0^* - I_0]$$

Here again, k is a control number, between 0 and 1. The larger the value of k chosen, the closer will production fluctuations follow sales fluctuations about the forecast and the smaller will be the reserve-inventory requirements.

Each of these alternatives is useful in certain types of plants, depending, for example, on whether the cost of production fluctuations comes primarily from fluctuations about some long-run desired normal—e.g., overtime and undertime costs, or work guarantees—or from changing the rate from one time to another—e.g., hiring, training, and layoff costs. Each in appropriate circumstances will lead to smoother production, at the expense of extra inventory to maintain the desired level of service.

Both of these control procedures will lead to modifications in the production level covering a continuous range of amounts. Sometimes, of course, it is necessary to make a change in the production level of a fixed size or no change at all. For example, changing the production rate may mean adding or cutting off a shift or bringing another machine or line into operation. To illustrate how the rules described can be adapted to this type of condition, note that the production level indicated by each rule is made up of two parts:

1. A tentative level. In the first rule, this is the preliminary plan. In the second, the tentative level is the level already planned for the preceding period.

2. A correction. In both rules, the correction is some specified fraction (k) of the discrepancy between planned and actual inventory projected to the end of the period being planned.

Where a change in level is to be made, either rule can be modified to the following:

1. Fix a minimum limit on the size of adjustment that will be made.
2. If the indicated correction is less than this level, use the tentative level.
3. If the indicated correction exceeds this limit, use the tentative level plus the correction term.

Under this scheme the production level will respond to sales fluctuations in a manner roughly similar to the operation of a rule where adjustment of any size is allowed. However, the "error" or inventory discrepancy would be allowed to drift until it is large enough to justify a step-up or step-down of the production level.

Information flow

The *information flow* under control rules of the type described can be shown schematically as in Figure 8.3. The inventory of material on hand at the beginning of any period plus material on order during the period less demand during the period determines the inventory discrepancy versus the "normal" level for the period being planned. (The "normal" may be a fixed amount, the same for all periods, or it may vary from period to period according to a preliminary plan in the case of seasonal items.) The inventory

FIGURE 8.3 Information flow for production control

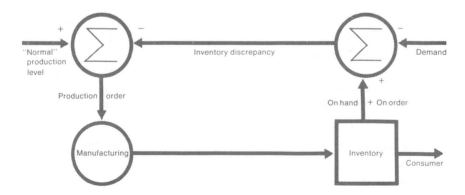

discrepancy plus the "normal" production level for the period being planned determines the production order or final plan. The "normal" production level may be the level set in a preliminary plan or the level planned for the preceding period. The control rule specifies how the "normal" level and inventory discrepancy are to be combined to obtain the production order or final plan for the period under consideration.

CHOOSING THE CONTROL NUMBER AND REVIEW PERIOD

The single-stage case

If the level of protection against stock run-out or emergency has been fixed, choosing two other elements will determine the control rule, and will dictate the amount of reserve inventory needed and the amount of production fluctuation to be experienced. These two elements are the length of the review period and the control number k.

The longer the review period, the less will be the clerical or scheduling costs of making a decision, since decisions will be made less frequently. However, a longer review period will usually mean a bigger reserve inventory and larger production-level fluctuations, since the total discrepancy between forecast and actual demand within each period may be expected to be larger.

If a value for the control number k is chosen close to 1, this will tend to reduce required inventory reserves, since production will respond more quickly to fluctuations in demand from forecast. By the same token, however, production fluctuations may be expected to increase.

Two rules of thumb or approximate formulas are sometimes useful in arriving at appropriate decisions concerning the length of review period and the control number k under the first type of control rule cited. These are:[2]

1. The expected magnitude of changes in the production level will be approximately proportional to $\sqrt{kP/(2-k)}$
2. The required reserve inventory will be approximately proportional to $\sqrt{[T(2k-k^2)+P]/2k-k^2}$
   where T represents the lead time and P represents the length of the review period.

For example, the illustration used with the warehouse-type rule for production control employed the following estimates or values for the lead time, control number, and review period:

[2] See Appendix B for derivation of these rules.

Lead time, T: 1 week
Control number, k: 1.0
Review period, P: 1 week

With these values the required reserve inventory was the equivalent of 25 hours per week, and the expected magnitude of changes in the production level from the preliminary plan *in either direction* would be slightly under 5 hours. (The magnitude of production fluctuations can be estimated from a historical examination of discrepancies between forecast and actual demand.[3])

When the control number k is 1, the first rule of thumb gives $\sqrt{1/(2-1)}$ $= 1.0$. If the control number were changed to 0.5, the rule of thumb would give $\sqrt{0.5/(2-0.5)} = \sqrt{1/3} = 0.58$. That is, changing the control number from 1.0 to 0.5 would cut the magnitude of changes in the production level from 5 hours to 0.58×5, or 3 hours per period.

On the other hand, when the control number is 1 (and the lead time T and the review period P are both 1 week), the second rule of thumb gives $\sqrt{[1(2-1)+1]/(2-1)} = \sqrt{2} = 1.41$. If the control number k were changed to 0.5, the rule would give $\sqrt{[1(1-0.25)+1]/(1-0.25)} = \sqrt{1.75/0.75} = 1.52$. Required inventory would be increased by the ratio $1.52/1.41$, or to 108 per cent of the level required when k equaled 1. The reserve inventory for $k = 0.5$ would be 108 per cent of 25 hours, or 27 hours.

If the control number k were left equal to 1, and the review time were lengthened to 2 weeks, the second rule of thumb would give $\sqrt{[1(2-1)+2]/(2-1)} = \sqrt{3} = 1.73$. In this case, reserve-inventory requirements would be increased by the ratio $1.73/1.41$, or 122 per cent. Reserve-inventory requirements would be 122 per cent of 25 hours, or 30.5 hours.

Figure 8.4 shows the magnitude of production fluctuations depending on the value of the control number k and the length of review period chosen. Figure 8.5 shows reserve-inventory requirements related to the value of the control number k and the length of review period.

The multistage case

The production-control rules described above have been discussed in terms of single-stage processes—one manufacturing operation and an inventory of completed material. The same methods apply as well to multistage

[3] See Appendix B, p. 363.

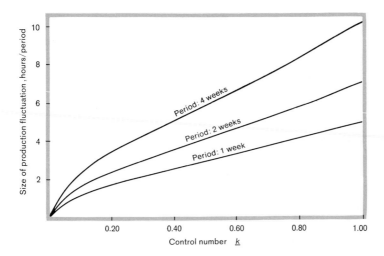

FIGURE 8.4 Magnitude of production fluctuations versus control number and length of review period

FIGURE 8.5 Reserve inventory required versus control number and length of review period

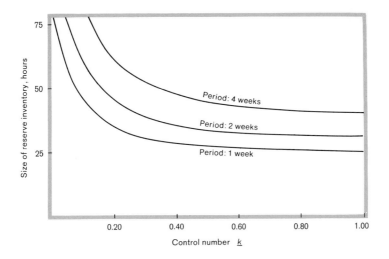

operations, or *cascaded* systems. A plant servicing a distant warehouse is a common example of a multistage process. This can be represented schematically as in Figure 8.6 Goods are manufactured and put in the plant inventory. From there they are moved to the field inventory, then to customers on demand. Customer demand governs the flow of goods through the two operations (manufacture and transport) and the two stock points (plant and field inventories).

The *information flow* for control of this process is similar to that described by Figure 8.3 and is shown in Figure 8.7. The field inventory on hand and on order at the beginning of the period plus the customer demand during the period determines the action taken at the end of the period, i.e., the beginning of the next period. Depending on the nature of the field inventory replenishment system, this may result in a shipment put in motion. Of course, the field-stock control might be of the fixed reorder type, in which case the notion of "period" would not apply; the relation between demand and inventory on hand and on order would be under essentially continuous surveillance. The lines of information flow would be the same in either case.

Note that in Figure 8.7 customer demand is transmitted directly to control plant-production operations. This is not necessary; in fact, it is not customary. In many production and inventory control systems in use today, the "demand" against which an early or intermediate operation is controlled is the direct demand by later operations on the inventory the operation in question supplies. For example, branch-warehouse replenishment orders may be used to control plant-finished inventory and final assembly or packing operations, or assembly-line parts requisitions may be used as the basis for controlling the level of parts-manufacturing operations. Although this is more customary, it is characteristically less efficient. Controlling all operations from field-warehouse replenishment to purchasing directly based on customer demand and demand forecasts characteristically makes smoother flow of goods possible, with less erratic fluctuations in operating levels and lower inventories.

FIGURE 8.6 Two-stage (plant and field warehouse) process

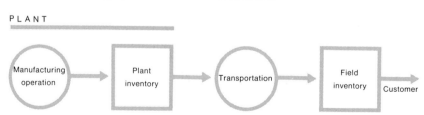

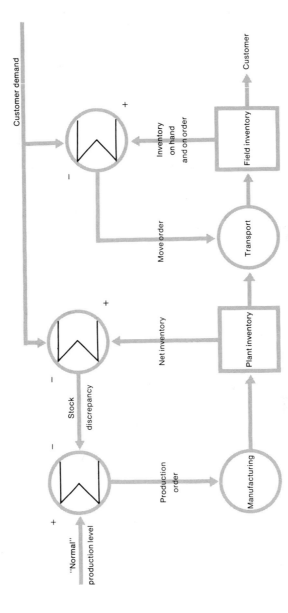

FIGURE 8.7 Information flow for production control, two-stage process

Two devices help make direct use of customer demand for control at all stages feasible. These are the base-stock system and the explosion method.

The base-stock system was described in Chapter 6 in connection with warehouse reorder rules; it is applicable to inventories at any stage. Under this system, for example, a field warehouse does not place replenishment orders as such; it reports at fixed intervals demand *on it* to the supplying plant. A replenishment shipment is initiated when reported demand reaches a predetermined point, set, for example, to allow economical shipping quantities. The direct purpose of this system is to control the transport operation, transferring material from plant-finished stocks to field stock points. The advantage lies in the availability of direct knowledge of customer demand which can be used in turn to control plant operations engaged in replenishing plant-finished stocks. The reported demand can, of course, be relayed to earlier plant operations for control of these.

The example of field warehouses has been used to illustrate the base-stock concept, but the existence of field stock points is by no means essential to the use of this system. From the point of view of inventory control, transportation between plant and field is exactly equivalent to any other operation in which inventories of one type are transformed into inventories of another. Where a plant services customers directly, the base-stock system can be used to control plant stocks and operations at each stage.

The concept of transmitting customer demand directly to control operating rates at each operation does not imply that each customer order must be reported. In some cases this may be desirable, as in some heavy-equipment industries, where individual orders may be very large and infrequent. In most cases, however, a periodic summary of demand is sufficient. It is necessary and sufficient that demand be transmitted to an operation as frequently as the production rate of the operation is adjusted.

The customer demand that is transmitted is something different from a simple summary of quantities of each item taken by customers during the period in question. Customer demand may be viewed as demand for the time of men and equipment represented by the physical objects the company sells. Remember that control over production level is exercised not in terms of the numbers of individual items made but in terms of some measure of output, such as operating hours, man-hours, machine hours, etc., common to all items made by the operation. The customer demand must be converted into this measure for control use.

The process involved is termed "explosion"; customer demand is expressed in quantities of individual items as "exploded" into demand for time of the operations involved plus quantities of purchased materials. The basic information required is an engineering parts and operations list for each end item: a statement of the operations required to make each item, the corresponding operation times per unit, plus the purchased parts and materials required per unit. Table 8.4 illustrates a highly simplified engineering parts and operations list. This table lists the number of hours required in each operation, the number of each purchased part, and the quantity of each raw material needed to make a given item. In the illustrative table, required times (hours) and quantities per 1,000 finished items are shown.

If customer demand in a particular reporting period for finished items were shown in Table 8.5, Table 8.4 could be used to convert this demand into demand for time of each operation for controlling production rates and for each purchased part and material for purchasing control. For example, multiplication of the first column of Table 8.4 by the corresponding quantities in Table 8.5 gives:

$$13,250 \times 2/1,000 = 26.50$$
$$10,500 \times 1/1,000 = 10.50$$
$$2,250 \times 1/1,000 = \underline{2.25}$$
$$39.25 \text{ hours}$$

That is, customer demand during the period was equivalent to demand for 39.25 hours of work in operation 1.

Construction and routine use of a table such as Table 8.4 gives a straightforward way of converting customer demand into demand at each operation for use in production rate or level control. The use of the base-stock system together with explosion of demand provides an efficient way for transmitting demand information back to each operation. Control procedures such as those described earlier in this chapter give means for using demand information together with inventory information to adjust the production level at each operation.

TABLE 8.4   Specimen engineering parts and operations list

(Requirements per 1,000 units)

End item no.	Operations						Purchased parts			Materials		
	1	2	12	13	14	16	12A1	12A2	14B	1936	1940	1975
13261	2		5	2		3	1,000		3,000		800	50
14993	1	3	2	1			2,000			1,500		200
14994	1	3	2		1			2,000		1,500		250
15532			3		2	3			4,000		1,500	150
15576			3		3	4		1,000	4,000		1,500	150

TABLE 8.5 Customer demand for end items, one reporting period

Item	Demanded quantity
13261	13,250
14993	10,500
14994	2,250
15532	7,500
15576	250

Note that the inventory position used at any stage is not the stock on hand but what might be termed "uncommitted but available" stock as of the end of the period being planned: the difference between (1) total production completed or planned to date and (2) customer demand to date and forecast through the processing lead time plus one review period. By the explosion method the information flow sketched in Figure 8.7 can be extended to any number of interrelated operations and the customer demand data used to control operating levels indirectly. Failure to provide this flow-of-demand information and reliance on replenishment orders from later stages to give intermediate operations-demand information effectively cuts the process into a sequence of independently operated units, each with an information flow like that in Figure 8.7. This cannot be more efficient, and is characteristically less efficient, than an integrated system in achieving reliable service and a smooth flow of product.

ALTERNATIVE CONTROL PROCEDURES—A SUMMARY ILLUSTRATION

The example that follows illustrates operating characteristics of types of control systems often found in business and some of the advantages of the control procedures discussed above. It is entirely fictional, but it is completely realistic. The company is smaller, and its situation simpler, than many real companies, to help keep the detail and arithmetic manageable without distorting the essential points. The same techniques and principles have worked for a variety of companies under all kinds of circumstances, and the illustration shows how some of the methods described can contribute to the ability of a company to manage its inventories. The progress of the company toward more efficient inventory management is described as occurring in stages. In fact, any one of these stages, from the original to the final, might be found to exist in the inventory-control practices of a number of sizable companies with reputations for progressive and efficient management.

Understanding of these control techniques and methods for diagnosing situations to choose appropriate ones helps short-cut the various progressive steps described in our fictional company.

Fixed-quantity reordering by branches

The Hibernian Bay Company produces a small machine, selling approximately 5,200 units annually for $100 apiece. The machining and assembly operations are conducted in a small plant employing largely semiskilled female help. The level of production can be changed fairly rapidly but at the cost of training or retraining workers, personnel-office expenses, and increased inspection and quality problems.

Customers are supplied from four branch stock points scattered about the country. These in turn are supplied by the factory warehouse. The factory and branch-warehouse stocking practices were haphazard and of concern to the company management. In total, nearly 4 months' stock was carried in branches, in the factory warehouse, or in incompleted production orders. A stock clerk in each branch who watched inventories and placed reorders on the factory warehouse was under pressure to be sure that stocks were adequate to fill customer orders. The factory-warehouse reorder clerk in turn watched factory stocks and placed production orders. Production runs or batches were each run through the plant as a unit. Fluctuations in production even with apparently sizable stocks caused the management deep concern.

The management decided to try to improve inventory practices. A research team was appointed; it suggested using "economical order quantities" as a basis for better control. The formula[4]

$$x = \sqrt{\frac{2As}{i}}$$

was used, where

A = fixed cost connected with an order (setup of machines, writing order, checking receipts, etc.)

i = annual cost of carrying a unit in inventory

s = annual movement

x = economical order quantity

The team found that each branch sold an average of 25 units a week, or 1,300 a year; that the cost of a branch's placing and receiving an order was

[4] See Chap. 4, p. 57.

$19 ($6 in clerical costs at the branch and factory, $13 in costs of packing and shipping goods, receiving, and stocking); that annual inventory carrying costs in the branches were $5 per unit, based on a desired 10 per cent return on incremental inventory investment. These indicated that each branch should replenish its stock in

$$\sqrt{\frac{2 \times \$19 \times 1,300}{\$5}} = \text{100-unit reorder quantity}$$

A system was set up in which each branch ordered in quantities of 100 units, on the average, every 4 weeks. This, in theory, would give each branch an inventory of one-half a reorder quantity, or 50 units. In addition, stock in transit from factory to branch was charged to the branch. Since the transit time was 1 week, stock in transit averaged 25 units for each branch.

However, though branch sales averaged 25 each week, sales fluctuated.[5] Enough had to be on hand when a reorder was placed to last until the order was received. While transit time, warehouse to branch, was 1 week, experience showed that delays at the factory might mean that an order would not be received at the branch until after 2 weeks. Statistical analysis of sales showed that sales in any one branch in 2 weeks would at times drop as low as 38 and at other times rise to 70. In view of the uncertainties of transit time and of biweekly sales rates and in order to keep the stock-out probability to less than 1 per cent, management computed that the maximum reasonable demand over the replenishment lead time was 67 units. The branches accordingly were instructed to order 100 units whenever the stock on hand plus on order was 67 units or less.

The presumed behavior would look like Figure 8.8, but actual behavior proved to be more like Figure 8.9. This gave an inventory on the average made up as:

Safety stock: 42 (order point, 67, less normal week's usage, 25)
Order cycle stock: 50 (one-half of 100-unit order)
In transit: 25 (1 week's sales)
Total: 117, or 4.7 weeks

The team found that the cost of holding a unit in inventory at the factory was $3.50 per year (at 10 per cent return on investment); that the cost of placing an order and setting up equipment for each order was $13.50; and,

[5] In the calculations that follow, it has been assumed that weekly demand is Poisson-distributed, fluctuating from period to period (independently in any one branch or among branches) about a mean demand rate D, with a standard deviation of $\sqrt{Dt}$, where t is length of time period.

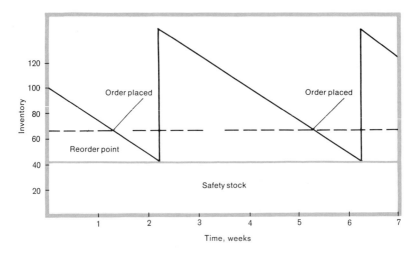

FIGURE 8.8 Branch economical reorder system—presumed operation

of course, that a total of 5,200 units was made each year. These indicated that each production order should be for

$$\sqrt{\frac{2 \times \$13.50 \times 5,200}{\$3.50}} = 200 \text{ units}$$

Factory processing time was 2 weeks; it would take 2 weeks for each

FIGURE 8.9 Branch economical reorder system—typical operation

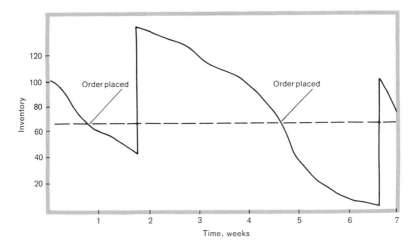

production order to be completed and reach the factory warehouse. The factory warehouse would need to place its replenishment order on the factory when it had enough on hand or on order to fill maximum reasonable demand during the next 2 weeks. *On the average*, the factory warehouse would receive one order a week from the branches (one every 4 weeks from each of four branches) under the new branch reorder system. In fact, because of the fluctuations in branch sales described before, it was found, after some experience with the new system, that orders on the factory warehouse from week to week fluctuated substantially. Table 8.6 shows the percentage of 1-week periods found when branch orders equaled any given amount. Table 8.7 shows the number of branch orders which experience showed the factory warehouse would have to fill in a 2-week period, the lead time required for the factory to replenish factory warehouse stocks. It was agreed that to give branch warehouses service adequate to maintain their own service, stocks at the factory would have to be high enough to fill demand 99 per cent of the time; i.e., a replenishment order would have to be placed when 500 units were on hand or on order. This meant a safety stock of 500 units minus 200 (normal usage), or 300 units. Cycle stock averaged half a run, or 100 units, and stock in process averaged an additional half run, 100 units. Total factory stock, then, was

Cycle stock: 100 units
Stock in process: 100 units
Safety stock: 300 units
Total: 500 units

Table 8.8 gives a picture of the apparent costs of the economical-order

TABLE 8.6 Number of branch orders from factory warehouse, per cent of weeks

No. of branch orders	No. of items ordered	No. of weeks	Per cent of weeks
0	0	28	35
1	100	28	35
2	200	20	25
3	300	4	5

TABLE 8.7 Number of branch orders from factory warehouse, per cent of 2-week periods

No. of branch orders	No. of items ordered	Per cent of 2-week periods
0	0	13
1	100	17
2	200	38
3	300	25
4	400	5
5	500	1
6+	600	1

TABLE 8.8   Costs, economical-order system

		Annual
Inventory	No.	cost
Factory	500 units @ \$3.50/yr/unit =	\$1,750
4 branch warehouses	468 units @ \$5.50/yr/unit =	2,340
Reorder cost		
Warehouses	52/yr @ \$19.00 each =	990
Factory	26/yr @ \$13.50 each =	350
		\$5,430

system. The stock of 968 units equaled less than 10 weeks' sales, a fairly substantial reduction, and the management felt that they had a better control since clerical procedures were set up to adapt readily to any changes in inventory charges (currently 10 per cent per year) or service-level requirements the management might choose to make.

Fixed-interval reordering by branches

But the factory still had problems. *On the average,* the warehouse would place one production order every 2 weeks. Experience showed that in 53 per cent of the weeks no orders were placed, in 44 per cent, one order, and in 3 per cent, two or more orders were placed, but orders did not always come every other week with regularity. Some weeks the factory had nothing to do, and in other weeks it had two or more orders at once. Figure 8.10 shows orders on the factory and production level for a representative period of weeks.

Factory snarls caused by these fluctuations occasionally caused the factory to miss deadlines. These in turn led on occasion to warehouse delays in filling branch orders and forced the branches to hold to the 2-week delivery time even though actual transit time was only 1 week.

An analysis showed that factory fluctuations were very costly. A statistical regression of costs against operating levels and changes showed that annual production costs were affected by the average size of changes in level rather than by the frequency of change. A few large changes in operating level were much more costly than frequent small changes. Investigations showed that under the economical reorder quantity system, production fluctuations were no larger than they had been, but the magnitude of the average change up or down actually equaled 60 per cent of the average production level. This was estimated to cost \$8,500 annually, bringing the total cost of the system, including costs of holding inventories, placing orders, and changing production rates, to \$14,000 per year.

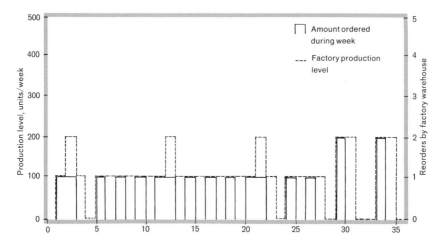

FIGURE 8.10 Factory orders and production level, economical reorder system

This led to the suggestion that the company try a new scheme so that orders on the factory warehouse and the factory would be more regular. A system with a fixed reorder cycle or period was suggested, under which branch warehouses would place orders at fixed intervals, the order being for the amount sold in the period just ended. The factory warehouse would ship the replenishment supply and order an equivalent amount from the factory. The factory warehouse in turn would be replenished within 2 weeks. Under this scheme each branch warehouse would need to keep its stock on hand or on order sufficient to fill maximum reasonable demand during one review period plus delivery time (tentatively taken as 2 weeks). The question to be determined was: How long should the reorder period (the time between reorders) be?

This question was answered as follows:

1. *Warehouse safety stock* needs were determined from branch sales fluctuations to allow for maximum reasonable demand over the period of the reorder interval plus 2-week maximum delivery period.[6] Maximum reasonable demand was computed on the basis of a 1 per cent chance of being out of stock once every 4 weeks (roughly the same level of service as in the economical reorder system). This was approximated by setting up the following set of service requirements corresponding to possible reorder periods under consideration:

[6] See Chap. 6, p. 135.

Length of reorder period (weeks)	Level of service = chance of run-out (per cent)
1	.25
2	.50
3	.75
4	1.00
5	1.25
6	1.50

The inventory requirements (safety stock) in each warehouse were then determined so that sales during a reorder period plus 2-week delivery period would not exceed stock on hand in more than the per cent of periods specified by the level of service. These requirements are summarized in Table 8.9. The expected demand during the review period plus lead time was 25 units per week; the safety stock represents the difference between the maximum demand and the expected demand during the review period plus lead time.[7]

2. *Cycle stock* would average one-half the typical shipment. Since a shipment would be made each period equaling the amount sold during the preceding period, the average shipment would be 25 units times the number of weeks in the period. Cycle stock would equal half this.

[7] As indicated in the footnote on p. 216, expected sales in t weeks equal $25t$, with a standard deviation $\sqrt{25t}$. The maximum demand to be protected under a review period of n weeks would be, therefore, $25(n + 2) + g\sqrt{25(n + 2)}$, where g would be chosen to give the desired degree of protection. The amount $g\sqrt{25(n + 2)}$ represents the safety stock. The number g depends, of course, on the level of protection desired. In the example calculation, the level of protection, and thus the appropriate value of g, depends on the length of review period chosen.

TABLE 8.9 Branch-warehouse inventory requirements

Length of reorder period (weeks)	Required level of service (per cent)	Maximum demand (at required level of service)	Expected demand (review period + lead time)	Safety stock
1	.25	99	75	24
2	.50	126	100	26
3	.75	152	125	27
4	1.00	179	150	29
5	1.25	205	175	30
6	1.50	231	200	31

3. *Stock in transit* would normally equal 1 week's sales, since this was the shipping time from factory to warehouse to each branch. However, the branches were set up to allow 2 weeks for delivery of orders placed, since the factory warehouse service had not been entirely reliable in the past. When deliveries were normal, therefore, the equivalent of one week's stock extra would be on hand. To be conservative, stock in transit was figured as 2 weeks' sales, or 50 units per branch.

The total branch-warehouse inventory would be the sum of these three. For example, if the reorder period were set at 2 weeks, the average inventory in each branch would be $26 + 25 + 50 = 101$ units.

The branch would place an order at the beginning of each period to bring total stock on hand or on order up to the maximum-demand level (Table 8.9). For example, if the reorder period were 2 weeks, an order would be placed to bring stock on hand or on order up to 126 units. By the end of the period, on the average, 50 units would have been sold, depleting the inventory on hand or on order to 76 units. The average inventory would lie halfway between—101 units, as noted above.

4. *Ordering costs* were found to equal $19 per order, with one order per period. A 1-week period means 52 orders per year; a 2-week period, 26 orders per year; etc.

5. *Factory safety stocks* were set to allow a 1 per cent risk that the warehouse would be unable to replenish all branch shipments. Since the factory warehouse would reorder each period and the lead time from the factory is 2 weeks, the warehouse would have to plan against sales for the review period plus the 2-week lead time. The factory warehouse would place an order on the factory each period, equal to orders placed on it, to bring the amount of stock on hand and on order up to the level of maximum demand over the length of the review period plus 2 weeks. The results are summarized in Table 8.10.

6. *Factory cycle stocks* approximately equal to one-half the sales in any one period would be in process or in the factory warehouse.

7. *Factory ordering costs* equaled $13.50 per period.

8. *Production change costs* were proportional to the reorder period-to-period changes in production level. Under this system these are equal to period-to-period changes in total sales in all branches, since branches transmit demand in the preceding period as reorders and the factory warehouse passes these on directly to the factory as a production order. The average magnitude of period-to-period fluctuations in sales was found to be about $11.5 \sqrt{n}$ units per period.[8]

[8] See Appendix B for the approximate relation between demand and production fluctuations under a fixed-period system.

TABLE 8.10 Factory-warehouse stock requirements*

(100 units average weekly sales)

Length of period (weeks)	Maximum demand (99% of the time)	Expected demand (review period + lead time)	Safety stock
1	341	300	41
2	447	400	47
3	553	500	53
4	658	600	58
5	762	700	62
6	867	800	67

* Expected demand over a review period of n weeks plus 2-week lead time would be 100 $(n + 2)$ units. Standard deviation would be $\sqrt{100\ (n + 2)}$. Maximum reasonable demand (with 1 per cent chance of run-out) would be 100 $(n + 2) + 2.33\ \sqrt{100\ (n + 2)}$.

Table 8.11 summarizes the costs of system operation as estimated for reorder periods varying in length from 1 to 6 weeks. Table 8.10 shows a 2-week reorder interval to be most economical for the company as a whole, so this was chosen. Every 2 weeks each branch would report sales in the preceding 2 weeks. The factory warehouse would ship a replenishment equal to reported sales and would place a production order for the combined total of reported sales. Costs were estimated to be $7,100 compared with $14,000 under the economical reorder quantity system. While the new system cut total inventories by over 40 per cent, most of the gain came from smoother production operations. Figure 8.11 shows weekly production for a representative period under the new system.

Further economies were apparent when the system was in operation. First, the reduction in production fluctuations made it possible to meet production deadlines regularly, cutting the effective lead time in deliveries to branches and thereby permitting modest reductions in branch safety stocks. Second, the inventory system was found well suited to "open" production orders: instead of issuing a new order with each run, the moderate fluctuations made it possible to replace production orders with simplified "adjusting memos" and to eliminate much of the machine setups.

Base-stock system for branch reordering

The success with the fixed-period system encouraged the company to go further, to test a base-stock system under which the branch warehouses would *report* sales periodically. The factory would consolidate these and

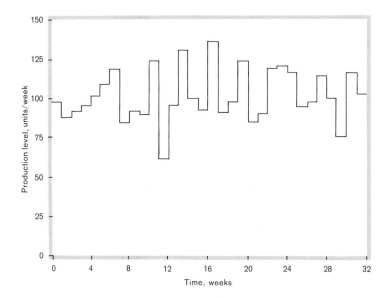

FIGURE 8.11 Production level, fixed reorder cycle

put an equivalent amount into production. Branch stocks would be replenished whenever reported sales since the last replenishment shipment exceeded a stated minimum shipping quantity. Whenever a shipment was to be made, the quantity shipped would equal reported demand since the last shipment.[9] Two questions to be decided were: How frequently should branches report sales? How big should the minimum replenishment shipment be?

Two possible advantages of this system compared with the fixed-period scheme were:

1. Branches might be able to justify weekly sales reports, reducing production fluctuations and safety stock needs further.
2. It might be possible to make less frequent shipments from factory to branches and make further savings.

Cost studies showed that the total cost, $19, of ordering and receiving goods could be broken down: $6 clerical costs in placing and recording the order, $13 in packing, shipping, and receiving.

[9] See Chap. 6, p. 141.

TABLE 8.11   Summary of reorder period cost comparisons

	Length of period (weeks)					
	1	2	3	4	5	6
Branch warehouses, each Inventory:						
Safety stock	24	26	27	29	30	31
Cycle stock	12.5	25	37.5	50	62.5	75
Transit stock	50	50	50	50	50	50
Total	86.5	101	114.5	129	142.5	156
Annual inventory cost (@ $5):	$ 435	$ 505	$ 575	$ 645	$ 715	$ 775
Ordering cost	990	495	330	250	195	165
Total	$1,425	$1,000	$905	$895	$910	$940
Total, four branches	$5,700	$4,000	$3,620	$3,580	$3,640	$3,760
Factory warehouse						
Safety stock	41	47	53	58	62	67
Cycle stock	50	100	150	200	250	300
Total	91	147	203	258	312	367
Annual inventory cost (@ $3.50):	$320	$515	$715	$903	$1,092	$1,285
Ordering cost	700	350	235	175	140	120
Total factory warehouse	$1,020	$865	$950	$1,078	$1,232	$1,405
Production change costs	$1,600	$2,250	$2,760	$3,180	$3,560	$3,900
Total system costs	$8,320	$7,115	$7,330	$7,838	$8,432	$9,065

The costs which might be affected were:

1. *Branch safety stock.* A 1-week reporting cycle could reduce branch safety stock needs from 26 to 24 units in each branch, as indicated in Table 8.11.
2. *Factory reserve stock.* A 1-week reporting cycle could reduce factory-warehouse reserve or safety stock from 47 to 41 units.
3. *Production changes.* The size and cost of changes in the production level would be cut if weekly reporting were introduced instead of reports every two weeks. Table 8.11 indicates that the cost of production changes would be reduced from $2,250 to $1,600 annually.

4. *Branch reports.* If branches reported weekly instead of every other week, reporting costs would be doubled. Each of the four branches would make 52 reports per year (at a cost of $6 per report) versus 26 per year under the 2-week replenishment system. Weekly branch reporting would cost $1,250 annually, compared with $625 with biweekly reports.
5. *Shipping costs and cycle stock.* Shipments under the base-stock system would be made independently of particular reports whenever reports from a branch indicated that enough had been sold since the last previous shipment to justify a new shipment. The optimum shipping quantity from factory to branch can be obtained from the formula given before:[10]

$$\sqrt{\frac{2 \cdot 13 \cdot 1,300}{5}} = 82 \text{ units}$$

(Note that the cost of shipment is $13, packing, shipping, and receiving, rather than $19, which includes the clerical costs of reporting or placing an order. Ordering and reporting are now separated.) The *minimum* shipment quantity would, however, not be the *average* shipment actually made to branches. Some weeks, cumulative reported demand would just miss justifying a shipment, in which case the shipment made the next week would substantially exceed the minimum. In fact, the average-size shipment would be approximately equal to the minimum limit plus one-half of the average amount sold in one reporting period. If the reporting period were 1 week, the difference between average and minimum shipments would be about 12 units. Since the "economical" shipping quantity appeared to be 82 units, this indicated a minimum limit of 70 units per shipment. With an average shipment quantity of 82 units, each branch would be expected to receive just under 16 shipments annually. The cycle stock in the branch would, of course, be increased from half the average shipment of 50 under the fixed biweekly replenishment system to half the new average shipping quantity of 82.

Table 8.12 summarizes the comparison of differing elements of costs between two systems: (1) a fixed-period system with biweekly branch reports of demand and replenishment shipments to branches, and biweekly production orders to replenish the factory warehouse; (2) a base-stock system with weekly branch reports and production-adjusting orders, and replenishment shipments to branches sent as reports from a branch indicated sales of 75 or more units since the last shipment to the branch. A modest reduction in cost, $290, appeared possible using the base-stock system.

[10] See p. 57.

TABLE 8.12 Comparison of differing elements of annual costs,
fixed-period versus base-stock system

	Fixed-period system	Base-stock system
Branch safety stock	$ 520	$ 480
Factory reserve stock	165	144
Branch reports	625	1,250
Production changes	2,250	1,600
Shipping cost	1,352	828
Cycle stock	500	820
Total	$5,412	$5,122

Base-stock system with leveled production

Cheered by its successes, the company decided to see if even further improvements might be obtained by cutting down further on production fluctuations. The production level under the base-stock system was adjusted each week to account for the full excess or deficiency in inventory due to sales fluctuations. It was suggested that production might be adjusted to take up only a fraction of the difference between actual and desired stocks, with added inventories used to make up the difference.

The two costs that would be affected are costs of changing production and costs of holding inventories at the warehouse, in particular, safety stocks. These are affected by the fraction of the inventory departure made up each week by adjusting production. The original base-stock system described above was equivalent to putting this fraction equal to 1.0.

The costs of inventories and production changes were estimated, making use of the two approximate rules quoted on page 207. The cost of required reserve stock in the factory warehouse was estimated as:

$$C_I = \$83.30 \sqrt{\frac{2(2k - k) + 1}{2k - k^2}}$$

When k, the control number, equals 1 (effectively the value under the base-stock system as initially established), the inventory cost is

$$C_I = \$83.30\sqrt{3} = \$144$$

the value shown in Table 8.12. Figure 8.12 shows the inventory cost for values of the control number k from 0 to 1.

The cost of production changes was estimated as:

$$C_P = \$1,600 \sqrt{\frac{k}{2-k}}$$

Again, when the control number k equals 1, the cost of production changes equals \$1,600, the amount shown in Table 8.12. The cost of production changes compared with the value of the control number k is also shown in Figure 8.12.

As Figure 8.12 indicates, setting the control number k equal to 0.05 minimizes the total of costs affected. The total of the two costs is \$555 if k is set at 0.05, compared with a total of \$1,745 if k is set equal to 1 (the initial base-stock system), a saving of \$1,190. The reserve stock required would cost \$555 and equal 159 units.

This procedure resulted in much smoother production operations, illustrated in Figure 8.13, compared with the earlier systems, illustrated by Figures 8.10 and 8.11.

In summary, this system worked as follows:

1. Each branch established a base stock of 169 units (70 units minimum shipment + 24 units safety stock + 75 units covering 3 weeks' average demand).
2. Each branch reported the volume of demand on it weekly.

FIGURE 8.12   Cost of production changes and safety stock versus rate of response to sales fluctuations (control number, k)

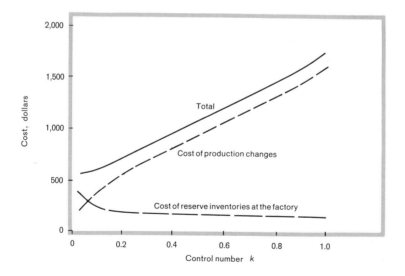

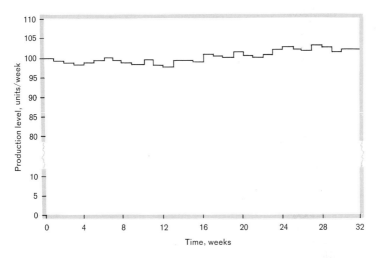

FIGURE 8.13 Production level, base-stock system. Control number $= 0.05$

3. Whenever reports from a branch showed that stock on hand or in transit to the branch had fallen 70 units or more below the base-stock level, the factory warehouse dispatched a shipment to make up the difference, i.e., to bring stocks on hand and in transit up to the base-stock level.
4. The factory warehouse in turn established a base stock equal to 459 units (300 units covering 3 weeks' average demand + 159 units reserve stock). Each week the following computation was made:

Stock on hand
+ Production in process

= Total stock on hand and in process
− Reported but unreplenished demand at branches

= Available stock
+ 100 units, normal production
− Base stock

= Excess (deficiency)

Using the chosen value of the control number k the normal production was lowered (increased) by 5 per cent of the computed excess (deficiency) of available stock compared with the base stock.

TABLE 8.13 Comparison of annual costs and required inventories, four alternative control systems

	Annual cost	System inventory (units)
1. Economical order quantity system	$14,000	968
2. Fixed-period reorder system	7,100	551
3. Base-stock system	6,800	551
4. Base-stock system with damped production response	5,600	669

These various changes in the method of controlling production and inventories led to step-by-step reductions in the cost of operation of factories and branches. The costs and total inventory required under the four systems are compared in Table 8.13.

While the foregoing example is wholly fictitious, it highlights some of the differences in operating characteristics among alternative control systems. The base-stock system with damped response turns out to be most effective in light of the demand, cost, and operating characteristics chosen for this particular illustration. In practice, demand and cost characteristics and the pattern of flow of goods are fundamentally what determine the choice of an efficient system, and the design of a system must start with analysis of these. Fortunately, technical methods such as those described in this and preceding chapters are available for designing a sound system based directly on fundamental demand, cost, and operating characteristics, short-cutting the step-by-step attack described in our fictitious example.

METHODS IN DEVELOPMENT

Development of improved control methods is far from a closed subject. A number of research groups are actively working in this field; some references to work of this type published so far are given in the bibliography on page 232. Although a number of technical approaches are being explored, the concepts underlying these studies are similar:

1. Control of production levels means setting a production rate in view of both a forecast of future demand and existing inventories, i.e., reacting to past operating results as these influence the capability of achieving planned objectives.
2. There is no point in fixing production rates or detailed plans any further

in advance than is absolutely necessary. If employment levels can be adjusted weekly, the control system should adjust employment a week in advance and not detailed employment schedules 1 to 6 months ahead. If a raw material must be purchased on a 6-month lead time, the control system should adjust inventories of this material in the light of forecast needs for 6 months.

3. The two related criteria governing design of a control system are stability and efficiency. Stability implies that the system should not cause over-correction, overresponse, or oscillation in production levels. As suggested earlier, a number of commonly used systems violate this criterion in various subtle ways. The system should make adequate but not excessive use of inventories to absorb demand fluctuations.

PROBLEMS

1. The Barbell Manufacturing Company produces a line of small home appliances selling for $400 each. Total demand has been running at the rate of 15,000 units per year. Distribution is handled by six regional branches throughout the country, each located to serve a market demand-ing about 2,500 units per year. Ordering cost at each of the branches is known to be $60 per order (clerical costs and shipping included) and inventory cost is set at $45 per year per unit.

   On a fixed-order basis of replenishment, how large should shipments to the branches be? At what intervals should replenishments be made?

2. In what quantities should the Barbell plant produce if machine setup costs are $150 and the cost per year to store the product is $25?

3. Find the total annual inventory and ordering cost for a branch ordering under this fixed-quantity rule.

4. Barbell's plan shows weekly demand and production at 300 units. Cur-rent inventory is at 350 units and the plan calls for a drop of 10 units per week over the next 10 weeks. Actual demand over the 10-week period develops as follows:

Week	Sales	Week	Sales
1	275	6	315
2	330	7	320
3	370	8	325
4	270	9	280
5	190	10	300

Tabulate the production and inventory levels, assuming a 2-week lead time on production changes, using a production control rule of the form P_{T+1} as given in the text, and control number:

a. $k = 1.0$
b. $k = 0.1$

5. Compute the expected changes in production level for both control situations in problem 4 above.

BIBLIOGRAPHY

Eilon, S.: *Elements of Production Planning and Control,* The Macmillan Company, New York, 1962.

Hanssmann, F.: *Operations Research in Production and Inventory Control,* John Wiley & Sons, Inc., New York, 1962.

Klein, Morton: "On Production Smoothing, October, 1960," *Management Science,* pp. 286–293, April, 1961.

Koepke, Charles A.: *Plant Production Control,* John Wiley & Sons, Inc., New York, 1961.

Kunreuther, H.: "Scheduling Short-run Changes in Production to Minimize Long-run Expected Costs," *Management Science,* vol. 12, no. 7, pp. 541–554, March, 1966.

McGarrah, Robert E.: *Production and Logistics Management: Text and Cases,* John Wiley & Sons, Inc., New York, 1963.

9

SCHEDULING
PRODUCTION

FORMS OF PRODUCTION ORGANIZATION

Production scheduling and related control systems strongly reflect the organization and functions of the production system. Two extreme organizational forms are generally recognized. These are the functional organization and the product-line organization. The functional form is better known as the "job-shop" organization, but it is found in many medium-sized and large companies whose product is quite different from that of the true job shop. The product-line organization is best known, probably, in the automotive industry. Because it is most often found in the automotive and similar industries where assembly operations are important, it is generally referred to as "assembly-line" manufacture; in fact, however, the same basic organization can be and is used in widely varying manufacturing operations.

Functional, or "job-shop," organization

In the functional organization, departments or work centers are organized about particular types of equipment or operations, such as drilling, forging, spinning, or assembly. Products flow through departments in batches corresponding to individual orders. These may be finished-stock orders on the plant or, in the extreme, individual customer orders. Theoretically, any sequence of operations from one department to the next is possible.

The functional type of organization is found in industries characterized by substantial basic-product diversity. It has the advantages of flexibility and adaptability to change in demand. Moreover, equipment is not specialized or tied to other units; as a result, better equipment utilization and lower equipment capacity requirements are in theory possible. On the other hand, the functional form of organization typically results in slow movement of product through manufacturing stages, resulting in sizable process-inventory requirements. For example, one frequently encounters manufacturing lead times of 1 to 3 months, although actual processing time of an order on equipment may be a matter of a few hours. The control and financing of the resulting process inventories can be exceedingly burdensome. Moreover, paper-work, order-routing, and scheduling costs typically are higher than in product-line organizations. Equipment change-over costs usually constitute a sizable and painfully recognized item, and more versatile and more highly paid personnel are required. Cost and production control are more difficult and expensive, with order expediting frequently a major expense.

Product-line, or assembly-line, organization

Under the product-line form of organization, all operations on a product or set of related products are combined. Equipment is devoted to a single product or product group. It is generally physically contiguous, and capacities of the several manufacturing stages are related to permit uniform product flow. Under this form of organization, individual product orders are merged and only superficial product differences, from the point of view of manufacturing procedures, exist within a given line.

This form of organization is typical in industries with stable demand and limited basic-product diversity. It has the advantages of rapid flow of product through manufacturing stages, resulting in lower process-inventory requirements and the need for less paper work in scheduling material, routing, and control. Opportunities for using specialized tools and less versatile people permit lowered operating cost. On the other hand, rigidity, extra equipment costs, sensitivity to disruption due to breakdown of component units of the line or due to fluctuations in output of individual units or stations, and feasible limitations on product diversity have limited the extended adoption of this form of organization.

Intermediate forms

Most manufacturing organizations contain elements of both organization forms, functional and product-line, and almost all products and product lines—whether several hundred or several tens of thousands of items—are capable of being manufactured under a wide range of organizational forms intermediate between the extremes of pure job-shop or assembly-line operation. Taking advantage of this latitude has been a source of considerable operating economy in some businesses and could be in many more. Analysis of specific product and processing characteristics has revealed opportunities for improvements, in inventory and production control, ranging from better forecasting to more efficient scheduling.

SEQUENCED OPERATIONS

Perhaps the most common form of intermediate manufacturing process between functional and product-line systems is that composed of sequenced operations. While having the job-shop characteristics of functional department and diversity of product, there exists a single direction of flow from one department to another. Thus departments can be thought of as existing in series. For example, in the Continental Stamping Company discussed below, all products move from preparation operations (all in a strict sequence) to shearing, to stamping or pressing, to machining, and end with packaging. While all orders or products will have their own sequence of manufacturing steps, these sequences correspond sufficiently so that departments can be put in one order or sequence which corresponds to the sequence of manufacturing steps on any product.

A producer of specialty paper products found that its products were made following a few basic sequences of operations, although one or more individual operations might be dropped in making any one product. This discovery stimulated the design of a scheduling and machine-loading system permitting a rapid balanced flow of product from one department to the next, resembling assembly-line scheduling much more closely than the traditional job-shop methods.

Another common characteristic frequently found together with sequenced operations is increasing product specialization. From stage to stage in the operation sequence in this case, products or components become more and more specialized. For example, in the Continental Stamping Company, a given kind of sheet metal may be cut into a variety of shapes and sizes, or a given size may be stamped into a variety of shapes. Another major industrial-equipment manufacturer had assumed that his plant's operations were characteristically job-shop, since each end item was individually designed and produced. Analysis showed, however, that the extremely diverse product line was or could be assembled from a limited line of a few hundred standard components. Although demand for individual end products was unpredictable, demand translated into component requirements showed considerable stability. Component requirements could be forecast with accuracy and produced on a regular rather than a sporadic basis, with resultant smaller inventory balances and reduced lead times.

Both the characteristics of increasing product specialization and sequenced operations make it possible to get away from the difficulties of an extreme job-shop operation. Order-for-order handling throughout the process can be dropped in favor of banks of inventories and continuous manufacture of components or process items.

BATCHED PRODUCTION

Another intermediate form of organization is one in which product lines are set up to handle a variety of products on a batch basis. For example, in the plant of a commercial-finishes manufacturer a single manufacturing line, such as the auto-wax and cleanser line, performs all steps in the manufacture of the finished product going over the line, including blending, packaging, sealing, and cartoning. However, a basic-line change-over is required to go from one product to another, with perhaps a clean-out of blending equipment or a resetting of conveyors and handling equipment to accommodate a different-sized package. The extent to which this type of line organization can be utilized in the manufacture of a diversified product line depends on the extent to which basic-product design and manufacture can be adapted to a set of essentially similar manufacturing steps and on the extent to which the costs of changing these stages over from one product to another can be reduced.

When this type of organization can be efficiently set up, it permits taking advantage of some of the simplicities of product-line scheduling, with the remaining inventory-control questions being reasonably straightforward ones relating to the appropriate size and sequencing of individual batches and required protective stock levels. The ability to design products around such a manufacturing organization appears likely to be an important determinant of how far companies with diversified lines can go in taking advantage of the growing opportunities for automation. While a variety of developments are making automatic machinery more and more flexible in an increasing number of fields, automatic equipment seen to date has been limited in flexibility to modification within the same basic set of operations.

Recognition of the characteristics of different production organizations and the capability of manufacturing given products under a variety of organizational frameworks are fundamental in planning production scheduling systems (1) because the organization of the scheduling system must reflect the basic manufacturing organization, and (2) because it is frequently possible to achieve some of the advantages of one type of manufacturing organization or another through appropriate scheduling routines, without basic reorganization of the production facilities or responsibilities.

PRODUCT DIFFERENTIATION—EXPLOITING COMPONENT FAMILIES

The wide end-product lines of many companies sometimes, in fact, are made from groups or families of more or less related components which are assembled in different ways and in various combinations. The component family characteristics of the product line should be recognized and taken advantage of in establishing production scheduling and control methods.

It is usually possible to construct a product-component table, an illustrative portion of which is shown in Table 9.1.

The degree of joint usage of individual components among the variety of end products depends upon the care taken in engineering products to make end-product differences as superficial as possible, from the point of view of manufacturing methods. A wide variety of end products can be obtained even within a given automotive line when the differences in fittings, colors, fabrics, and finishes are considered. Great care has been taken, however, in designing the product and manufacturing methods to make these differences as superficial as possible. The same basic parts and assembly process are used for all of them.

Electronic instruments, radio, and television equipment are another gen-

TABLE 9.1 Product-component table showing end-product numbers using specified subassemblies

End-product no.	Subassembly no.													
	15 A	15 B	36	38	61 A	61 B	61 D	67 B	92 A	92 B	97	101	109	113
C 3293	X		X		X				X					
C 3368	X		X		X					X				
D 1982		X			X						X			
G 15A3		X		X		X						X		
G 6972		X		X		X							X	
G 6972A		X		X				X						X

eral field of manufacture which exhibits a wide variety of end products. Here, however, there has been substantially less done to achieve basic uniformity in component design. To some degree the differences in products may be inherent and basic. However, recent advances in product design to permit the use of automatic wiring and assembly equipment indicate that many of these differences are in fact a matter of engineering design rather than a basic requirement of the product. Where each product is designed individually, there is less opportunity to exploit the concept of product family or group.

Changes in products or merchandising requirements may call for major revisions in manufacturing methods and component design and use, to prevent planning and scheduling problems from getting out of control. The trend in typewriter styling is a good example of how an evolution in merchandising may lead to serious inventory and planning problems short of major changes in manufacturing methods. Early typewriter-manufacturing methods were based essentially on a single model. Gradually a modest variety of type and carriage sizes was introduced. Variety remained small enough and demand sufficiently concentrated in a few styles, however, to permit use of established manufacturing methods. These methods, designed for a very limited product line, happened to be so organized that the characteristics of an individual unit observable to the customer, such as type style, carriage width, color, and keyboard, were fixed at the outset.

In recent years, style has swept the typewriter field. Distinctive type styles and variety of color have become normal. Thus manufacturers are faced with the problem of establishing large stocks to service a variable and highly diversified demand in the face of a long manufacturing lead time, or of redesigning products and manufacturing methods so that style variations can be incorporated closer to or in response to actual demand.

The reason for concern with the engineering of product families is clear. When each product is designed individually with specialized components, the result is a manufacturing and assembly process which exhibits the characteristics of a job shop in all their difficult extremes. Each order from a customer or for finished-stock adjustment must be serviced individually throughout the plant. Opportunity for economies through economical order quantities is lost, and uniformity in employment in individual departments can be achieved only at the expense of substantial processing lead times.

As the number of individual components is reduced, the sales volume per component increases. More efficient reorder methods and controls become effective. More advantageous terms for purchased items may be possible. Inventories can be reduced and/or lead times can be cut. When opportunities for component standardization are fully utilized, it is sometimes found that the demand for individual components is relatively uniform, even when the demand for individual end products employing these components is highly erratic and uncertain. This is the result of averaging the demand for an individual component over a large number of end products. When this turns out to be true, it frequently becomes possible to forecast the total requirements for an individual component accurately, even when the precise end use of these components is not known. Components with these characteristics can be set up on a product-line system, taking advantage of the opportunities for lessened inventories, lead times, and labor fluctuations which such systems offer.

THE SCHEDULING FUNCTION

The principal function of production scheduling is to obtain a smooth, timely flow of product through manufacturing steps. It starts with the specification of what to make, from customer orders or from the operation of the inventory-control system. It includes the loading of items to be made into manufacturing centers, and covers the dispatching of manufacturing instructions to operating centers.

The scheduling system must work within the limits of established production plans and inventory budgets. It is essentially the process by which an organization reacts to existing demand or order commitments, making use of capital facilities, material, and people that are available or will be within the allowed lead time. Scheduling, then, is a short-term function aimed at responding to current demand and output fluctuations compared with plan.[1]

The objectives of the scheduling function are to prevent unbalanced use of time among departments and work centers, to keep labor on hand employed, and to meet established lead times. The scheduling methods used are closely allied to the production planning and inventory control methods used, such as those discussed in earlier chapters. These methods determine the resources available for scheduling. On the other hand, the lead times which the scheduling system permits in turn have a strong influence on inventory stocks and policies.

Earlier chapters have described methods for setting operating levels in processing or manufacturing centers, setting inventory balances at established stock points, and deciding when and in what quantity to replenish

---

[1] The interpretation of "current" depends on company circumstances, markets, and products. It means basically meeting requirements at the end of the established lead time for processing or procuring materials.

inventories. Scheduling, then, is primarily concerned with conversion of items drawn from one set or stage of stock points into items to go into a following stock point. In other words, it covers the make-up of a production order, from requisitioning of stocked parts or materials needed to delivery of the item ordered either to stock for use elsewhere or to the customer.

In a "pure" job shop, then, where no standard items are made, the scheduling function covers the whole process from drawing on raw-material balances (or, if these are specially purchased, requisitioning these) through converting stages to completion of each customer order. In other companies, a production order may cover manufacture of standard parts for stock from raw materials; another order may cover assembly of stock parts into subassemblies, or conversion of one type of stock in process into another (conversion of greige yard into yarn dyed a particular color).

Sometimes, even when the production or processing steps are fairly well standardized, other requirements, such as government regulations, may make it necessary to keep a batch or lot identified from raw material to finished item. In this case, there are no available inventories in process, i.e., no stock points in the terminology used in earlier chapters. In-process inventory is in the form of partially completed orders which are not available for use on other orders. A production order may cover a number of individual operating steps, but the item is considered available only when all of these steps are completed. The scheduling function is concerned with getting a production order completed on time, i.e., transferring material from one stock point to another in the established lead time.

Production orders may be for a specified quantity, such as the amount ordered by a customer or an economical replenishment lot, to be made as one batch. Or they may be "open" orders, with the rate of production or the quantity of the item to be completed by a given time adjusted from time to time.

Scheduling practices depend in detail on the nature of the product and facilities, although considerable effort has gone into the development of techniques—board displays, filing systems, card systems, etc.—to facilitate scheduling and control of progress on orders scheduled. Conventional scheduling techniques or procedures are typically designed to cope with the complexities of job-shop scheduling, where each order is unique and no predetermined sequence of operations exists. Most such procedures are basically schemes for recording and keeping track of center loadings, expected delivery times, and work progress. In examining approaches to scheduling, it is helpful to break these into:

1. Techniques for deciding which item to make and how to make it.

2. Methods for loading production orders, i.e., fitting orders to available facilities.
3. Methods for dispatching orders and watching progress.

Special-production orders

The ultimate source of information on what to make is a customer's order. In a job-shop or special-order business, the customer's order directly stimulates scheduling action. In many businesses with mixed stock and special orders it is necessary to process a special order by itself through at least some operating centers.

The first step in scheduling a customer order is to convert it to the detailed form needed to specify how and from what it will be made. The information needed includes:

1. *Engineering description.* This may include drawings suited to shop use with specifications and tolerances, chemical formulation and processing requirements, etc.
2. *Bill of materials.* An accurate and complete statement of the items to be used in manufacture is needed. Where these are stock components or parts, this should be indicated and the component number or reference should be shown. Where special materials, components, or parts are needed, items to be purchased should be indicated.
3. *List of operations.* This should show the detailed routing of the order from selection of items to be processed through each processing stage to completion. The specific type of processing equipment or machine needed at each stage should be shown, together with any special equipment or tooling required.
4. *Reasonable time estimates.* The list of operations must show the estimated time to complete each specific operation. Estimates may be based on standard times, if these are available; they may be set by special time study or methods analysis; or they may be arrived at based on judgment of an experienced estimator, the foreman, or on comparison with a similar operation in the past.

The operation routing, time estimates, and bill of materials will normally be summarized in a single document, variously called the job layout sheet, operation master, operation routing list, etc. Figure 9.1 illustrates a typical operation master. Responsibility for preparing the operation master list may be a part of the duties of the production control section, although it is not directly a scheduling or control job. In some companies, especially in those

Cust. Order No.:		Date:		Promised:

<table>
<tr><td rowspan="3">Address</td><td>S.O. No.:</td><td>Contract No.:</td><td>Print Nos.:
133-3369
-A37</td></tr>
<tr><td>Div.:</td><td>Lot:</td><td></td></tr>
</table>

Job No.: 36360	Quantity: 200	Lot No.: —	Description: Buckle Joint #13363

Material:

Part Nos.:
One ea.: #3369 Head; #8822 Rocker Arm; #7763 Pin

Oper.	Dept.	Description	Time			Latest Start Date	Date Insp.:
			Setup	Run	Total		
31	30	Draw parts					
36	30	Assemble per print	.90	.0220	5.300		
38	30	Press pin	1.25	.0083	2.910		
43	40	Stamp	.75	.0032	1.390		
49	40	Inspect	.40	.0167	3.740		
40	40	Deliver to ass'y stores					

FIGURE 9.1 Operation master list

dealing in technical products, the work layout and write-up of specifications is assigned to the engineering department; in others it may be a part of the methods-engineering, the industrial-engineering, or the production-engineering department; in still others, a special estimating unit for special orders may be responsible for layout.

Where the customer order is sufficiently special so that the salesman or sales department cannot quote a price or estimate delivery directly, the order or request for bid must go through a number of steps. In a typical special-products business, for example, the sales department will initiate the request, preparing a special-order estimate form. This will identify the customer, describe the item wanted, with reference to customer drawings or sketches, and indicate the quantity and delivery date desired. Figure 9.2 illustrates a typical special-order estimate.

The estimate form must then go to the production-engineering or estimating unit, the unit responsible for making up actual job routings, to specify the parts, components, or materials to be used, required operations, and necessary special equipment, tools, or fixtures. They may estimate the quantity of materials and operating times and extend these to get cost, or they may estimate quantities only, with the estimate then going to a cost unit for cost extensions. The estimate will then normally go to the production-scheduling unit for a check on availability of processing time in each operation, from which a tentative delivery date will be set, often in terms of weeks after receipt of the final order.

Preparation of a special-order estimate clearly involves a good deal of work, and the information it contains is valuable, once a firm order is received. In the case of a sizable order, the work of preparing the estimate may have required the preparation of a detailed and essentially complete operations master list. A copy of the job estimate then will normally be filed in the estimating or production-engineering unit for referral when a firm order is received.

Once a firm order is received and approved by the sales and credit departments, it can move to the estimating or production-engineering unit to make the detailed layout. When this is complete, as expressed by the operation master with necessary drawings, the job documents can be reproduced.

The number of documents required to move a special order through a plant of moderate size is staggering. These include:

1. Copies of the operation master for production scheduling, cost accounting, and the departments concerned. Sometimes each department will receive a full operation master; in other companies, each department will receive a reduced master, showing only fixed data (customer name, order number, etc.) plus data pertaining only to the particular operations in the department.
2. Job tickets, showing the data pertaining to each operation individually, for use by foremen in assigning work, by workers in reporting work, and by timekeepers and the cost unit in accounting for payroll and shop cost.

Customer:

Address:

Request No.:

Date:

Reply by:

Sales Code:

Description:

Similar to:

	Yes	No
Previous Order:	☐	☐

Drawings:

Material to be supplied by:	Us	Cust.		Tools to be supplied by:	Us	Cust.
1. _____	☐	☐		On hand:	☐	☐
2. _____	☐	☐		New:	☐	☐
3. _____	☐	☐				

Est. Cost Mfg. Div.:			
Material: 1			
2			
3			
Shop hours: 1			
2			
3			
Assembly hours: 1			
2			
3			
Tooling:			
Est. Completion			
Eng. and tools			
Material			
Shop			
Assembly			
Inspection			

Date:_____ Approved:_____

FIGURE 9.2 Typical special-order estimate

Copies of job tickets are sometimes used by the production-scheduling unit, rather than a copy of the operation master.

3. Material requisitions, to authorize removal of parts, components, or materials from stock.

4. Tool or equipment requisitions.

5. Move tickets, for use in controlling the movement of an order from one department or center to another.

6. Purchase requisitions, to authorize the purchasing agent to procure special purchased items.

A number of types of techniques are used to facilitate reproduction. Ozalid masters for the route sheet are sometimes used. Ditto masters are used with devices to permit selective printing of pertinent information on job tickets, move tickets, requisitions, etc. Where punched-card equipment is used for cost accounting, payroll, or loading, the operation master may be converted directly to punched cards. Each card will show order-identification data and the information from a line of the operation master. The cards when reproduced and interpreted can be issued for direct use as job tickets, material requisitions, or move tickets. Sometimes a ditto master will be used with punched cards: the master is used to write the necessary information on the card in normal form, and the same information is then punched in the card for loading, cost accounting, or material-usage calculations. Figure 9.3 illustrates a typical set of order papers.

Where the customer order is for a nonstock standard item, a permanent operation master can be kept on file. This can be reproduced with the variable information particular to the order, such as customer identity, order number, and quantity added. Some companies have found that many "special" orders call for particular combinations of standard attachments or groups of operations. Standard operation masters can be set up for these individual subsets of operations and reproduced in the combination called for by the special order. This is an example of assembly of special-order documents themselves from "stock" components.

For example, a paper-products manufacturer who makes up specialty products for the college trade, such as pads, notebook fillers, and bound notebooks with special embossing or printing, uses the following system in filling special orders. Orders are made up from stock components such as fillers, binding supplies, and covers. Operations follow the same sequence as for similar stock items except for the addition of certain extra steps. These extra steps are basically the same for any special order for one class of product. Operation masters covering these sets of special steps have been prepared, with space for including special descriptive data (the insignia to

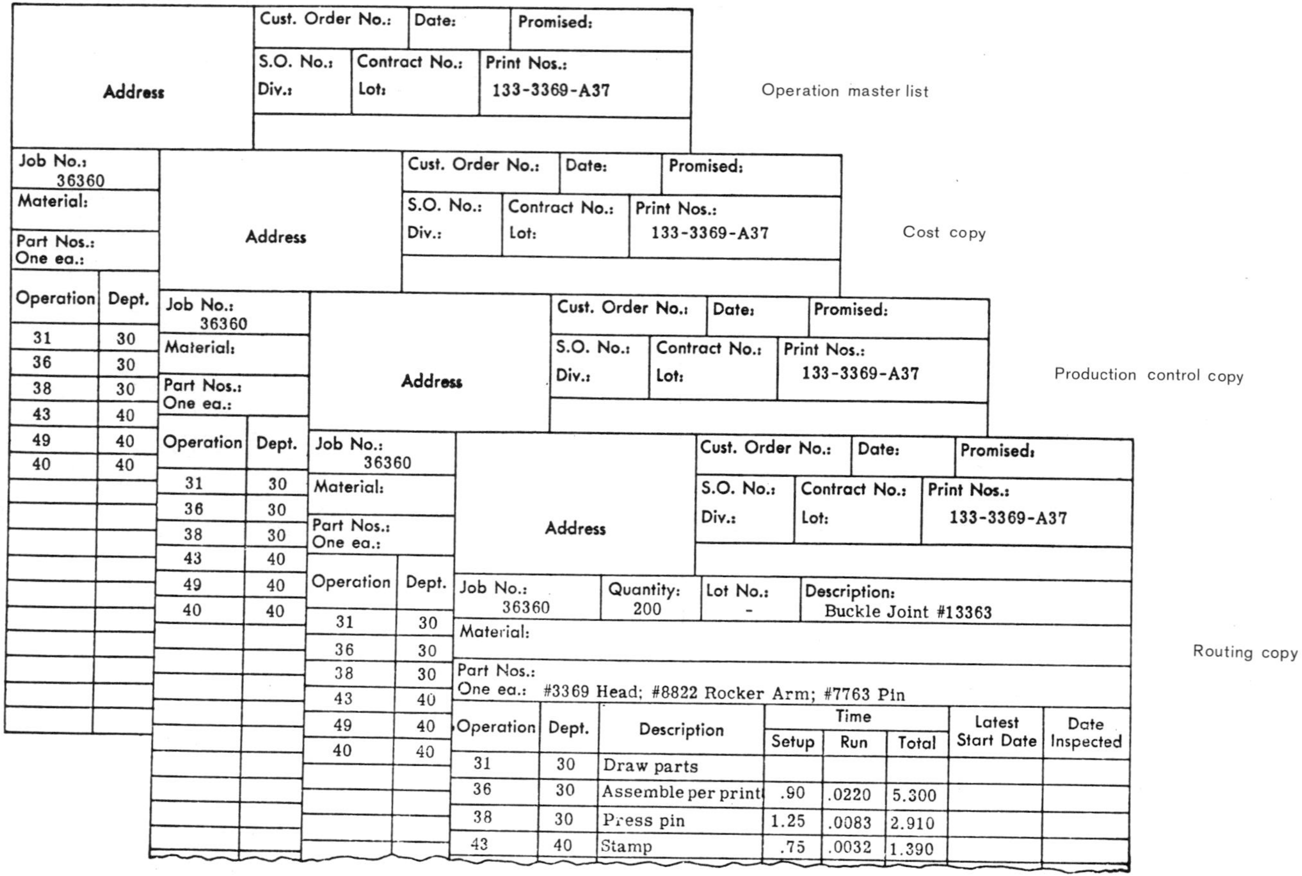

Operation master list

Cost copy

Production control copy

Routing copy

Print Nos.: 133-3369-A37

Cust. Order No.: | **Date:** | **Promised:**
S.O. No.: | **Contract No.:** | **Print Nos.:** 133-3369-A37
Div.: | **Lot:**

Address

Job No.: 36360
Material:
Part Nos.: One ea.:

Operation	Dept.
31	30
36	30
38	30
43	40
49	40
40	40

Routing copy / Production control copy

Description: Buckle Joint #13363
Quantity: 200
Lot No.: -
Job No.: 36360
Material:
Part Nos.: One ea.: #3369 Head; #8822 Rocker Arm; #7763 Pin

Operation	Dept.	Description	Setup	Run	Total	Latest Start Date	Date Inspected
31	30	Draw parts	.90	.0220	5.300		
36	30	Assemble per print					
38	30	Press pin	1.25	.0083	2.910		
43	40	Stamp	.75	.0032	1.390		

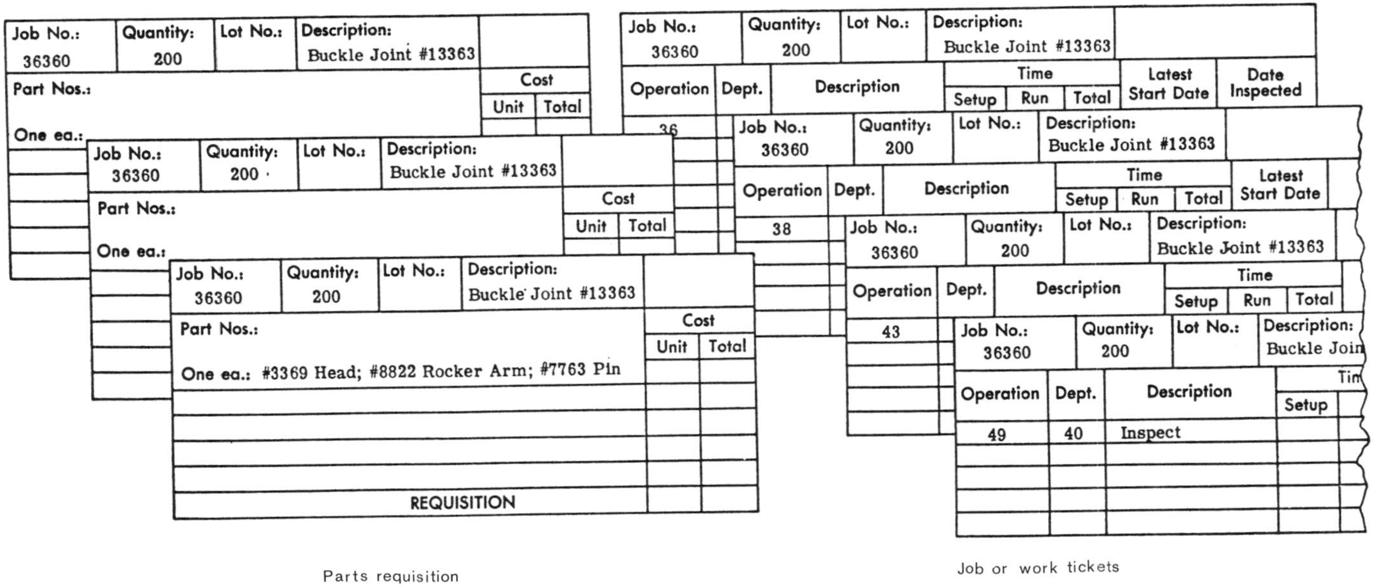

Job No.: 36360 | Quantity: 200 | Lot No.: | Description: Buckle Joint #13363

Part Nos.:

	Cost	
	Unit	Total

One ea.:

Job No.: 36360 | Quantity: 200 | Lot No.: | Description: Buckle Joint #13363

Part Nos.:

	Cost	
	Unit	Total

One ea.:

Job No.: 36360 | Quantity: 200 | Lot No.: | Description: Buckle Joint #13363

Part Nos.:

One ea.: #3369 Head; #8822 Rocker Arm; #7763 Pin

	Cost	
	Unit	Total

REQUISITION

Parts requisition

Job No.: 36360 | Quantity: 200 | Lot No.: | Description: Buckle Joint #13363

Operation	Dept.	Description	Latest Start Date	Date Inspected
36				

Job No.: 36360 | Quantity: 200 | Lot No.: | Description: Buckle Joint #13363

Operation	Dept.	Description	Time		Latest Start Date
			Setup	Run	Total
38					

Job No.: 36360 | Quantity: 200 | Lot No.: | Description: Buckle Joint #13363

Operation	Dept.	Description	Time		
			Setup	Run	Total
43					

Job No.: 36360 | Quantity: 200 | Lot No.: | Description: Buckle Joint

Operation	Dept.	Description		
			Setup	
49	40	Inspect		

Job or work tickets

FIGURE 9.3 Illustrative set of order papers

be used, the name to be printed, etc.). These are used as supplements to operation masters for stock items to prepare the special-order documents.

When the operation master for the order has been prepared, showing quantities and times required for each operation, the order is ready for loading; i.e., it is ready for assignment of specific completion dates for each step. Loading may be done before or after the full set of order documents is prepared. Some companies find it convenient to enter scheduled completion dates on the master so that they will be reproduced on the individual-order documents automatically. Others enter scheduled completion dates on the individual-order documents after they have been prepared, especially if standard operation masters have been used.

Production orders for stock items

Where the inventory of a stock item is controlled under a reorder system of the type described in Chapter 6, the decision of how much of which items to make is built into the system. Under a periodic-reorder system, a new production order for the item is placed each week. Under a fixed-reorder system, a new production order is prepared whenever the quantity on hand or on order falls below the reorder point. Under a base-stock system, where end-product demand is exploded into demand for the component or item in question, a production order is prepared at each review for reported demand during the preceding period, or whenever reported demand since the previous order exceeds a minimum economical quantity.

The necessary papers covering a stock item, whether a finished item or part or item in process, should normally be prepared in advance. The only steps necessary are the assignment of an identifying order number, the specification of quantity, and the reproduction of order documents. The order is then ready for loading.

The required completion date of an order for a stock item is determined by the system: the date the order was initiated plus the established lead time for the item. The established lead time sets the limit of scheduling flexibility within which the item must be loaded. Clearly, if the operations of the company are to proceed on a rational basis, stock-replenishment lead times must be realistic. On the other hand, once set, lead times must be adhered to, and stock-production orders must be scheduled as expeditiously as special items. If lead times on stock items are not met, the disruption to subsequent operations can be painfully expensive. If established stock lead times do not have to be met, inventory levels are too high and the production system is not in fact under control.

In a control system operating with a fixed or minimum run length, the appropriate run length can be reviewed by reference to the current usage rate and a table, graph, or nomogram for determining run length, such as those described in Chapter 4. In a base-stock system, the base-stock level should be increased or decreased by the amount of increase or decrease in the minimum run length, and a run should be scheduled to bring the total quantity of the item on hand or scheduled up to the new base-stock level.

SCHEDULING TECHNIQUES

Run-out list for selecting items

The systems described in Chapters 7 and 8 are useful in planning and controlling over-all inventory levels and production operating levels. They do not, however, necessarily indicate how much of which particular item to make. This is a day-to-day decision to be made in the face of actual demand and inventories on hand. If any type of "damped" response to inventory fluctuations is employed, some decision must be made how to allocate available production time among the items in question.

One approach to this question rests on the concept of run-out time, the time when inventory on hand plus production of the item already scheduled will be used up. The object is to assign available production capacity in such a way that run-out times for all items are the same.

The inventory of each item expected on hand at the end of the period being scheduled is:

Inventory on hand or scheduled in production on the scheduling date
+ Scheduled production of the item
− Expected usage of the item during the period

= Inventory expected on hand, end of period scheduled

This expected inventory divided by the current usage rate gives the expected time over which demand for the item is covered.

This formula can be applied equally well to the total inventory of all items produced by the facility being scheduled as long as inventories, production, and usage are expressed in commensurable units, e.g., machine hours or man-hours. Since the total production to be scheduled is known from the employment plan or over-all control, knowledge of total inventory on hand and an estimate of expected usage is all that is needed to determine how long the total expected inventory will last—the total run-out time.

The production of each item should then be scheduled so that the run-out time for the item is the same as for the inventory as a whole. This can be done as follows:

1. Multiply the usage rate for the item by the run-out time for the total inventory planned for the end of the period scheduled.
2. Add expected usage during the period scheduled.
3. Subtract the total of inventory on hand or currently scheduled in production. This gives the production of the item to be scheduled.

To illustrate, Table 9.2 shows the calculation for eight stock numbers.

The steps in the calculation are as follows: First, the inventory of each item on hand (column 9) is multiplied by the required production time per unit and totaled. This gives the total inventory on hand expressed in machine hours (column 1, 189.0 hours). Let us suppose that the planned production time for the week is 74.6 hours (column 2) and that the esti-

TABLE 9.2   Schedule of production by item, week of November 5

(1) Inventory on hand (in machine-hour units)	(2) Total planned production (machine hr.)	(3) Estimated weekly usage (in machine-hour usage)	(4) Estimated ending inventory (1) + (2) − (3)	(5) Run-out time (weeks) (4)/(3)
189.0	74.6	78.3	185.3	2.365

Item schedule

Item code	(6) Expected usage (dozens)	(7) Desired inventory end of week (5) × (6)	(8) Total require- ments (dozens) (6) + (7)	(9) Inventory on hand (dozens)	(10) Scheduled production (dozens) (8) − (9)	(11) Scheduled production (machine hr.)
732	46	109	155	121	34	6.1
1684	26	61	87	81	6	1.1
1699	92	218	310	247	63	12.6
1736	111	262	373	197	176	32.0
1744	43	102	145	129	16	3.2
1759	10	24	34	32	2	.5
1802	52	123	175	128	47	11.2
1811	12	28	40	12	28	7.9

mated weekly usage is 78.3 hours (column 3). The total weekly usage expressed in machine hours is obtained by multiplying the usage of each item (column 6) by the time required to produce one unit and totaling. The estimated inventory at the end of the week, expressed in machine-hours, is:

Inventory on hand:	189.0 hours
+ Hours of production planned:	74.6
− Estimated weekly usage:	78.3
= Inventory at end of week:	185.3 hours

If these items are used at the rate of 78.3 machine-hour equivalents per week, the inventory will last 2.365 weeks, on the average (column 5). We would like to have stock equal to 2.365 weeks' usage in each item at the end of the week (column 7), to which must be added requirements for the current week, to get estimated total requirements (column 8). From this is subtracted the inventory on hand, to obtain required production (column 10). Required production by item multiplied by the production time per unit gives the machine hours to be devoted to each item in turn. The calculation process guarantees that the total of times assigned to individual products will equal the planned time.

There is no reason why the item schedule must be worked out with the same frequency with which the production level is fixed. It may be desirable, for example, to plan operating levels monthly and set up detailed item schedules weekly, or to fix operating levels weekly and set up item schedules daily. In fact, sometimes one finds companies arriving at the employment plan or planned level of operations by making out a detailed item schedule; then the item schedule is accepted as fixed. If the production level is set over a moderately long time, e.g., a month, the fixed item schedule over this period may require substantial safety stocks, since each item must be protected. However, if the production plan is based on total inventory, a safety stock to protect the total inventory from depletion is all that is required. Frequent adjustments of the item schedule can be used to keep the total inventory in balance among individual items.

Run-out lists with economical run lengths

A run-out list can be used for scheduling production in an operation which makes a number of stock items which are to be made in economical fixed or minimum batches or lots, and where the operating level has been set, for example, by the control techniques described in Chapter 8. Some examples include: a machining center making parts for stock; an assembly line used to make a series of items; a paint, petroleum, or powder-blending operation; a textile-dyeing operation. In cases such as these, either setup costs or physical limitations, such as equipment capacity, will dictate batch or run sizes, and items must be scheduled in batches or runs to meet these conditions.

The procedure in this case is to divide inventory on hand (or in production) for each item by the estimated usage rate. This gives the run-out time if no extra production is scheduled. Then standard lots are scheduled, beginning with the item with shortest run-out time, until the total time scheduled equals the planned production time. For example, suppose run lengths for the items listed in Table 9.2 had been established as shown in Table 9.3. Table 9.4 shows the run-out time by item based on inventory on hand and expected usage. Items 1811, 1736, 1802, and 732 have the lowest run-out times, in that order. The total machine hours to produce these items in standard runs is 79.5. Thus runs of items 1811, 1736, and 1802 would be scheduled for completion and a run of item 732 scheduled to start. The run

TABLE 9.3   Established run lengths by item

| Item | Established run length | | Item | Established run length | |
	Dozens	Machine hours		Dozens	Machine hours
732	90	16.0	1744	90	18.0
1684	35	6.2	1759	40	10.4
1699	120	24.0	1802	100	23.8
1736	140	25.5	1811	50	14.2

TABLE 9.4   Run-out times by item

Item	Inventory on hand (dozens)	Expected usage (dozens)	Run-out time (weeks)	Item	Inventory on hand (dozens)	Expected usage (dozens)	Run-out time (weeks)
732	121	46	2.63	1744	129	43	3.00
1684	81	26	3.11	1759	32	10	3.20
1699	247	92	2.68	1802	128	52	2.46
1736	197	111	1.77	1811	12	12	1.00

of item 732 would be continued into the following week, with the extra 4.9 hours subtracted from available time the following week.

The estimated inventory at the end of the period, together with new run-out times, is shown in Table 9.5.

If two or more machines or process units are operating in parallel, the same procedure can be followed. Items are assigned to units in sequence, starting with the item with shortest run-out time, until all machines are loaded.

Adjusting product mix in continuous production

Where items are in continuous production on multipurpose equipment, the principle of run-out time can be employed to adjust machine assignments. In the spinning operations of the textile industry, for example, several types of yarn may be produced on a battery of spinning frames. The assignment of spindles to yarn grades must be kept in adjustment with yarn requirements. In spinning and similar continuous operations, the allocation of equipment among products can be determined in each scheduling period by fixing the proportion of equipment producing each item so that the expected run-out time is constant among all items.

The same type of calculation is made as that illustrated in Table 9.2. The objective is to make minor periodic adjustments in the assignment of producing units to products so that stocks of items produced are kept in balance and major reassignments are not required.

Where a single unit or line is producing a series of items in sequence, such as an assembly line producing a number of models of an appliance,

TABLE 9.5 Estimated inventory end of period, new run-out times

Item	Opening inventory (dozens)	Scheduled production (dozens)	Estimated usage (dozens)	Inventory end of week (dozens)	Run-out time (weeks)
732	121	90	46	165	3.58
1684	81	...	26	55	2.11
1699	247	...	92	155	1.68
1736	197	140	111	226	2.04
1744	129	...	43	86	2.00
1759	32	...	10	22	2.20
1802	128	100	52	176	3.38
1811	12	50	12	50	4.16

or a packaging line packing a product in several sizes, a variety of approaches may be used. In such a case it is usually necessary to balance the sum of the times scheduled for individual products against some predetermined operating level for the line. The approaches which can be used include the following:

1. Where change-over cost is high, a run-out list can be used together with established run lengths, as illustrated by Tables 9.3, 9.4, and 9.5.
2. Where change-overs are not serious, a run-out list may be used, as in Table 9.2.
3. Where the item inventories can be kept under continuous watch or are reviewed frequently, and change-over from one item to another can be accomplished on short notice, the change-over rules described in Chapter 6[2] can be used.

ASSIGNMENT TO MACHINE OR PROCESS-UNIT GROUPS

The production order being scheduled may pass through one or several departments or common pools of employees and may require time on a variety of types of equipment. The types of equipment may perform basically different functions, such as drill presses and grinders. They may be of different sizes, such as presses with different capacities, mixing vats of varying sizes, or packaging lines equipped to handle cartoned and bulk-packaged material. In this case, each item must carry a designation of the type of equipment preferred or required to process it on the operation master list. The job of loading is to fit the production order onto the machine or process centers required, in the uncommitted time available and within a total time no greater than the promised delivery time on special items or lead time on stock items.

The first essential piece of information needed is a list of available equipment and processing time. For convenience, like machines should be grouped into single centers. In the simplest circumstances, where each machine or processing unit is operated independently of others, i.e., by separate employees, the number of machines in each group multiplied by the number of hours to be worked each day gives the total time available for processing orders. In other circumstances, individual employees in a department may work on a number of types of machines. Loading may have to be consistent with the capacities of individual machine groups as well as the total time available of employees working in the area.

[2] See pp. 150–152.

Table 9.6 shows a typical equipment table for a machining department. The machine types are listed on the left, with the number of each. The table shows two-shift operation (8 hours) time available on each machine type. At the bottom is shown the number of employees scheduled for the week and planned employee hours. Note that under the planned level of operation there are substantially more machine hours available in total than man-hours. Machine group 82-A, circular grinders, can be loaded to a total of 480 hours in the week; machine group 82-J, small presses, can be loaded to a total of 560 hours in the week. The total load which can be scheduled for Department 82 is 1,200 man-hours, since a total of 30 employees is planned.

Table 9.6 shows the time which is available to be assigned to individual production orders. Practice varies in placing responsibility for assigning time. In some companies, the production-scheduling unit will assign orders against the total production time in the department, i.e., the number of employee hours or total operating hours. Assignment to machine group and individual machine and operator is left to the department foreman, dispatcher, or time clerk. In other companies, the production-scheduling unit will assign orders against the time of the individual machine group; this practice is preferred where orders cannot be switched among machine groups to balance time. Normally, the assignment to machines and operators is left as an on-the-spot job to be done by the foreman, dispatcher, or time clerk.

TABLE 9.6   Machine hours; department 82 (forming)

Group no.	Type	No.	Available hours (2 shifts)
82-A	Circular grinders	6	480
82-B	Rad. grinders, small	4	320
82-C	Rad. grinders, medium	3	240
82-F	Lathe, medium	4	320
82-H	Lathe, large	2	160
82-J	Press, small	7	560
82-K	Press, medium	3	240
82-L	Press, large	2	160
82-N	Broach	2	160
82-Q	Horizontal mill	2	160
82	Employees, 1st shift	20	800
	Employees, 2d shift	10	400

Loading step by step

Sometimes an individual production order may call for a number of operating steps, and the order of these steps may vary considerably from item to item. Or, a special production order may call for operations in several departments which must be loaded to match the required operating sequence. In such cases, an attempt may be made to schedule order loads step by step to account for interactions among steps or departments. As an individual order is loaded, each operation is checked to determine which operation imposes the greatest delay on the order. This may be done more or less formally; however, the following five steps are, in general, required.

1. Determine the required hours at each operation and the time thereafter to complete the job if no loading delays occur (frequently taken as the total of required hours on subsequent operations plus 1 day for moving between subsequent operations).
2. Find the earliest date the required hours can be scheduled onto each operation.
3. Find the possible completion date dictated by each operation by adding the time under (1) to the date under (2); the operation with the latest date is the "bottleneck."
4. Schedule the bottleneck operation as early as possible, i.e., on the date under (2).
5. Schedule subsequent operations as early as possible, consistent with the route sheet; schedule prior operations as late as possible.

Experienced personnel familiar with the existing load can complete these steps quickly and reasonably accurately. Some flexibility exists in shifting the timing of operations prior to the bottleneck to fit in subsequent orders.

Such detailed loadings, however, often can become meaningless if production routing orders are issued to the factory promptly after orders are loaded. Prompt issuance of routing orders on manufacturing authority gives individual departments certain practical flexibility in scheduling orders, even to the point of delaying some orders to move up other orders not yet due. These "rearrangements" may be made even to the extent of delaying some orders past their due dates, usually in order to make better use, from the point of view of the individual department, of people immediately on hand, machines available, or existing setups. This type of "informal rescheduling" at the department or work-center level quickly results in overdue orders, departmental load fluctuations, and large in-process stocks. The in-process stocks are not planned or controlled; they become necessary to act as buffers, uncoupling successive departments to make up for the lack or failure of "organization" through scheduling.

Graphical methods

LOAD CHARTS

A load chart or register is the simplest type of control over the time requirements of orders assigned. This type of control is often entirely adequate, especially where a run-out list is used to select stock items for manufacture. The most critical items are loaded first, i.e., items with the shortest calculated run-out dates; then items with successively greater run-out times are loaded, as capacity permits.

Loading systems of this type are based generally on maintenance of work-load reports or graphs, which show the cumulative work load for each center represented by the unprocessed order backlog. The work-load report may be drawn up in a variety of ways, using mechanical and display techniques such as those described below. In its simplest form the report may show the total backlog in hours or days for each department or center, with no attempt to display the effect of a large backlog in one center on completion opportunities in another. As an operation on a job is completed, the work done, represented by the *estimated* time for that operation, is subtracted from the approximate backlog. This type of load control is easy to maintain, it gives an approximate idea of job-completion lead times which can be quoted, and it shows up work-center imbalances, for labor and equipment procurement. A simplified example of a work-load report of this type is shown in Figure 9.4.

Here a spread sheet or chart is used to keep a running subtotal of load by machine type as well as a running total of personnel load. When the capacity of any machine or processing-unit type is reached before the total personnel load is reached, a decision must be made whether to skip subsequent items calling for that type of equipment or, if possible, to shift items to alternate available equipment.

For example, Figure 9.4 shows the load on a department after the department is about 70 per cent loaded (in terms of planned employee hours). As the production order for each item is loaded, the bar line opposite each center or machine group is extended by an amount which represents the time requirements of the production order on that center. The scale used in drawing in each line is adjusted so that a line of a given length is the same proportion of total time available in any production center. For example, each day in Figure 9.4 represents 20 per cent of the total time available.

Figure 9.4 shows that when the assigned load from the run-out list has reached 70 per cent of total time available in Department 31, the time

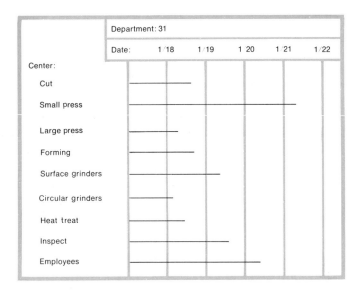

	Department: 31					
	Date:	1/18	1/19	1 20	1/21	1/22
Center:						
Cut						
Small press						
Large press						
Forming						
Surface grinders						
Circular grinders						
Heat treat						
Inspect						
Employees						

FIGURE 9.4 Machine-load report, week ending January 22

commitment for small presses has reached nearly 90 per cent of available time. In going down the run-out list, then, to select additional items for manufacture, the scheduler may try to avoid items which require small-press time. Or he may reexamine items already loaded to see if any of these can be shifted to the group of large presses, which are lightly loaded. When orders have been selected which total to available employee time but do not overload any individual machine group, the production orders are available for dispatching.

There is no reason why the load report, Figure 9.4, must be kept in chart form. Some companies find it more convenient to use a ledger form, such as Figure 9.5.

Each column in Figure 9.5 refers to one machine group. The total number of hours available is entered in the first row under each machine group, and under the column representing total load. Then space is available for entering, as each item is loaded, the order or item number, the required time on the center or centers affected, and the remaining hours available for loading. Where punched-card or internally programed equipment is available to use in loading, computations of run-out time, selection of items for scheduling, and maintenance of running totals of load can be done routinely as part of the equipment program.

Department: 31   Week ending:

Center:	Cut	Small Press	Large Press	Forming	Surface Grinders	Circular Grinders	Heat Treat	Inspect	Total Employees
Time Available:									
Order # Req'd Time: Available:									
Order # Req'd Time: Available:									
Order # Req'd Time: Available:									
Order # Req'd T...									

FIGURE 9.5   Machine-load report

GANTT CHARTS

A variety of display boards are used to make detailed production scheduling and control data available for easy inspection, many of which date back to the Gantt chart. The Gantt chart is designed to display load and work progress as a function of time, e.g., planned load and progress by machine center, or planned versus actual progress on individual orders. Gantt charts make use of a horizontal scale marked in time units. A series of horizontal lines, each representing a controlled machine or order, is used to display control data. The following symbols are used to indicate status of orders or planned usage of machines:

> *Gantt Chart Symbols*
> Start of an activity
> End of an activity
> Light connecting line indicates period of
>   proposed activity
> Heavy line shows progress of activity
> Planned nonproduction time, e.g., repairs,
>   maintenance

To illustrate some of the uses of a Gantt chart in machine loading, let us look at a manufacturing process for a hypothetical device. This is an instrument made to stock, in runs of 1,000. It is one of a family using interchangeable components; it contains one specially machined part which determines its sensitivity characteristics. The manufacturing steps are: (1) the special part is cut from steel stock and formed on a press; (2) it is then assembled with other stock parts into a sensing unit; (3) stock components are assembled into a casing and base; (4) the casing and base are painted and then baked; (5) the sensing unit is assembled with the casing to complete the instrument.

The times required to complete each of the operations are shown as:

Operation	Time (hours)	Center	Department
1. Cut part	4	Shear	50
2. Form part	4	Small press	50
3. Assemble sensing unit	50	Assembly B	60
4. Assemble casing and base	15	Assembly C	20
5. Paint casing	3	Paint rack	30
6. Bake casing	30	Paint oven	30
7. Assemble instrument	40	Assembly A	10

First we might look at the manufacturing process, using a Gantt chart to help determine how long a lead time should be allowed. Inventories of materials and components have, let us assume, been set to give immediate service in filling production-order requirements. Figure 9.6 shows schematically on a Gantt chart what the processing time of the part might be.

FIGURE 9.6   Lead-time calculation, full-batch operation

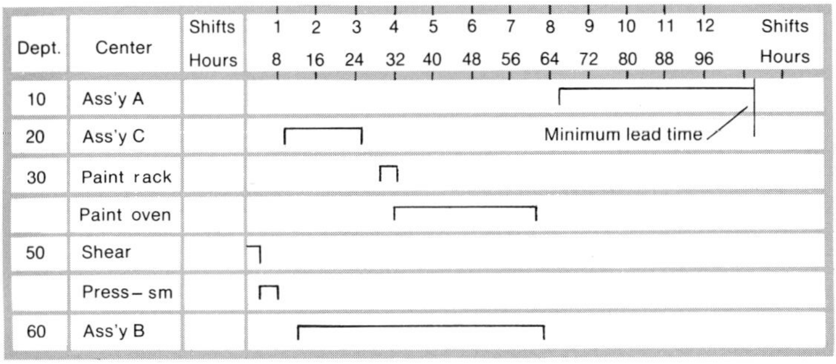

As a first estimate, let us suppose that each operation is to be completed before the next one is to begin—i.e., the order is to be moved from center to center in a single unit—and that one-half of a shift (4 hours) is to be allowed for moving parts from one department to another. Starting with the first operation, a line equivalent to 4 hours is drawn opposite Department 50—Shear. Then a line equal to 4 hours is drawn in for the second operation, Department 50—Small press, from the 4th to 8th hours. Next 4 hours must be allowed to move parts to Department 60—Assembly B, and 50 hours for assembly of the sensing unit. An additional 4 hours must be allowed to move sensing units to Department 10—Assembly A, and then 40 hours for assembly into the final instrument.

Final assembly is to start 66 hours after the beginning of fabrication. Thus the painted and baked casing must be completed by the 62d hour, to allow time for moving. Baking must begin 30 hours earlier, with 3 hours allowed for painting, both in Department 30. Casing assembly must be completed in Department 20 by the 25th hour and must begin on the 10th hour. Clearly, then, the assembly and painting of the casing and base can be completed within the time allowed for making the sensing unit. The total time required to make the unit is 106 hours, or 2 hours over 13 shifts. A lead time of 18 shifts should be ample, allowing time for unexpected delays.

The lead time of 18 shifts was worked out on the basis that one operation would not begin until the preceding operation was entirely completed. This is often the practice in plants operated like job shops. Another possibility would be to start an operation, such as instrument assembly, as soon as preceding operations had gone far enough to provide an adequate supply of parts. Figure 9.7 shows how this can be put to use to cut the lead time in the example to a minimum of about 8½ shifts, or an allowed lead time of perhaps 13 shifts.

FIGURE 9.7 Lead-time calculation, lapped operation

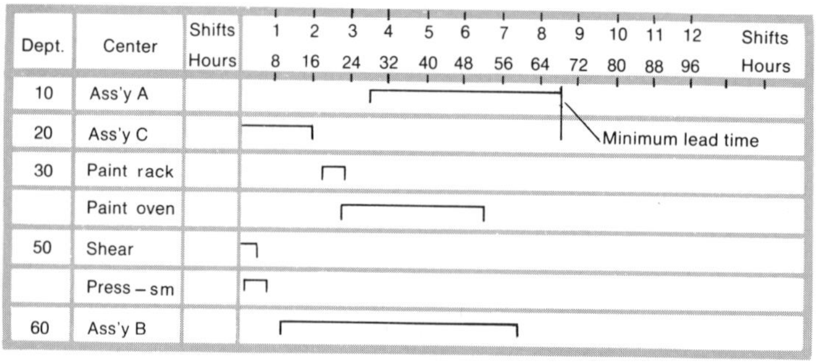

Dept.	Center	Shifts	1	2	3	4	5	6	7	8	9	10	11	12	Shifts
		Hours	8	16	24	32	40	48	56	64	72	80	88	96	Hours
10	Ass'y A														
20	Ass'y C												Minimum lead time		
30	Paint rack														
	Paint oven														
50	Shear														
	Press – sm														
60	Ass'y B														

The lead time for standard items can be worked out once and then incorporated in the inventory-control system and on the operation master list, for example, by showing the length of time before completion date by which each operation must be completed. In the instrument example, if the lead time based on full-batch operation were used, the operation master might show assembly of sensing unit to be completed by due date minus 44 hours. Then, as each production order is placed, with a known due date, the latest allowed completion dates for all steps are automatically determined.

A Gantt chart can also be used to load a particular production order on equipment in the face of existing equipment. Suppose, for example, that on June 10 Order No. 9972 for 1,000 instruments is prepared for loading, and under the lead-time commitment the order is to be completed for delivery to finished inventory by June 23. Figure 9.8 shows a typical Gantt chart covering the operating centers affected by Order No. 9972. The unnumbered lines indicate orders previously loaded; in practice, an order number can be written in over the commitment. The lines numbered 9972 show the load commitments to complete this order. As indicated, the order should be completed in the fore part of June 23, just within the indicated lead time.

Forms of the Gantt Chart. A Gantt chart for machine loading can be drawn up on paper, with entries penciled in. Where the chart is used for

FIGURE 9.8   Gantt chart for machine loading

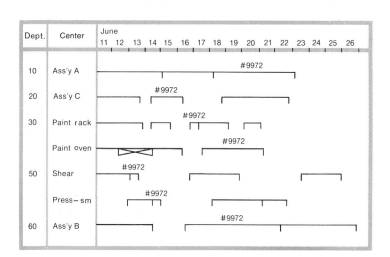

control as well as for original loading, or where changes are frequent, the need for continuing erasures and corrections may make the chart awkward. Various devices can be used to increase the effectiveness of display and flexibility for making changes. For example, a hard-board sheet with colored adhesive tapes for indicating the load can be used. Pertinent order data can be noted directly on the tape, and tapes can be removed or shifted as circumstances require. A perforated panel board can be used with strings or pegs to indicate loadings.

A number of office-equipment suppliers offer commercial forms of the Gantt chart. These, such as the Productrol Board and the Schedugraph, are designed to overcome the inflexibility of drawn lines and the corresponding difficulty of making corrections and schedule changes. In the Productrol Board, two lines of holes replace the line on the chart; pegs with strings attached are used to display "lines" representing planned and actual progress. Colored strings and numbered pegs can be used to increase the information shown.

The Schedugraph is basically similar, except that overlapping flaps replace the lines of holes. The bottom of each flap is a transparent pocket. As each job or operation is scheduled, a card with a colored bottom border is made up to show pertinent information, cut to length corresponding to the time estimated for the operation, and inserted in the appropriate pocket under the appropriate part of the time scale. Inserts can then be used to indicate production against the scheduled load.

All such systems are basically display boards, to indicate loads and to point out troublesome points, either when production is falling behind schedule or where machine imbalances are leading to excessive advance loadings.

OTHER TYPES OF LOADING DEVICES

A number of other types of techniques can be used for assigning and keeping track of machine or center loads. One common technique is to set up a register for each machine center, for each time period considered. Anyone familiar with an old-fashioned hotel register can recognize this approach. As each order is loaded a notation is made on the register for each machine showing the estimated time the order is due to go on the machine and the estimated time off.

Some companies find it convenient to use open boxes with a section for each machine, each period. As an order is loaded a copy of the job ticket can be inserted in the box section for reference. A running total of time assigned each section may be maintained. Other companies have found tag systems convenient, with tags representing orders hung on hooks representing machine capacity. Such a system is less flexible and less easy to interpret than a chart loading system in conventional machining operations. However, it is often quite satisfactory where time estimates are not precise, or where the best measure of load is the number of orders assigned. Some mixing operations, such as paint or chemical blending, and sometimes dyeing operations, show this characteristic.

Loading sequenced operations

Many manufacturing organizations produce a wide line of products through a more or less well-defined production process. The product flows from one department to another in a single direction, although there may be more than one department or process at any stage. Despite the one-directional flow of product—contrasted with the "pure" job shop—even standard products required for inventory replenishment may be processed under job orders through a more or less functionally organized system. Sometimes the resulting schedules, lead times, and process inventories exhibit the worst characteristics of those of the true job shop, in spite of the opportunities for a more thoroughly organized scheduling system which the production process makes possible.

The operations of the Continental Stamping Company, illustrated in Figure 9.9, exhibit one-directional flow, and the scheduling system designed illustrates what can be done to minimize job-shop difficulties. The problem is one of scheduling about 150 orders varying from 1 to 1,000 units of different items released daily. There are several operations to be performed; a given order may pass through as few as six or as many as eight departments. Most departments contained a number of types and sizes of equipment, and the load on each had to be controlled. Personnel within a department could be shifted freely among equipment assignments.

A system for planning employment in each department and controlling total finished inventory balances was set up, using the concepts of Chapter 7. The only two working inventories were finished stocks of standard items and raw materials; a base-stock system was set up to control these. The scheduling system was designed to load the individual departments and centers or equipment pools uniformly to scheduled capacity, processing the orders for individual items generated by the inventory-control system plus special customer orders. The method has two characteristics: (1) orders for stock items are allowed to remain unreleased up to a maximum of a few days to form a backlog of unreleased orders, with the maximum delay added

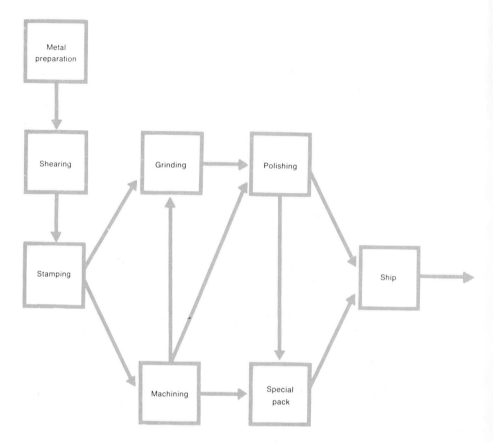

FIGURE 9.9 Illustrative production process

to the manufacturing time to obtain the lead time used for inventory calculations; (2) production orders are released daily in such a way that each machine group is provided with one day's work.[3]

AN ILLUSTRATION WITH TWO DEPARTMENTS

These principles can be illustrated by the simpler case of loading two departments, with one type of equipment in each. The output of the first, Department A, forms an in-process inventory which is drawn on in turn by Department B. A common procedure is to assign orders to Department A

[3] C. G. McGee, "Operations Research in the American Thread Company," *Operations Research,* vol. 4, no. 5, pp. 587–598, October, 1956.

for processing as they arrive, to be done as soon as possible. In effect, an "inventory" of orders for stock or in-process material, or special customer orders, is built up before Department A. Department A draws upon the backlog of orders for production. This inventory of orders can be used to level out fluctuations in labor utilization in Department A; the larger the inventory of orders is, the more nearly uniform the work load in Department A can be, relative to fluctuations in demand. It is of course necessary to arrive at some compromise between lead time, or delay in processing orders, and fluctuations in the level of production at A.

Let us assume that the order demand contains on the average a fair utilization of the production capacity of both Departments A and B, and that the full daily output of A on the average represents a full daily load for Department B (the two departments are in balance). However, if the orders processed in Department A are chosen at random for the advantage of Department A only, it can be anticipated that the daily load produced for Department B will fluctuate, just as the load on Department A, represented by orders, fluctuates. While each day a group of orders will be chosen for processing in Department A, which represents a fixed load equal to Department A's capacity, these may represent a widely fluctuating load on Department B. Department B therefore must go through the same process as Department A.

An in-process inventory will be built up between Departments A and B, and Department B will draw on this inventory to obtain its daily work load. The larger the inventory, the more opportunity exists for Department B to achieve a uniform work load. It is to be expected, therefore, that the Department B foreman may allow the inventory to be built up somewhat in order to give himself flexibility. It is also possible that certain individual orders which make their way into this in-process inventory will be delayed there substantially longer than the average delay, if these orders happen to be a bit more difficult than run-of-the-mill orders. This has been found to happen even where the priority or work order has been established by the central production unit. These orders are the type that expediters must search out and get processed.

The problems arising from individual department-by-department scheduling and the use of in-process inventories to act as buffer stocks between departments can be seen from this restricted example, although extension to a series of departments is not difficult to visualize. This type of scheduling, frequently found in processes having some of the characteristics of job-shop operations, can result in long lead times for orders processed, fluctuations in actual lead times compared with average or expected lead times, sizable process inventories serving as buffers between individual departments, and sizable finished-inventory stock to provide adequate service to customers in the face of long production lead times.

The inventories between individual operations or departments in series perform two functions. First, they are necessary because of the transit and scheduling time between one operation and the next. Second, they serve to uncouple the department from the random fluctuations in sales demand. Under the scheduling system described above, which is found commonly, the input to each department exhibits random characteristics similar to the sales input to the plant as a whole. This results from each department's selecting for its own work orders which are convenient for itself, without reference to the needs or requirements of subsequent departments.

Suppose, however, that when the daily load is made out for Department A, orders are selected for processing so that, first, the load in Department A is balanced to utilize its capacity and, second, the load also represents a uniform balance on Department B. The extent to which this can be done depends again on the size of the inventory of Department A and on the nature of the correlations in work loads for Departments A and B represented by individual orders, as well as on the size of individual orders relative to the daily capacity of Departments A and B.

Selection of a work load for Department A which is balanced in both Departments A and B permits a reduction of the inventory needed between Departments A and B, except in so far as these are needed to meet transit requirements and to protect against uncertainties in production in either department. The only inventories required between Departments A and B are those needed to fill the functions of product-line inventories, i.e., smoothing out short-term production or load fluctuations and providing transit stocks.

As a next step, instead of giving Department A the inventory of orders and allowing Department A to draw on these as required, with the restriction that A's load be balanced with respect to Department B also, it is possible to hold all orders in a central location and issue an order load to Department A period by period. The orders issued to A in each period would be those which could be accommodated on Department A's equipment in one period. These orders would be chosen, first, so that no order would be held up before processing more than some stated number of periods and, second, so that the total order load sent to Department A would provide a balanced load for both A and B.

This is illustrated in Figure 9.10. Each cell in the figure represents one production order. There are 18 outstanding orders; the number in the box in the upper left-hand corner is the order number. In the lower right is the work load it represents (e.g., in machine hours) in A; in the upper left is

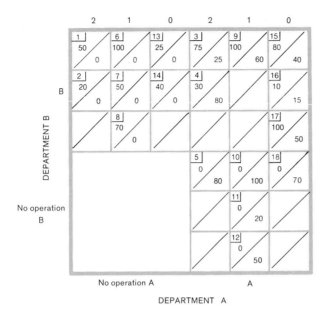

FIGURE 9.10 Scheduling procedure, order backlog holding time

the work load for B. The orders are classified according to the number of days they have been held. No order may be held more than 3 days. If Department A has a planned capacity of 225 machine hours per day and Department B has a planned capacity of 250 machine hours per day, the scheduling operation consists of choosing orders from Figure 9.10 so that the load on each department matches its capacity as closely as possible and all orders held 2 days are scheduled. Table 9.7 illustrates this process. The first column shows available capacity. The second column is the total load of orders which must be scheduled, orders 3, 4, and 5 in Department A, and orders 1, 2, 3, and 4 in Department B. The third column shows the

TABLE 9.7 Department loading schedule

	Daily capacity	Load—orders held 2 days	Avail-able	Added load	Total loaded today	Net over/under
Department A	225	185	40	35	220	−5
Department B	250	175	75	80	255	+5

capacity available for handling other orders. The fourth column shows the load of additional orders scheduled to fill capacity. These are orders 11 and 16 for Department A and orders 8 and 16 for Department B. These result in a total load shown in the fifth column, with the difference between load and capacity shown in the final column. Department A is underloaded by 5 hours, and Department B is overloaded by 5 hours. These differences will be used to adjust available capacity the next day, adding underload to capacity of Department A and subtracting the overload from Department B.

It would have been possible to get an exact balance of orders to capacity in one of the departments—for example, by using a combination of orders 11, 13, 14, and 16 totaling 35 hours in A and 75 hours in B. However, this would have resulted in a serious overload in B the following day from current 1-day orders which must be scheduled the next day. Scheduling order 15 would have balanced A exactly, leaving B with 80 hours, but this would have resulted in overloads in both A and B from orders which must be scheduled by then. In general, it is not possible to match capacity exactly day by day, but discrepancies can be corrected in the following day's schedule.

This is illustrated in Figure 9.11. The load in hours is represented by the two axes, horizontal for Department A and vertical for Department B. The dashed lines represent ideal daily loads for each department, and their intersection represents the ideal joint load—250 hours for B and 225 hours for A. The load actually scheduled in Table 9.7 is represented by the open circle—220 hours for A and 255 hours for B. Then the target for the next day is represented by the solid point—230 hours for A and 245 hours for B, to make up the discrepancy.

AN APPLICATION

The general principles described above can be extended to several departments where there is a uniform direction of flow from one department to the next in the production process. This can be done as follows: First, a flow chart such as Figure 9.12 (corresponding to the operations in Figure 9.9) must be laid out showing the departments of operations to be scheduled and the directions in which production flows. Second the minimum transit time between operations must be set. Then departments must be grouped and arranged in sequence, and each group must be assigned a lead time corresponding to its position in the flow chart. The lead time for one department exceeds the lead time for the next preceding department by at least the minimum transit-time allowance; this means that the lead time assigned any department will tend to be governed by the most complex process routing feeding into that department.

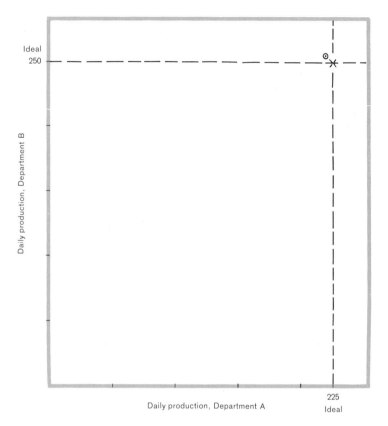

FIGURE 9.11 Scheduling procedure, released versus ideal load

   As an order is received it is first converted into a list or statement of the times required to complete the order in the various departments into which it must flow. These are then filed in order at the time of receipt. Some maximum order delay, i.e., a maximum number of periods which the order will be allowed to remain unscheduled, is set.

   The Continental Stamping Company established a maximum delay of 5 days in processing orders. Each day, the scheduling proceeds as follows. First, all orders received 5 days before are selected and scheduled. Then a "trial balance" is made to find the amount of available capacity in each machine center. Then other orders on hand are selected to build up as nearly as possible a balanced load, department by department. This is a trial-and-error process which can be facilitated by various sorts of punched

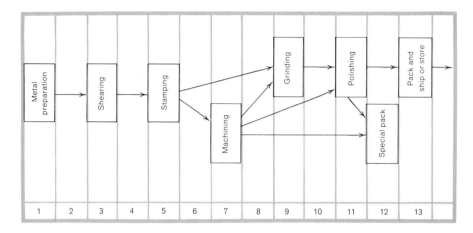

Lead time, days

FIGURE 9.12   Production control flow diagram—Continental Stamping Company

or needle-sort cards, together with moderate practice on the part of the scheduling clerk. In the case of the Continental Stamping Company, for example, edge-punched cards are used. One card is prepared for each order showing the departments and centers through which it must pass, the hours required in each center, and the last day for scheduling. The cards can be rapidly manipulated by the clerk to find orders matching available capacity.

A table similar to Table 9.8 is maintained by the scheduling clerk.

The capacity shown for each department is based on the planned employment. In all cases except Metal Preparation the employees within a department are freely transferable among centers. The capacity by center in Metal Preparation is based on planned employment by center. In all other cases, center capacity is based on machines available and planned hours of operation. As noted above, the employment or production plan is worked out weekly, using base-stock and explosion methods described in Chapter 6. Note that the load scheduled on any one day is for the next day's work in the Metal Preparation Department, for work 3 days hence in the Shearing Department, for work 9 days hence in the Grinding Department, etc. Each department is fed a balanced load a day at a time, and the load is chosen to provide a balanced load on each of the following departments. When the orders are scheduled for the day, a job ticket for each order is sent to each department to process the order, showing the operation, allowed time, and planned date for running. This gives the foreman advance information for

TABLE 9.8   Loading schedule, by department or center

Department or center	Capacity			Pri-ority load	Avail-able	Added load	Total load	Over/ under	Comment
	Nor-mal	Net over/ under	Avail-able						
Metal preparation	88	−1	89	46	43	42	88	−1	
Clean	56	−3	59	20	39	38	58	−1	
Saw	32	+2	30	23	7	4	30	0	
Shearing	320	−6	326	180	146	143	323	−3	
Shears A24	200			91	109	90			
Shears A31	184			89	95	53			
Stamping	432	+4	428	237	191	186	423	−5	
Presses D33	320			154	166	77			
Presses C46	248			83	165	109			
Machining	280	−12	292	171	121	125	296	+4	
Drill presses	296			160	136	118			
Multiple drills	32			6	26	1			Light de-mand
Lathes	32			5	27	6			
Grinding	240	−8	248	186	62	59	245	−3	
Grinders N67	144			78	66	26			
Grinders N81	120			110	10	10			Heavy load, small orders
Universal grinder	32			5	27	13			
Circular grinder	16			3	13	10			
Polishing	160	+20	140	86	54	65	151	+11	
Ball mill	144			60	84	41			
Buffers	32			10	22	15			
Tank polish	32			16	16	9			
Special pack	40	+2	38	23	15	12	35	−3	
Pack	80	−3	83	46	37	36	82	−1	

making assignments, planning setups, and ascertaining that orders he is to process are available from preceding departments on time.

Weekly summaries are made from daily reported production tickets, and each department reports weekly the total allowed time by center for process-ing material on hand but unprocessed. Most departments work with 1 day's orders ahead. These figures are used to correct release figures to keep in-process orders in balance.

The final column of Table 9.8 allows for scheduling clerk's notes on load on hand versus capacity. He is in a position to notice developing bottlenecks and can bring these to the attention of the production supervisor before a serious bottleneck develops.

Some points worth noting about this type of scheduling process include the following: (1) The bigger the maximum delay allowed in scheduling an order relative to the scheduling period, the more uniform loading is possible in the individual departments; (2) the more frequently scheduling is done, i.e., the shorter the scheduling period, the lower the in-process inventory can be, and the faster can material be processed through the departments. For example, in the case described, a change in the scheduling period from 1 day to 1 week would mean increasing the total processing time from roughly 13 days to roughly 6 weeks.

The disadvantages of the system described are that it requires frequent scheduling and detailed control and communications to know what has been done and to keep loads in individual departments realistic. There are, in addition, no large buffer inventory stocks between departments to protect against major fluctuations introduced by equipment breakdowns and the like. (In general, the typically large process stocks in job-shop-managed plants do not serve this function either; they are not properly balanced to do so.) In return for these disadvantages, substantially lower process inventories can be obtained, and major cuts in required lead times, delayed orders, and expediting become possible even while uniform utilization of labor and good service to customers is maintained.

THE DISPATCHING FUNCTION

Once the production order has been drawn up, routing and time requirements determined, and the order loaded on operating centers, the production-control center has the general responsibility for informing operating centers and departments of work to be done and completion dates, and for reviewing progress against orders released. This is the general function of dispatching.

Order release, routing, and records

A primary dispatching job is to make up the production-order set, including necessary job tickets, material requisitions, and the like. As indicated earlier, a number of reproducing or copying systems have been devised for selective reproduction of job tickets, material requisitions, and move tickets from an operation master list, specially prepared or kept on file. The production-order papers, including drawings, will normally be sent to the first department in the sequence, to move with the order in process to subsequent departments. Frequently job tickets will be forwarded directly to each department as an indication of work ahead.

The practices and habits of dispatching vary greatly among manufacturing plants. This is partly a reflection of differences in the organization or physical processes of the manufacturing unit, but many times these differences are arrived at without particular thought.

Under a thoroughly decentralized or noncontrolled system, the production-scheduling group may make up a routing list, showing operations to be performed, departments or machine centers, anticipated processing times (based on experience or time standards), and estimated completion dates (based on existing center loadings). The routing list issued as soon as possible after the order is received represents authority given the factory to complete the order. Under a noncontrolled system, no progress reports are made as the order moves from operation to operation. "Expediters" to find delayed orders and encourage foremen to give them priority in processing are a normal, essential, costly, and disliked part of a system of this type.

Under this system, control may be exercised on an exception basis: Each foreman or time clerk may be required to submit a report weekly, or even daily, showing orders due for completion since the previous report but held up for some reason. This report gives the production-control unit information needed to adjust loadings. Where an order is held up because parts or materials are not available, or where the delay will cause difficulty in meeting lead times or customer promise dates, this gives expediters warning in time to take some corrective action.

A more tightly controlled alternate system is often employed, where labor tickets or other reports of actual production, filled out on the floor as each step is completed and then sent to the office for cost and production-control use, are used routinely to show order progress. This control provides a basis for following up promptly on orders which may be falling behind schedule. The reports of work completed can be recorded on the load charts or load registers to show progress compared with plan, as a basis for re-scheduling of orders, if necessary.

A third basic alternate is sometimes employed, where the route sheet is made up and each operation tentatively scheduled but instruction or authority is issued for only one operation at a time. As each step on an order is completed, the tentative schedule and promise date are checked and compared with the work load ahead of the next center. The production-scheduling group is then in a position to control priorities and movement of orders directly.

Materials

Another dispatching function of the production-scheduling unit is often to check on availability of parts or materials before release of an order. Normally, if intermediate inventories are properly controlled, stocks will be on hand. This is a particular characteristic of inventories controlled against exploded customer demand under a base-stock system. From time to time, unanticipated usage, delays in processing parts replenishment production orders, or delays in receipt of materials from suppliers will cause depletion of inventory on hand.

In a closely controlled system it is often considered desirable to be sure parts or materials are on hand or will be by the time they are needed, before releasing production orders. This makes it possible to readjust loadings to assign orders which can be worked on. Where this is not done, plants have sometimes found themselves with operating centers working below capacity, even with sizable backlogs of orders for processing, because the orders that were released were unworkable for some reason. If such orders do reach the floor, there is a tendency for them to be put aside and forgotten even when material becomes available. And after these orders have been released to the floor, the production-scheduling unit's job of rescuing them is made doubly difficult. Review of material availability before release of production orders keeps unworkable orders in the control of the production-scheduling unit, where they can receive expediting attention appropriate to the need.

Other dispatching functions of the production-scheduling unit include maintenance of a log or record of releases, an order-status file for answering inquiries,[4] an expediting list, and often a file of drawings and other data descriptive of the order.

Control over complex intermediate operations

Normally the flow of materials into semifinished or finished inventory compared with orders scheduled will provide an adequate basis for control of production against schedule and for spotting and correcting delays. In some cases, however, as in the Continental Stamping Company, there may be a large number of detailed operations in separate departments or centers between consecutive formal inventory control points. The inventory in these stages is process stock being operated on or in transit from one operation to another. This series of process steps forms one "operation" in the terms of Chapter 2.

Where a single operation in terms of inventory control is made up of a group of process steps, intermediate control over flow in the individual processes is often important. This is particularly true where the processing time is several days, since a failure or delay in an early step in the operation

---

[4] Ability to give a prompt, definite, and reliable answer to a customer's inquiry and ability to recognize and report delays to customers (before they report them to you) are an important competitive advantage, especially in a special-order business.

may not be observed at the inventory-control point, so corrective action may not be taken for several days. Intermediate control over flow through each process can be obtained through the use of job or production tickets. These are turned in daily by each center, and they show the jobs or items processed and good production achieved. They will frequently also record scrap or waste for cost control and as a basis for issue of supplementary authorization for withdrawal of items from preceding stock points to replace spoiled material.

Charts, of a type such as the Gantt chart described earlier for loading, are useful devices for recording and displaying production reports. To illustrate how these can be used, let us reexamine the chart shown in Figure 9.8 (page 261). Remembering that this chart was prepared as of June 10 for loading orders to be processed later, let us assume we are examining progress as of the end of June 16. In order to refer to Figure 9.8 directly, let us assume no more orders have been scheduled in the interim since June 10.

Figure 9.13 shows how the chart might appear with production reported and recorded on the chart in the conventional manner. The line drawn in under the loaded time for each order represents reported progress at the review date. For example, Department 10 and the shearing center, Department 50, are well ahead of schedule. Department 10 is ahead about 1 day's production and is nearly ready to start Order No. 9972. On the other hand,

FIGURE 9.13 Gantt chart: progress control

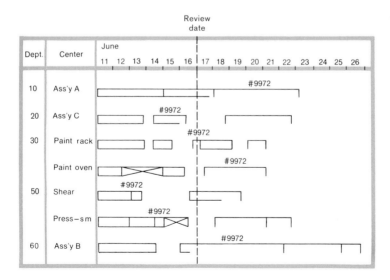

Department 20 is more than a full shift behind schedule, and this is apparently holding up painting on Order No. 9972 in Department 30. The paint-rack center has gone on to the next job. The small press in Department 50 was delayed 12 hours, delaying the completion of work on Order No. 9972 and the beginning of assembly work in Department 60. Department 60 is now nearly 7 hours behind schedule.

The time blocked out by a diagonal cross represents time not available because of a delay or holdup of work. (See the paint-oven and small-press centers in Figure 9.13.) For example, the diagonally marked-off space of the small press indicates that a previous delay has pushed back work in this center 12 hours. This time which was not loaded previously cannot be loaded, since it is needed to complete orders now behind schedule.

The chart with order numbers and progress against jobs shown gives the production-control unit a convenient way of assessing problems and possible alternatives for eliminating or avoiding trouble. For example, a serious difficulty can be avoided on Order No. 9972 if movement of material from Department 20 to the paint rack is expedited so that painting and baking can begin just as soon as the order now being processed by paint rack is completed. This would permit completion of the order with at most a 6-hour delay at final assembly, possibly less if movement from Departments 30 and 60 to Department 10 were expedited.

PRODUCT-LINE CONTROL

Where the product-line organization is used, the loading and control problem is easier. Loading by means of run-out lists and the like is possible. The control problem is not so much one of following individual orders from center to center as it is a job of seeing that the flow through each center is on schedule, that bottlenecks are not allowed to develop.

A number of recording techniques can be used to display production information as reported, to spot potential bottlenecks. One system designed for control of product flow through a complex chain illustrates how these data can be used for control over flow. Under this system, the first step is to lay out the product line as shown in Figure 9.14, using distinctive symbols for various important functions which may occur. Each operation is positioned in the line of flow. The normal processing time from each operation to the end is determined, and the operations are numbered, starting with the operation with lowest processing time remaining, i.e., closest to the end of the line.

The next step is to make up a chart showing the cumulative delivery

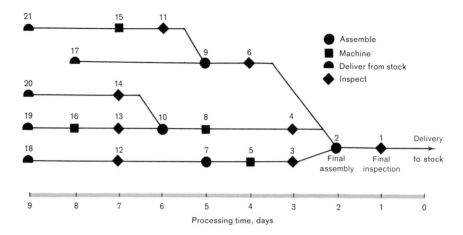

FIGURE 9.14   Product flow and processing times for each operation in the chain

schedule to inventory which is to be maintained; this is illustrated in Figure 9.15. Using the cumulative delivery schedule shown here, cumulative requirements to date through each operation can be determined by reading the quantity shown on Figure 9.15 corresponding to the current date plus the operation processing time. For example, at the beginning of delivery, operation 16, with a processing time of 8 days (Figure 9.14), should show cumulative production of 400 units.

FIGURE 9.15   Cumulative delivery schedule

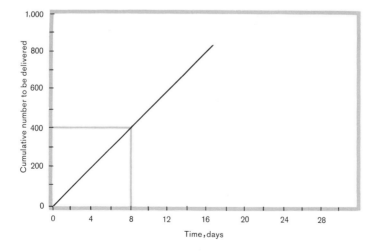

These readings can be combined on a single chart, such as Figure 9.16, for comparison with actual production. A distinctive color and marking may be used for each class of operation. Comparison of actual results with schedule will indicate areas where bottlenecks are developing and attention is needed. For example, the illustration in Figure 9.16 shows that deliveries have fallen behind schedule and threaten to delay production within a few days. In addition, assembly operation 10 is far behind schedule and is holding up operations 8 and 4. Lack of attention will shortly affect final assembly and inspection output.

This general method, modified to meet the requirements of the individual line, and operated graphically or mechanically, has been found to be a simple but effective product-line control device. For example, a peg board can be set up to display the information shown in Figure 9.16. Each horizontal line on the board represents one operation, and each hole represents a fixed number of units, e.g., 10 or 50. Actual production can be shown by running a string horizontally across the board to the hole which represents

FIGURE 9.16   Comparison of actual results with schedule

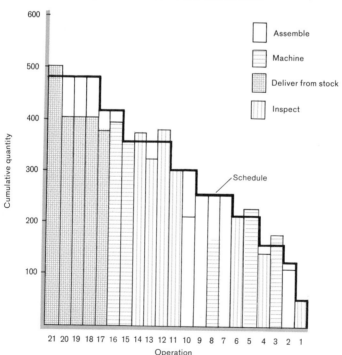

the quantity nearest actual cumulative through-put. The schedule can be shown by running a string of distinctive color from line to line down the board indicating the current scheduled amount. Use of strings of distinctive color to represent types of operations or individual feeder lines will help the scheduler determine at a glance which operations are on schedule and which are falling dangerously behind.

LINEAR PROGRAMING IN PRODUCTION SCHEDULING

Certain applications of linear-programing methods have been made to scheduling a variety of items among a number of alternate processing methods. In particular, the petroleum-refining industry has been making increasing use of this technique for laying out gasoline-blending programs, for joint use of distillation, catalytic cracking, and related refining units, and for scheduling heating-oil production. References to work in this area are included below.

EXERCISES

1. The Production Scheduling Department of a textile firm showed the following records at the end of an operating period for the nine grades of a particular fabric it produces:

Grade	Forecast usage 1,000 yards per week	Available stock on hand and on order
M-1	42.8	81.8
M-2	92.5	93.0
M-3	151.6	162.0
M-4	20.5	55.6
M-5	27.5	91.3
M-6	61.5	39.4
M-7	90.0	170.0
M-8	120.8	181.2
M-9	60.0	125.8

Prepare a run-out list showing the sequences in which production orders for the several grades of fabric should be released.
2. If all grades of fabric in problem 1 are produced at the same rate in a

single production unit, and if this unit has a capacity of 750,000 yards per week, what quantities of each grade should be produced in order to bring all items to an equal time supply?

3. Because of marked variations in demand for the several grades of fabric, it is decided to cycle the production of the various grades of fabric according to the methods of Chapter 4 (see pages 67–72 and Appendix A). For each fabric grade compute the inventory fraction to be reached before changing over to produce another item. Describe how you would systematize this form of control in this fabric production operation.

BIBLIOGRAPHY

Charnes, A., W. W. Cooper, and A. Henderson: *Management Models and Industrial Applications of Linear Programming*, vols. I and II, John Wiley & Sons, Inc., New York, 1961.

Clark, Wallace: *The Gantt Chart*, Sir Isaac Pitman & Sons, Ltd., London, 1938.

Garett, J. William: "Three Heuristic Rules for Sequencing Jobs to a Single Production Facility," *Management Science*, vol. 11, no. 8, June, 1965.

Ignall, E., and Linus Schrage: "Application of the Branch and Bound Technique to Some Flow-shop Scheduling Problems," *Operations Research*, vol. 13, no. 3, pp. 400–412, May-June, 1965.

Moore, F. G.: *Production Control*, 2d ed., McGraw-Hill Book Company, New York, 1959.

Sisson, Roger L.: "Methods of Sequencing in Job Shops: A Review," *Operations Research*, vol. 7, no. 1, pp. 10–29, January-February, 1959.

Szwarc, W.: "Solution of the Akers-Friedman Scheduling Problem," *Operations Research*, vol. 8, no. 6, pp. 782–788, November-December, 1960.

Vazsonyi, Andrew: "The Use of Mathematics in Production and Inventory Control: II, Theory of Scheduling," *Management Science*, vol. 1, nos. 3–4, pp. 207–223, April-July, 1955.

10

PHYSICAL-DISTRIBUTION PROBLEMS

THE PHYSICAL-DISTRIBUTION PROCESS

Distribution refers to all those operations and activities of the firm which are associated with the movement of the firm's product from the production operation to the user or consumer, either for final consumption or for use as an industrial intermediate. By this broad definition, distribution involves not only the physical-distribution functions of warehousing and transportation, but also the marketing functions of promotion, pricing, sales, and service. All such distribution activities are important in production and inventory control. Promotional efforts will affect demand rates; changes in pricing and service policy will similarly produce changes in the market.

The logistics system of the firm is the system for organizing and managing the flow of materials, components, supplies, and other resources from suppliers through the process of the firm, to customers. Manufacturing firms typically acquire resources, convert them to new forms and combinations, and distribute them to customers. The products may flow to industrial customers as materials, supplies, or components, or they may be consumer products distributed to ultimate consumers. The physical-distribution system encompasses the activities concerned with the movement of the finished product from the final process stage to the customer.

Our principal interest here is in physical distribution in the context of the larger task of industrial logistics management. In order to assure a smooth flow of materials through the production process into storage and an economical flow from storage to market, it is necessary to consider the inter-actions among the separate functions of physical distribution and their costs. For example, the stocking policies at field warehouses will affect the timing and quantities of replenishments ordered from the factory inventories. Freight rates for full-car and less-than-carload shipment and customer de-livery requirements will affect the selection of locations of field warehouses. If the firm has several plants supplying product to several markets, the unit costs of production at each plant and the transportation costs from each plant to each market must be considered in allocating warehouse replenish-ment orders among the several plants.

This chapter will take up some of the more important problems in physical distribution and describe methods of dealing with them.

THE FUNCTIONS OF PHYSICAL DISTRIBUTION

Allocation of production and stock location

Many companies operate systems of plants or field warehouses and in planning production must face a series of questions concerning where to make, where to ship, and where to stock a product. The answers to all of these questions influence the operation of a planning and control system. Here are some examples.

A steel fabricator operates two plants, one in Pennsylvania and one in Indiana. The company serves a nationwide market for a line of several hundred stock items in which freight is an important cost element. Orders range from small orders for several items totaling a few hundred pounds to orders totaling one or more carloads. The company has been forced to face questions such as the following:

1. Should one or both plants be set up to make a full line of products? This would eliminate the need to split many orders between the plants, with a resulting cut in freight and handling costs. On the other hand, it would mean shorter, less economical runs at each plant (since total production would be split). It would also mean an increase in the number of stock points to be controlled and a larger total inventory investment.
2. If both plants do not make a full line, should the finished plant inventory include a full line? This would permit consolidated shipment of mixed orders but it would mean transshipment of stocks between plants to stock one plant's inventory with items made only at the other plant. It would also mean extra inventory. If complete finished stocks are carried at each

plant, what orders should be filled from them? What orders should be filled from the inventory at Plant A of items made only at Plant B? For example, it is normally uneconomical to ship a full carload from Plant A, incurring the extra costs of shipment from B to A and extra handling cost, when the order could have been filled directly from Plant B at carload freight rates. How should a mixed order be assigned?

3. Should field warehouses be set up? What territories should they serve? What orders should they fill? For example, field warehouses might fill only small orders or portions of orders which would move at premium freight rates, or they might fill all orders for items they stock. What items should a warehouse stock, and how much should be carried?

A food processor operates a series of plants scattered through the country and distributes its products through several district warehouses. The warehouses serve to give prompt service to local customers. Some questions which periodically face this company include:

1. How should district warehouses be assigned to plants for servicing, in view of freight costs, demand in the warehouse territory, and plant capacity? How do demand fluctuations influence the assignment? For example, it may be more economical to assign a warehouse to a more distant plant with higher freight cost, even though adequate capacity is theoretically available in a nearer plant. This may happen if better balancing of loads gives more flexibility in meeting demand fluctuations and thus cuts inventory needs.

2. When should additional capacity be installed, and in which plant?

A moderate-sized office-equipment manufacturer makes a line of standard office machines, but these can be manufactured with a variety of combinations of special features. Prompt delivery and availability of machines for field demonstration are important. A large competitor is able to manufacture in volume machines with combinations of special features and stocks the machines in his field offices. Should the smaller company attempt to stock all items in field locations? What items should be stocked in the field? Should machines with special features be stocked in the factory or made to order?

An automotive manufacturer must supply dealers with spare parts for repair work. The manufacturer operates four regional assembly plants which also serve as spare-parts depots. In addition, the company operates a number of district offices and parts warehouses. Some questions the company faces include:

1. Which district warehouses should be serviced from a regional plant?

Should districts order some parts directly from the manufacturing plant or supplier?

2. What items should dealers be encouraged to stock? How is the choice of parts and size of dealer parts stock affected by the volume of repair business a dealer does? What items should a particular district warehouse or a regional depot carry?

3. If dealer or district-warehouse space is limited, how can this space best be used? What items should be carried, and in what quantities? How should stocks of individual items be replenished?

These are the types of questions that must be answered by many companies. The answers to some of them can be approached by using techniques for analyzing reorder rules and inventory balances such as those described in Chapters 4 and 6. Some techniques for attacking other aspects of these problems are outlined below.

Balancing plants and warehouses

One common situation is the following: A company operating a series of plants and warehouses has established total capacity or planned operating levels in its plants to meet anticipated total field-warehouse demand. However, individual warehouse requirements must be assigned to particular plants to minimize total freight cost. This type of problem, as stated, is well suited to use of linear-programing techniques[1] and, in fact, is one of the earliest applications of this method.[2]

To illustrate how this method can be used, let us suppose the following schedule of plant outputs and warehouse requirements has been set up:

Plant	Planned output (tons)	Warehouse	Expected requirements (tons)
A	3,000	1	1,000
B	2,000	2	2,500
C	1,000	3	5,000
D	4,000	4	1,500

[1] See Chap. 7, p. 177, and Appendix C, p. 365.
[2] See, for example, Frank L. Hitchcock, "The Distribution of a Product from Several Sources to Numerous Localities," *Journal of Mathematics and Physics,* vol. 20, pp. 224–230, 1941.

TABLE 10.1 Freight rates between plants and warehouses

Warehouse	Plant			
	A	B	C	D
1	10.00	12.50	13.50	14.00
2	12.50	11.00	10.50	12.00
3	9.00	12.00	11.00	10.00
4	12.50	12.50	9.00	13.00

Note that the total planned output equals total requirements. The fact that an equal number of plants and warehouses are used is not important; any number of either might be used.

Table 10.1 shows the freight rates assumed to apply between the plants and warehouses. The task is to allocate production to the warehouse to minimize the total freight bill. One possible plan is shown in Table 10.2. Under this plan, for example, all of the output of Plant A would go to Warehouse 3, the output from Plant B would be split equally between Warehouses 1 and 4, etc. This is a feasible plan but not necessarily the plan with the lowest freight cost.

To get the minimum-cost plant, the first step is to construct a possible or "feasible" plan, like that in Table 10.2. In principle, any possible plan will do as a starting point; but if a reasonably good guess as to the most economical plan can be made at the start, the subsequent calculation is reduced. Where the plan is revised periodically to account for changes in output, requirements, or freight costs, a good starting point for making the revision is the previous minimum-cost plan, with the minimum revision needed to make the plan balance to new outputs and requirements.

The only rule that must be followed in building a possible plan is this:

TABLE 10.2 Possible allocation of production

Warehouse	Plant				Total
	A	B	C	D	
1	. . . . .	1,000	. . . . .	. . . . .	1,000
2	. . . . .	. . . . .	500	2,000	2,500
3	3,000	. . . . .	. . . . .	2,000	5,000
4	. . . . .	1,000	500	. . . . .	1,500
Total	3,000	2,000	1,000	4,000	

Alternately assign the complete output of one plant to one warehouse or to as few warehouses as are necessary; this will normally leave the last warehouse considered with some remaining requirements. Fill these requirements from one plant or as few other plants as necessary. Then assign the total remaining capacity of the last plant used to one warehouse or as few of the remaining warehouses as necessary.[3]

The next step is to construct a value table as shown in Table 10.3.[4] The entries in Table 10.3 are the freight rates from Table 10.1 for the allocations called for under the plan.

The row and column values (e.g., the 9.50 in the second column opposite Warehouse 1 and the 3.00 under Plant B) are assigned so that each entry in the table is the sum of the corresponding column and row figures. This can be done as follows:

1. Pick any column or row, e.g., column A, and arbitrarily assign it the value 0.
2. Then whenever an entry appears in that column in Table 10.3, use it as the corresponding row value. (For example, the value 9.00 appears in row 3 under A. This is chosen as the row value for 3.)
3. Subtract this row value from any other entry or entries in the row; use the difference as the corresponding column value. (For example, 9.00 subtracted from 10.00 in row 3, column D, gives a column D value of 1.00.)

TABLE 10.3   Initial-value table—1

	Plant	A	B	C	D
	Col. value	0.00	3.00	−.50	1.00
Warehouse	Row value				
1	9.50	. . . . .	12.50	. . . . .	. . . . .
2	11.00	. . . . .	. . . . .	10.50	12.00
3	9.00	9.00	. . . . .	. . . . .	10.00
4	9.50	. . . . .	12.50	9.00	. . . . .

[3] See comments on "degeneracy," pp. 289–292.
[4] The method used here to get the minimum-cost solution is known as the "transportation" method, due to G. B. Dantzig. It is applicable to problems of the type discussed in this chapter. See G. B. Dantzig, "Application of the Simplex Method to a Transportation Problem," *Activity Analysis of Production and Allocation,* Cowles Commission Monograph no. 13, Tjalling C. Koopmans (ed.), John Wiley & Sons, Inc., New York, 1951.

The row and column values shown in Table 10.3 were calculated as follows:

1. Column A assigned the value 0.00.
2. The value 9.00 in row 3, column A, used as the row 3 value.
3. Row 3, column D value, $10.00 - 9.00 = 1.00$, column D value.
4. Column D, row 2, $12.00 - 1.00 = 11.00$, row 2 value.
5. Row 2, column C, $10.50 - 11.00 = -.50$, column C value.
6. Column C, row 4, $9.00 - (-.50) = 9.50$, row 4 value.
7. Row 4, column B, $12.50 - 9.50 = 3.00$, column B value.
8. Column B, row 1, $12.50 - 3.00 = 9.50$, row 1 value.

The value table can now be completed by filling in the other entries equal to the sum of the corresponding row and column values, as shown in Table 10.4.

The next step is to test the tentative plan to see where an improvement can be made. This is done by subtracting the entries in the table of freight rates, Table 10.1, from the corresponding entries in the completed value table, Table 10.4, as shown in Table 10.5. Wherever an assignment has been made the difference will be zero. If all differences are zero or negative, this shows that the plan is the best possible. If any difference is positive, this shows an assignment that can be made to cut total cost. In Table 10.5 the difference under Plant B and opposite Warehouse 2 is positive, equal to $3. This indicates that this assignment can be used to improve the plan, at a net saving of $3 per ton on any material so assigned.

The next step is to improve the plan along the line indicated in Table 10.5. The plan is reproduced, with changes indicated in parentheses, in Table 10.6. The mark $(+)$ under Plant B shows the increase indicated by the test calculation. Since any change must be compensated for by an off-setting change in the same row or column, we can eliminate from consideration all rows or columns with only one entry, e.g., Plant A and Ware-

TABLE 10.4 Completed-value table—1

Plant		A	B	C	D
Col. value		0.00	3.00	-.50	1.00
Warehouse	Row value				
1	9.50	9.50	12.50	9.00	10.50
2	11.00	11.00	14.00	10.50	12.00
3	9.00	9.00	12.00	8.50	10.00
4	9.50	9.50	12.50	9.00	10.50

TABLE 10.5   Test of plan—1

	Plant			
	A	B	C	D
Warehouse 1:				
Value	9.50	12.50	9.00	10.50
Freight	10.00	12.50	13.50	14.00
	−.50	0	−4.50	−3.50
Warehouse 2:				
Value	11.00	14.00	10.50	12.00
Freight	12.50	11.00	10.50	12.00
	−1.50	3.00	0	0
Warehouse 3:				
Value	9.00	12.00	8.50	10.00
Freight	9.00	12.00	11.00	10.00
	0	0	−2.50	0
Warehouse 4:				
Value	9.50	12.50	9.00	10.50
Freight	12.50	12.50	9.00	13.00
	−3.00	0	0	−2.50

TABLE 10.6   Revision of plan—1

Warehouse	Plant				Total
	A	B	C	D	
1	. . . . .	1,000	. . . . .	. . . . .	1,000
			(0)		
2	. . . . .	+ (500)	500	2,000	2,500
3	3,000	. . . . .	. . . . .	2,000	5,000
		(500)	(1,000)		
4	. . . . .	1,000	500	. . . . .	1,500
Total	3,000	2,000	1,000	4,000	

house 1, and then any other rows or columns with only one entry remaining, e.g., Warehouse 3 and then Plant D. (The mark (+) counts as an entry.)

Any increase in Plant B–Warehouse 2 must be offset by corresponding decreases in the same row or column. The smallest number to be decreased is 500 under Plant C–Warehouse 2. This leads to the changes shown in Table 10.6, or the revised plan shown in Table 10.7.

The revised plan shown in Table 10.7 can now be tested in the same way, the results of which are summarized in Table 10.8. This shows opportunities for allocating production from Plant A to Warehouse 1, and from Plant D to Warehouse 4, with the plan revision shown in Table 10.9. This plan can be tested in the same way, with the result shown in Table 10.10. Since the test shows no positive differences, this means that no further change can be made in the plan to reduce freight cost. The final minimum-freight-cost plan is shown in Table 10.11.

This procedure, once familiar to a clerk, can be worked through rapidly. It arrives at a solution in a finite series of steps, each step coming closer to the solution. It can also be used on punched-card or internally programed equipment to compute a minimum-cost plan.

In the course of computing the minimum-cost program, a condition may arise, either in the initial program or in a subsequent step, where the plan breaks into two parts or more. The total requirements for some part of the warehouses is just matched by some one or more (not all) of the plants. Table 10.12 is an example of such a program, using the data from the example. Plants A and C and Warehouses 2 and 4 form one self-contained group, and Plants B and D and Warehouses 1 and 3 another. This is known in the technical literature of linear programing as a *degenerate* solution. It creates a difficulty, since the value table, such as Table 10.4, cannot be constructed.

TABLE 10.7 Allocation of production—2

| Warehouse | Plant | | | | Total |
	A	B	C	D	
1	. . . . .	1,000	. . . . .	. . . . .	1,000
2	. . . . .	500	. . . . .	2,000	2,500
3	3,000	. . . . .	. . . . .	2,000	5,000
4	. . . . .	500	1,000	. . . . .	1,500
Total	3,000	2,000	1,000	4,000	

TABLE 10.8   Test of plan—2

	Plant			
	A	B	C	D
Warehouse 1:				
Value	12.50	12.50	9.00	13.50
Freight	10.00	12.50	13.50	14.00
	2.50	0	−4.50	−.50
Warehouse 2:				
Value	11.00	11.00	7.50	12.00
Freight	12.50	11.00	10.50	12.00
	−1.50	0	−3.00	0
Warehouse 3:				
Value	9.00	9.00	5.50	10.00
Freight	9.00	12.00	11.00	10.00
	0	−3.00	−5.50	0
Warehouse 4:				
Value	12.50	12.50	9.00	13.50
Freight	12.50	12.50	9.00	13.00
	0	0	0	.50

TABLE 10.9   Revision of plan—2

Warehouse	Plant				Total
	A	B	C	D	
1	+(1,000)	(0) 1,000	. . . . .	. . . . .	1,000
2	. . . . .	(2,000) 500	. . . . .	(500) 2,000	2,500
3	(2,000) 3,000	. . . . .	. . . . .	(3,000) 2,000	5,000
4	. . . . .	(0) 500	1,000	+ (500)	1,500
	3,000	2,000	1,000	4,000	

TABLE 10.10 Test of plan—3

	Plant			
	A	B	C	D
Warehouse 1:				
Value	10.00	10.00	7.00	11.00
Freight	10.00	12.50	13.50	14.00
	0	−2.50	−6.50	−3.00
Warehouse 2:				
Value	11.00	11.00	8.00	12.00
Freight	12.50	11.00	10.50	12.00
	−1.50	0	−2.50	0
Warehouse 3:				
Value	9.00	9.00	6.00	10.00
Freight	9.00	12.00	11.00	10.00
	0	−3.00	−5.00	0
Warehouse 4:				
Value	12.00	12.00	9.00	13.00
Freight	12.50	12.50	9.00	13.00
	−.50	−.50	0	0

TABLE 10.11 Final allocation of production

Warehouse	Plant				Total
	A	B	C	D	
1	1,000	. . . .	. . . .	. . . .	1,000
2	. . . .	2,000	. . . .	500	2,500
3	2,000	. . . .	. . . .	3,000	5,000
4	. . . .	. . . .	1,000	500	1,500
Total	3,000	2,000	1,000	4,000	

TABLE 10.12 Example of degenerate plan

Warehouse	Plant				Total
	A	B	C	D	
1	.....	1,000	.....	.....	1,000
2	2,500	.....	.....	.....	2,500
3	.....	1,000	.....	4,000	5,000
4	500	.....	1,000	.....	1,500
Total	3,000	2,000	1,000	4,000	

Henderson and Schlaifer outline a technique for handing degenerate programs.[5] If a degenerate plan arises, the following steps are followed if there are fewer plants than warehouses:

1. Divide one unit of material by twice the number of plants.
2. Choose any convenient number less than this quotient. Add this number to the planned output of each plant.
3. Add the equivalent *total* to the requirements of any *one* warehouse.

If there are fewer warehouses than plants, the rule can be reversed; i.e., divide one unit by the number of warehouses, add a convenient number smaller than the quotient to the requirements of each warehouse, and add an equivalent total to the output of some one plant. If the number of plants and warehouses is equal, either form of the rule can be used. Then the problem can be solved in the way outlined before. When the final answer is reached, the fractions of units can be rounded to the nearest whole number.

Balancing with different plant costs

The "transportation" method was illustrated by an example with two rather strong restrictions:

1. It was assumed that plant output in total exactly matched total warehouse requirements.
2. No allowance was made for plant cost; i.e., it was assumed that (*a*) there were no differences in cost among plants, and (*b*) there was no change in out-of-pocket unit cost in any one plant if volume changed.

[5] Alexander Henderson and Robert Schlaifer, "Mathematical Programing—Better Information for Better Decision Making," *Harvard Business Review*, p. 98, May–June, 1954.

Many times one of the questions to be answered in planning is how much of the available capacity of each plant to employ. There also may be a possibility of expanding the capacity by overtime or second-shift operation at premium cost. In these cases, differences in plant cost and an excess of maximum plant capacity over field requirements must be taken into account.

An excess of capacity over requirements can be taken into account by setting up a dummy warehouse, with requirements equal to the difference between maximum plant output and field requirements. The freight costs to this dummy warehouse from any plant are set equal to zero. "Shipments" from any plant to the dummy warehouse represent planned unused capacity at that plant. For example, suppose in the previous illustration that the capacity of Plant A were 5,000 tons instead of 3,000 tons. This would give a surplus of production over requirements of 2,000 tons. Then the plants and warehouses would be shown as:

Plant	Capacity	Warehouse	Expected requirements
A	5,000	1	1,000
B	2,000	2	2,500
C	1,000	3	5,000
D	4,000	4	1,500
Total	12,000	Unused capacity	2,000
		Total	12,000

If out-of-pocket unit costs differ from one plant to another, these can be accounted for as part of the "freight rate." Choose the lowest-cost plant as a base and set its unit cost equal to zero. Calculate the difference between actual unit cost at any plant and the base-plant unit cost. Add this difference to the freight cost from the plant to each warehouse, except the dummy or unused capacity, to get a new set of "freight costs." These effectively account for differences in delivered cost by combining freight cost with differences in manufactured cost.

When the possible use of extra premium capacity arises, this can be handled by splitting each plant into two or more "plants," each representing one type or level of operation, each with its own capacity, and with the freight rates from the "plants" being the base rate plus any unit premium cost.

Suppose, for example, that we are planning the operations of four plants serving four warehouses. Maximum normal capacity in the four plants is

12,000 units; maximum overtime capacity is 1,000 units. Total estimated field requirements are 10,000 units. The individual capacities, costs, and premium rates might appear as shown in Table 10.13. These can be converted to the form of Table 10.14 for designing an allocation plan using the transportation method. Table 10.14 defines a transportation problem with seven plants and five warehouses.

Graphical techniques

Sometimes consumers or sources may be very numerous and scattered over wide areas. For example, we may be concerned with plants or warehouses serving hundreds or thousands of customers. Or we may be concerned with picking up raw materials such as timber, pulpwood, or farm crops from a great many small sources. The computational load of handling allocation problems by linear-programing means may well be too great if each indi-

TABLE 10.13 Data for allocation plan

	Plant				Warehouse require-ments
	A	B	C	D	
Regular capacity	5,000	2,000	1,000	4,000	
Overtime capacity	500	0	100	400	
Normal unit cost	$100	$102	$105	$95	
Overtime unit cost	$115	.....	$122	$110	
Freight rate to:					
Warehouse 1	10.00	12.50	13.50	14.00	1,000
Warehouse 2	12.50	11.00	10.50	12.00	2,500
Warehouse 3	9.00	12.00	11.00	10.00	5,000
Warehouse 4	12.50	12.50	9.00	13.00	1,500

TABLE 10.14 Allocation plan using "transportation" method

	Plant							Warehouse requirements
	A	A-OT	B	C	C-OT	D	D-OT	
Cost premium	$5	$20	$7	$10	$27	0	$15	
Capacity	5,000	500	2,000	1,000	100	4,000	400	
Warehouse 1	$15.00	30.00	19.50	23.50	40.50	14.90	29.00	1,000
Warehouse 2	$17.50	32.50	18.00	20.50	37.50	12.00	27.00	2,500
Warehouse 3	$14.00	29.00	19.00	21.00	38.00	10.00	25.00	5,000
Warehouse 4	$17.50	32.50	19.50	19.00	36.00	13.00	28.00	1,500
Unused capacity	0	0	0	0	0	0	0	2,000

vidual consumer or city, for example, is treated separately. Sometimes these can be grouped and an approximate freight rate used, or they can be treated as if all were located in some one principal market in each broad area. Even this can be tedious, however. Frequently, graphical techniques can be used to get the minimum-cost solution.

One such method[6] makes use of the fact that the pattern of freight rates from any point, e.g., plant or warehouse, is normally quite regular, forming a pattern such as that shown in Figure 10.1. Where freight costs follow this pattern, a graphical technique can be used which is rapid and as precise as the data will warrant.

The raw material needed to apply this method is:

1. *A set of cost maps.* These maps, similar in nature to Figure 10.1, show lines or contours of constant transportation cost from each source. One map for each source is needed. Maps can be prepared by plotting known freight costs from the source on the map at the corresponding destination point and then sketching in the lines by eye.
2. *A demand map.* This shows consumption by market or market area; the estimated consumption can be plotted directly on the map.
3. *Cost-difference maps.* These can be constructed directly from the cost maps. Each line on the difference map represents a line where a constant differential exists in the cost of shipping from one source compared with another. For example, the 0 cost-difference line is drawn through points where the transportation costs are equal from either source.

Figure 10.2 illustrates cost lines or contours and cost difference lines for two sources. These would normally be drawn on separate maps. The cost lines for Source A are marked on the left, those for Source B on the right. For example, the line marked 2.50 at the upper left-hand corner of Figure

[6] See M. L. Vidale, "A Graphical Solution of the Transportation Problem," *Operations Research*, vol. 4, no. 2, April, 1956.

FIGURE 10.1 Characteristic freight-cost pattern

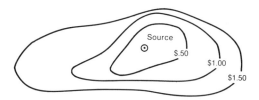

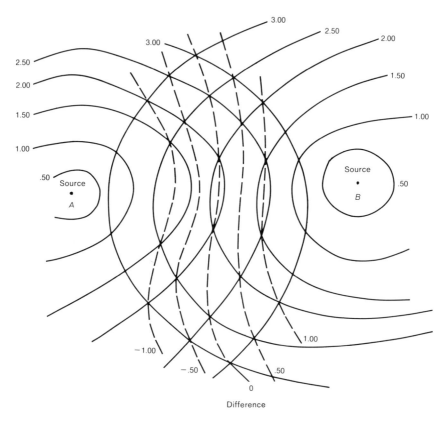

FIGURE 10.2   Illustration of cost and cost-difference lines

10.2 which continues through the center to the lower left is the line representing points to which shipments can be made from A for $2.50.

The dashed lines running generally vertically between the two sources are cost-difference lines. Note, for example, that the 0 cost-difference line, i.e., the line where costs are equal from either source, goes through the intersection of the equivalent cost lines from the two sources. The other cost-difference lines shown are labeled in terms of the cost advantage to Source B. For example, the 1.00 cost-difference line shows the points which can be served for $1 less for freight, per unit, from B than from A.

Some points of interest about the cost-difference lines are:

1. A boundary between any two areas served by two sources should always follow a cost-difference line.

2. If the production costs at the two sources are equal and if capacity is not limited, the boundary should follow the 0 cost-difference line. If the production cost of one source is higher by a fixed amount, the boundary should follow the cost-difference line for this difference. For example, in Figure 10.2, if the cost at A were $0.50 per unit higher than at B, the boundary should follow the −.50 difference line.
3. When three or more sources are involved, the boundary between any two areas follows a cost-difference line between the corresponding sources. When three or more sources are involved, the boundaries never intersect in pairs but only in groups of at least three.

Examples of use of this technique to solve problems of allocating markets to plant or warehouse sources include:

1. *Several sources, total production equal to total requirements.* First, a rough sketch of a market breakdown is made. Then one source is chosen, and some difference line between it and a neighboring source is picked more or less arbitrarily as a possible boundary. Then a second difference line is chosen which defines the market for this first source so that consumption equals its capacity. The intersection of these two difference lines automatically defines a third difference line, which with one of the first two forms part of the tentative boundary for a second market area. Another difference line intersecting with it can then be found to define the market area for a second source, so that consumption balances production.

   The work proceeds in this fashion, with one boundary added at a time, being sure that demand balances capacity in each area defined and that each tentative boundary is a cost-difference line chosen to go through the intersection of two boundaries already picked. If all market areas can be bounded in this way, without violating either condition, the answer is found. If the last boundary cannot be fitted in meeting both conditions, the procedure must be repeated starting with a new initial boundary. Usually, when the last boundary will not fit, one can quickly see the way in which the initial boundary should be moved.
2. *Several sources, unlimited capacity, equal unit costs.* The boundaries between markets are the 0 cost-difference lines. Each source will operate at the level necessary to meet demand in its market.
3. *Several sources, unlimited capacity, differing unit costs.* The boundaries between markets are the cost-difference lines chosen so that production plus transportation cost from the sources on either side is equal along the line. Equivalently, the excess unit production cost over the lowest cost can be added to the freight rates for each source. Then the boundaries follow the 0 cost-difference lines of the new "freight" costs.

4. *Several sources, differing unit costs, excess total capacity.* First, the procedure in paragraph 3 is followed; then a check is made to see if the demand in the market area assigned any source exceeds its capacity. If so, the boundary must be moved inward to lie on favorable cost-difference lines until demand just equals capacity. If in making this adjustment the demand in any adjoining area or areas equals its source capacity, the boundaries of such areas must also be moved inward. All adjustments must leave boundaries on cost-difference lines and intersecting three or more at once.

This type of graphical technique is in one sense a trial-and-error method in that there is no direct step-by-step way to work directly toward an answer. On the other hand, it does give a test whether a particular market division is best and an indication of the nature or direction of change if the tentative division fails the test. Some practice in using the cost-difference maps will quickly permit the user to develop skill in making adjustments easily and efficiently to reach the right answer.

OPERATING LEVELS AND COSTS

Relationship between operating levels and costs

Both the linear-programing and graphical techniques for allocation of demand to plants are based on the assumption that unit production cost at any one source is constant; it does not change with volume. Note that we refer to out-of-pocket or direct costs, not total costs including distribution of fixed charges. Often this is a fair assumption. Frequently, however, it is not true, particularly where the source is a plant. Often out-of-pocket unit costs *increase* as output increases. Some reasons for this include use of less efficient equipment and use of overtime or premium-shift time.

The loss of flexibility and increase in inventory requirements is often an important but overlooked cause for increased unit out-of-pocket cost as output increases.[7] Since the differences in freight cost from one source versus another tend to be small near the boundary between two market areas, it is often desirable to move the boundary in toward a plant operating at capacity. Somewhat more is paid in freight, but often the extra cost is more than compensated for in inventory and operating savings. Where inventory cost and loss of flexibility are important, the relation between rate of produc-

---

[7] See, for example, Appendix A, p. 356ff., for an analysis of inventory costs versus capacity where product cycling takes place.

tion and cost can be estimated with the help of techniques described in Chapters 6, 7, and 8.

In some cases where unit cost changes with volume, linear-programing methods can be used. One special case was mentioned above, where output above a specified rate was produced at overtime or shift-premium cost. In other cases the same technique can be used. For example, Figure 10.3 shows a possible relation between *total* out-of-pocket cost and output rate. The solid line illustrates the actual assumed relationship, while the dashed-line segments illustrate a possible approximation with straight lines. Figure 10.4 shows the marginal *unit* out-of-pocket cost corresponding to the total-cost curve and the approximations in Figure 10.3.

Just as overtime production was set up as a separate "plant" for plan calculations, the approximate cost levels in Figure 10.4, with their corresponding volume limits, can be set up as separate "plants" for planning purposes. For example, using the approximations shown in Figure 10.4, we might set up, for planning purposes, one "plant" with a unit cost of $1.50 and a maximum capacity of 2,150 units and a second "plant" with a unit cost of $2.50 and a capacity of $5,000 - 2,150 = 2,850$ units. The more detailed the approximation, i.e., the more approximate cost levels and volume limits chosen, the closer will the result be to the actual cost relation.

Graphical techniques can also be used to arrive at an allocation plan where marginal unit cost depends on volume. The procedure works in this way:

FIGURE 10.3 Total out-of-pocket cost versus output rate

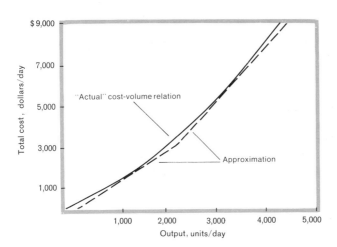

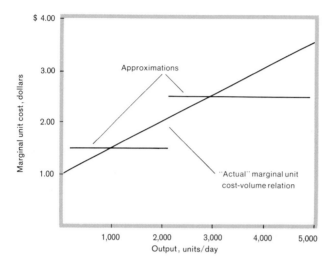

FIGURE 10.4 Marginal unit out-of-pocket cost versus output rate

1. Choose a unit cost for each plant, c_i^0. Then work out the market allocation by the method sketched earlier for several sources with unlimited capacity but with differing unit costs. This will result in a market allocation and a production volume assignable to each plant.

2. Find the marginal unit cost, c_i^1, corresponding to the production volume for each plant, i; if the two sets of costs differ, the allocation should be adjusted. Reallocate the markets using as unit production costs the average $(c_i^0 + c_i^1)/2$ for each plant, i. This process can be repeated until the unit costs used in the market allocation and the marginal unit costs corresponding to the assigned production under the market allocation are equal.[8]

   For example, if the marginal unit cost-volume relation shown in Figure 10.4 applied to some one of the plants, we might start by assuming a unit cost of $2 for this plant (corresponding to an output rate of 2,000 units per day). Then the market would be assigned. If the resulting market allocation required an output of 3,000 units per day, this would correspond to a marginal unit cost of $2.50, as shown in Figure 10.4. Then we would use ($2.00 + 2.50)/2 = $2.25 as a new assumed unit cost and repeat the market allocation.

[8] See M. L. Vidale, *op. cit.*

Methods of examination

Both the linear-programing and graphical-allocation techniques have been described in terms of planning the use of existing plant with existing capacity. However, they can be used equally well to test the desirability of additions to capacity at any points or of a new plant or warehouse source at any additional point. All that is needed is an estimate of the unit out-of-pocket operating cost of production with the new capacity, or if a new location (plant or warehouse source) is being considered, the unit out-of-pocket operating cost and the transportation rates to markets or receiving warehouses. The assumed or proposed plant changes can then be set up and used as if they existed in fact. The effect of the proposed changes on allocation plans can be determined and the effect on cost calculated. This gives a measure of the payoff which must justify the increased investment. The same procedure can be used to test the feasibility of closing some source, by calculating a plan without the source, computing out-of-pocket and transportation costs under this plan, and comparing the change in these to any out-of-pocket savings estimated to result from closing the source.

FIELD WAREHOUSING

Economical shipment of small orders

One reason for stocking an item in a field warehouse in addition to holding inventory at the producing plant is to provide local delivery of small customer orders. This may help cut freight costs by allowing for bulk delivery to the field stock point and delivery at premium transportation rates only over the last leg of the journey. Figure 10.5 illustrates the alternative patterns of shipment that might be considered. Under pattern (a), the field warehouse is replenished in economical lots and the customer order is filled

FIGURE 10.5 Alternative shipping patterns

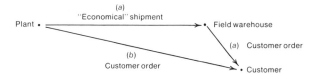

directly from the warehouse. Under pattern (b), the customer order is filled directly from the plant.

There is no reason why both patterns cannot be used simultaneously in one distribution system. In fact, if the customer order is large enough to move at minimum freight costs, it is generally desirable to ship direct from the plant, using the field warehouse to fill small orders only.

The warehouse can normally service any small orders where the unit cost of movement from plant to warehouse plus the unit handling cost at the warehouse plus the unit premium freight cost out of the warehouse is equal to or less than the unit premium freight cost direct from the plant. The economical servicing area for the warehouse can be determined by the graphical techniques described earlier. The plant and warehouse are considered as alternative sources, the warehouse source carrying a unit "production-cost" premium equal to the freight cost from plant to warehouse plus warehouse handling cost. Freight or transportation rates used are in this case the premium rates which apply to small shipments. With this information, then, the boundary between the warehouse-serviced area and the plant-serviced area or between two warehouses can be mapped out.

If an item is carried in the warehouse, extra inventory will be required; the amount required depends on the type of reorder or replenishment rule used.[9] The increased inventory of the item is required for three reasons:

1. *Stock in transit.* On the average, inventory in transit will equal the transit time from plant to warehouse times the shipment rate of the item through the warehouse.
2. *Economical order stock.* On the average, there will be inventory at the warehouse equal to one-half the shipping quantity from plant to warehouse.
3. *Safety stock.* Normally the transit time from plant to customer via the warehouse will be greater than when the item is shipped directly to the customer. Stock to cover maximum demand over the increase in delivery time must be carried.

The relative economy of carrying an item in a field warehouse can be determined, first, by defining the order size to be filled from the warehouse and the market area the warehouse will serve. Then, the expected demand for orders within the established size limit from the warehouse serving area must be determined. A proposed replenishment rule must be chosen and inventory requirements, replenishment-order size, and replenishment-order frequency must be estimated by the methods described in Chapter 6. Inventory levels should be set to provide the same delivered service time to cus-

[9] See Chap. 6.

tomers as on direct shipments from the plant. The cost comparison can then be made:

Cost of Direct Shipment	Cost of Warehouse Service
Total volume of customer orders considered	Total volume of demand considered
$\times$ Average premium freight rate, plant to customers in warehouse area	$\times$ Freight rate to warehouse
_____	_____
= Direct-shipment freight cost	= Plant-warehouse freight bill
	+ Number of replenishment orders times order cost
	+ Warehouse inventory carrying cost
	+ Warehouse direct handling cost
	+ Transit inventory carrying cost
	+ Demand volume times average premium freight rate, warehouse to customers
	_____
	= Cost of service via warehouse

It is often possible to justify field-warehouse stocks to cut premium freight on small orders, especially for items that move regularly in moderate volume. However, the smaller the volume of demand for the item, the less favorable the field warehouse often looks in comparison with direct shipment.[10] This is due to the fact that the cost per unit put through the warehouse will tend to rise rapidly for smaller-volume items because of the increased cost per unit of replenishing inventory and holding inventory. The number of replenishment orders and warehouse inventory requirements will be smaller for low-volume items, but they do not drop in proportion. Thus the unit cost goes up.

Local service for prompt delivery

Another reason for carrying items in a local or field warehouse is to give prompt delivery to local customers. For example, a local warehouse may be able to provide same-day or next-day service on customer orders within a radius of a hundred miles or more. A factory shipment to fill the order might not arrive for 2 weeks. The question that must be answered with respect to each item is: Should it be carried in the local warehouse, or is the extra cost too great?

[10] Demand volume here is in terms of orders for small shipments, for example, l.c.l. or l.t.l.

Often in addition to local and plant inventories there is the possibility of setting up a regional warehouse, intermediate between the two. The regional warehouse might service the market areas of several local warehouses on certain items not carried locally. A local warehouse may often serve as regional stock point for certain items.

The warehouse serving area is, in this case, usually dictated by availability of transportation, not by inventory-policy considerations. The serving area in turn gives a basis for an approximate estimate of the demand for any particular item which the warehouse might carry. Inventory requirements to service this demand can be determined by use of techniques such as those described in Chapter 6. First, a replenishment rule such as a fixed-order system, fixed-period system, or base-stock system is chosen. The estimated volume can be used to calculate reorder size or frequency. The desired reorder point can be estimated, equal to maximum demand over the replenishment cycle.

However, once inventory and operating requirements are estimated, the question still remains: Is this worth while? This question normally cannot be answered directly because speed of service to customers and warehouse cost are not commensurable.

The first question management must answer, arbitrarily if necessary, is: How much premium per unit are we willing to pay to cut delivery time x days? The answer may be found by filling out a table such as Table 10.15. Another way may be to sketch the information from two or three alternative tables graphically, for discussion and choice.

The second step that is needed is an estimate of the penalty per unit paid because of local warehousing. As noted above, unit inventory and replenishment costs tend to go up rapidly as the volume handled goes down. Figure 10.6 shows the characteristic form of relation between inventory penalty as a per cent of cost and physical units moved through the warehouse. This can normally be arrived at to a fair approximation covering all items or all items in a major group, from the analysis of inventory replenishment.

The third step is to combine these in a "policy" chart such as Figure 10.7. The curve in Figure 10.7 is the dividing line between characteristics which

TABLE 10.15   Delivery-cost policy

We will pay a premium per unit (per cent)	To cut delivery time to customers (days)
0	1
0.25	2
1.0	4
3.5	8
4.0	16

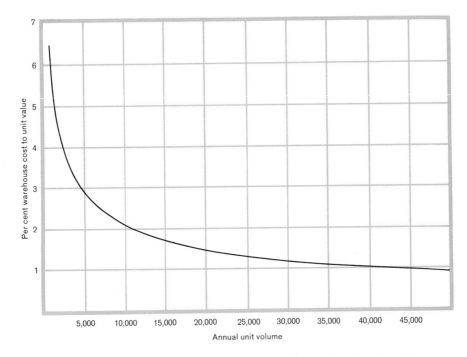

FIGURE 10.6 Illustrative relationship between annual volume of an item through a warehouse versus inventory and replenishment cost

determine that an item will be carried and those which indicate that it should not be carried.

To construct the chart, we first pick an arbitrary annual volume, e.g., 2,500 units. From Figure 10.6 we find the estimated premium, 4 per cent. From Table 10.15 we find that we will pay 4 per cent only to cut delivery time by at least 16 days. So we plot a point on the chart corresponding to 2,500 units on the horizontal axis and 16 days on the vertical axis. Likewise, annual volume of 40,000 units indicates a cost premium of 1 per cent, which corresponds to a 4-day reduction in delivery time. By continuing in this way, we can plot a series of points and draw the line through them.

To use the chart, we estimate the annual volume of an item through a warehouse and the extra delivery time from the next nearest point, e.g., a regional warehouse or plant. If the point representing the combination of these factors falls above the line in Figure 10.7, the item should be stocked locally. If the point for the item falls below the line, the item should not be stocked locally. For example, suppose one warehouse area required an estimated 10,000 units of an item annually, and a local stock would cut customer delivery time by 8 days. Then the point representing 10,000 units and an 8-day cut in delivery time lies above the line in Figure 10.7, so the item should be stocked locally. Suppose another warehouse area requires an estimated 25,000 units of the same item, but a local stock would cut delivery time to the customer by 3 days. Then, the point corresponding to 25,000 items and a 3-day cut lies below the line in Figure 10.7, so the item should not be stocked locally.[11]

The particular numerical values chosen in this example are not important. The general principle applies in any similar problem, whether the policy toward extra cost for faster delivery is more or less liberal than that shown in Table 10.15.

Once this procedure has been applied to determine which items to carry in local warehouses, it can be used again to see which remaining items might be stocked in regional stock points. Here, of course, the demand

[11] See H. W. Karr and M. A. Geisler, "A Fruitful Application of Static Marginal Analysis," *Management Science*, vol. 2, no. 4, p. 313, July, 1956; or M. A. Geisler and H. W. Karr, "The Design of Military Supply Tables for Spare Parts," *Operations Research*, vol. 4, no. 4, p. 431, August, 1956, for an approach to allocation of limited space among items, applicable to the field-warehousing problem.

FIGURE 10.7   Illustrative "policy" chart for warehouse-stocking decisions

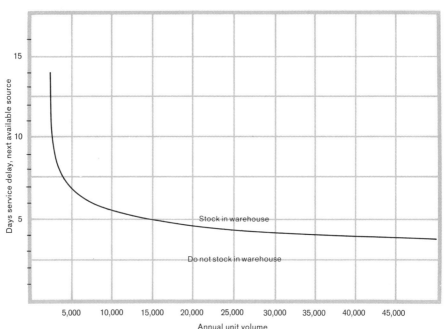

volume used is that for the whole region, and the delivery-time difference is that between plant shipment and regional-warehouse shipment to a customer.

PROBLEM

1. A heavy-chemicals manufacturer purchases raw materials which he processes and packages at three regional plants. Because of the differences in labor costs and transportation the delivered price of the raw materials from each source to each processing plant varies from as little as $200 per ton to $1,400 per ton. Limitations in the available supply make it necessary to purchase from all sources. The delivered prices for the coming month are as follows:

Delivered price of raw materials, dollars per ton

From	to Plant I	II	III
Source A	$ 400	$1,900	$ 800
Source B	600	600	200
Source C	1,000	800	1,400
Source D	200	1,200	400

The production plan calls for 102,000 tons for the coming month, which are available in the following amounts:

Source A	15,000 tons
Source B	24,000 tons
Source C	21,000 tons
Source D	42,000 tons
	102,000 tons

Plant capacities are such that this production is scheduled for the three plants in the following amounts:

Plant 1	21,000 tons
Plant 2	27,000 tons
Plant 3	54,000 tons
	102,000 tons

What quantities of raw materials should be shipped to each plant from each source, in order to minimize the total purchase and shipment cost?

BIBLIOGRAPHY

Charnes, A., and W. W. Cooper: "The Stepping Stone Method of Explaining Linear Programming Calculations in Transportation Problems," *Management Science*, vol. 1, no. 1, pp. 49–69, October, 1954.

Cooper, Leon: "Location-Allocation Problems," *Operations Research*, vol. 11, no. 3, pp. 331–343, May-June, 1963.

Feldman, E., F. A. Lehrer, and T. L. Ray: "Warehouse Location under Continuous Economies of Scale," *Management Science*, vol. 12, no. 9, pp. 670–684, May, 1966.

Ford, L. R., and D. R. Fulkerson: "Solving the Transportation Problem," *Management Science*, vol. 3, no. 1, pp. 24–32, October, 1956.

Glassner, B. J.: "Cycling in the Transportation Problem," *Naval Research Logistics Quarterly*, vol. 11, no. 1, pp. 43–58, March, 1964.

Heckert, J. Brooks, and Robert B. Miner: *Distribution Costs*, 2d ed., The Ronald Press Company, New York, 1953.

Holladay, J.: "Some Transportation Problems and Techniques for Solving Them," *Naval Research Logistics Quarterly*, vol. 11, no. 1, pp. 15–42, March, 1964.

Koopmans, Tjalling C. (ed.): *Activity Analysis of Production and Allocation*, Cowles Commission Monograph no. 13, John Wiley & Sons, Inc., New York, 1951.

Longman, Donald R., and Michael Shiff: *Practical Distribution Cost Analysis*, Richard D. Irwin, Inc., Homewood, Ill., 1955.

Simpson, K. F.: "A Theory of Allocation of Stocks to Warehouses," *Operations Research*, vol. 7, no. 6, pp. 797–805, November-December, 1959.

Smykay, Edward W., Donald J. Bowersox, and Frank H. Mossman: *Physical Distribution Management*, The Macmillan Company, New York, 1961.

Szwarc, W.: "The Transportation Problem with Stochastic Demand," *Management Science*, vol. 11, no. 1, pp. 33–50, September, 1964.

Vazsonyi, Andrew: *Scientific Programming in Business and Industry*, John Wiley & Sons, Inc., New York, 1958.

Vidale, M. L.: "A Graphical Solution of the Transportation Problem," *Operations Research*, vol. 4, no. 2, April, 1956.

11

DESIGN
OF
A
PRODUCTION-
CONTROL
SYSTEM

SCOPE

A production-control system is only a part of the system of information flow and control in a business organization. The methods and information for production planning and control are necessarily closely related to other planning and control functions such as engineering, cost control, capital planning, and sales planning and control. Production control is a central or important element in any business information and control system, since certainly the decisions made exert a strong influence on the profitability of the company, its ability to provide service, and its capacity for coping with uncertainties which may arise.

Since production planning and control systems are only part of the general information system and intimately related to other planning and control operations, it is difficult to draw a line specifying cleanly where production planning and control systems start and stop. For example, production-planning methods are strongly influenced by the capital-budget program of the company, by plans which may exist for plant expansion and the location of warehouses and other facilities. In turn, the analysis underlying production-planning methods can be used to evaluate proposed capital expenditures. The cost and accounting systems of most companies make use of much of the same information on production accomplished, shipments, and stock movements that are essential feedback elements in the production-control system. Certainly procedures devised for production control should recognize the needs of the cost and accounting activities; where possible, many of the procedural and data-processing activities may be combined. The production planning and control system relies on engineering data for knowledge of the relation between raw materials, intermediate products, and finished items and for information concerning new processes and products which may be devised, as well as for estimates of operating times. In turn, information concerning production planning and control problems can have an important bearing on engineering decisions, e.g., in the design of products to make use of standard components and subassemblies or to be easily adapted to special customer specifications. Though the interrelationships between production-control and other information systems are important, and though it is desirable, where possible, to design integrated procedures and processing methods to service a number of systems, we must draw the line somewhere.

For purposes of discussion of organization problems, therefore, we might think of a production planning and control system as a system for establishing operating and inventory levels in existing facilities to meet forecast demand and for adjusting operating levels and replenishing inventories to take account of actual demand as it materializes. In some circumstances, it may be feasible to restrict the operations and inventories considered to a portion of the total process. For example, branch-warehouse and factory finished-stock controls and methods of branch-warehouse replenishment may in some circumstances represent a broad enough scope for effective work on system design. In other cases, the planning and control procedures within a plant may give adequate scope for work. As a general rule, however, it is desirable, where possible, to look at the planning and control problem, from raw materials to customer, as a unit. Raw-material control procedures will influence the ability of manufacturing or processing operations to supply finished stocks. The reliability of deliveries to plant finished stocks from operating units influences the ability of the plant to service warehouse demand. In turn, the nature of branch-stock control can seriously affect the problems faced by a plant in maintaining operating levels and servicing branch needs, as illustrated in Chapter 8.

ORGANIZING TO DESIGN A PRODUCTION PLANNING AND CONTROL SYSTEM

The design of a production planning and control system is characteristically neither an easy nor a short job. In the first place, the system must be responsive to a number of needs and policies of the company concerned.

It is by no means a function of the manufacturing organization alone, since performance of the system should reflect sales and financial policies as well. In the second place, a soundly conceived system must be based on a good deal of detailed information about the products of the company, demand characteristics, and the processes and capacities of the manufacturing and distribution organization. Demand statistics and cost data in the detail required are often not available from existing conventional records. The collection and analysis of this information takes time, and a thoroughgoing revision of production-control procedures from analysis through trial and full installation can easily take from 6 months to 2 years in a company of moderate size and complexity. This is a full-time job for skilled people, and if the results are to be worth while, it cannot be hurried unduly.

Experience has shown that it is useful to set up two distinct groups to approach the design of a production planning and control system. One is the analysis, or work, team, and the other is a supervisory committee.

The analysis team

The analysis team is the group that does the detailed day-to-day work necessary to design, test, and install the system. This group must investigate manufacturing and distribution processes, to specify the types of decisions needed to control them and the information required to make these decisions. It must lay out the information system and specify the decision rules for use in routine operation. The analysis team is the group that works out on paper how the system is supposed to work, and designs and supervises operating trials to test the efficiency and feasibility of the system. The team should also have the responsibility, either directly or jointly with a systems and procedures unit, for the design of forms and clerical procedures and for training operating personnel in their use. The team should include at least one person who will have continuing responsibility, after completion of the installation program, for design of improvements, review of the operation of the system, and for making the analyses needed from time to time to demonstrate the effects of alternative policy decisions, as a guide to management in setting policy.

Fundamentally, members of the analysis team need analytical skill and ability to use and interpret numerical data. This type of skill is characteristic, for example, of a good imaginative industrial engineer, quality-control engineer, or physical-research scientist. Skill and aptitude in the use of mathematical techniques is also important, since these are very valuable in understanding the way various decision rules operate in detail. Methods of mathematical statistics are essential to the making of necessary statistical analyses of characteristics of demand and for planning and supervising effective trials of the system. At a later stage, skill in the design of clerical procedures is important, to translate a system which is sound from a logical point of view to one which operating people can use. Finally, knowledge of company processes, operations capabilities, people and personalities, and sources of data by at least some of the team members is important.

It is impossible to lay down a hard-and-fast rule for the size of the analysis team. Increasing the size of the team by no means guarantees anything like a proportionate reduction in the time required to do the job. Design of the system requires thought and analysis. While two or three good minds may speed up this process, the rate of progress is far more dependent on the quality of the individuals than on the sheer number assigned. Most companies are not in the fortunate position of being able to free more than two or three skilled analytical minds to work on a job of this sort. Experience suggests that a team of two to six analysts, with clerical and computational help available to them, forms an effective group. In addition to having the analytical skills and knowledge mentioned above, these people must be known to be discreet and trustworthy, since to do an effective job they must obtain the frank opinions of people throughout the organization on operating policies, methods, and problems.

The supervisory committee

The functions of the supervisory committee are initially to advise the analysis team on policy matters and to make information and people available to the team where needed. As the work progresses, the committee has the important function of reviewing plans and progress for operating acceptability, of reaching tentative conclusions and making recommendations about organizational questions, and of reviewing trials of the system for operating acceptability. Members of the committee should represent the points of view of the sales, production, and financial organizations, and of general management. Other members may be included as circumstances indicate. For example, representatives of purchasing, engineering, or existing production-planning organizations might be added. A minimum of one or two responsible members of management and a maximum of five or six probably set the limits on committee size.

Sometimes, in a desire to have all points of view represented, a company may assemble a very sizable committee to review the analysis team's work. However, the problems which a large committee creates in organizing meetings and in promoting effective, frank discussion should be borne in mind.

One student of organization[1] has suggested (with tongue in cheek) that the most effective size of a committee is 0.7 of a person. Though it may be argued that his study is based on somewhat different circumstances, the gain in effectiveness from a small committee can be substantial.

Many companies have found it effective to plan meetings monthly between the review committee and the analytical team. These meetings should not, in any sense, be formal affairs with the analytical team expected to make any sort of full-dress presentation; if they were, all of the team's time would be spent getting ready for the meetings. The team should be expected to have at each meeting a concise statement of what has been accomplished since the last meeting compared with plan, the program for the coming period, an indication of some of the problems and difficulties encountered, some of the approaches or ideas under development, and information needs for pushing the work ahead.

The principal objective of these meetings is to obtain the reaction of committee members as representing the various points of view of the company management. The meetings also serve the important function of giving the analysis team a chance to learn more about the policies under which the system must operate and the kinds of management decisions and problems to which it should contribute information. Committee members will also, of course, have available for the team suggestions concerning sources of information it may require.

Generally the review-committee members should not attempt to take a detailed role in the analysis itself. The job of the committee is to review and counsel. There is a delicate balance which must be maintained between active interest and guidance from the committee and interference in the details of methods of approach. In commenting on developing ideas, committee members must also recognize that, particularly in the early stages of the work, the ideas put forth by the analysis team will be largely in the form of points of view or tentative approaches. Committee members should very properly raise questions about these ideas and indicate the operating issues which they think are involved, but if too many ideas are firmly quashed early in the work on the grounds that "they won't work," the committee will guarantee an unimaginative and probably an ineffective result.

As the work develops and the proposed system is plotted out, the supervisory committee has an important role to play in raising questions about proof of feasibility and effectiveness and in helping define operating trials which will be convincing to company management and operating personnel.

[1] Bruce S. Old, "On the Mathematics of Committees, Boards, and Panels," *The Scientific Monthly*, vol. 63, pp. 129–134, August, 1946.

Analysis tasks

DESCRIPTION OF OPERATIONS

The analysis team's fundamental job is to describe what information is needed and how it should be used to regulate production. There are three closely related aspects to this task, on which work must necessarily go along simultaneously from the beginning. These aspects may be obvious, but they can stand specific recognition. The first is a description of the production and distribution system to be controlled and physical and policy restrictions on it. The second is a description of the stimulus to which the production and distribution system reacts—in short, characterization of customer demand. The third is a definition and measurement of the costs of operating the process and the control system, in so far as they are affected by the production planning and control methods used.

Describing the production and distribution process under study means that a number of aspects of the system must be identified. In the first place, the centers or pools of activity, groups of interchangeable personnel, and within these the important groups of interchangeable types of equipment, must be identified. It is essential to know what operating characteristics govern the use of one type of equipment versus another. The choice may depend on the physical characteristics of the product, the type of job to be done, the size of the piece handled, or the volume of product to be processed. Planning and loading decisions assume the availability of time estimates to do a job, and so the analysis team must know whether standard times or approximate time estimates are available, and how accurate these estimates are expected to be. Certainly in the first stages, specification of employment and equipment centers should not be too detailed. In the typical plant-warehouse system, usually from 6 to 15 stages would be an adequate number to start with. Of course, operations or inventory points which are geographically separated but which do fundamentally the same job, such as branch warehouses or parallel branch plants, can be treated as a single type of stage in the process.

The second important piece of information in describing the process is a description of the major classes of products made and the operations through which they pass. The direction of flow from one operation or operating pool to another must be identified. The characteristics of flow are also important— whether, for example, it is continuous, batch by batch, or continuous with variations in the type of product.

In most job-order operations, material moves from operation to operation in a batch. Many chemical processes exhibit this type of flow. Sometimes the flow of material is continuous, but the particular item moved changes from time to time. For example, a petroleum pipeline may be operating night and day pumping first one product for several hours and then another into separate storage facilities at the end. The flow off an automatic packaging line may be essentially continuous, although the line will be devoted first to one type of product or package size and then another.

In some operations, the flow of an individual item is essentially continuous. For example, in the textile industry a particular grade of yarn may flow from the spinning frames in frequent small batches. The output of a product assembly line may be a heterogeneous stream of items distinguished by color or other special features, so that the output of any particular style or color may be essentially continuous. The nature of the flow into or out of an operation has an important effect on the functions that inventories before and after the operation serve, and therefore on the size of the inventories required. Finally, an estimate of the characteristic range of processing times through a particular operation or operating center is an important type of data needed.

The characteristics of existing inventories in the system are valuable pieces of intelligence. The analysis team should seek answers to questions such as the following: What inventories are now maintained, and what functions can they be said to serve? Do they exist because of differences in the size of batch processed, because of uncertainty in the rate of usage or demand for the item, to absorb seasonal fluctuations in usage, to act as a buffer so that one operation can be loaded to some degree independently of another or, as is usual, because of some combination of these needs? Where are the inventories located, between which operations? Where established stocks are maintained, as distinguished from floor stocks of partially processed job lots, how many separate stock units are maintained, i.e., how many distinguishable items are carried? How much stock is carried, and what does this represent relative to the usage rate and the output rate of the supplying operation? What restrictions on inventory size exist in the form, for example, of floor space, shelf space, tank capacity, and the like?

EXISTING PLANNING AND CONTROL SYSTEM

One of the first things the analysis team will want to do is to gain an understanding of how the existing production planning and control procedures work. This covers the full scope of planning and control activities from forecasting customer demand through issuing purchase orders for raw material. In many companies this is not at all an easy job to do, since the planning functions may be only partially identified in formal terms.

Frequently, too, one finds inconsistencies between stated methods and practices or between one person's understanding and another's. It is important, therefore, to identify just who does what, and in what detail, and to learn how frequently the various planning and control steps are taken, what information is used, and who is told about the decision. Assembling the actual documents and forms used and following them through from one person to another is one way of getting a picture of how the system is supposed to work compared with how it actually works.

One of the most difficult aspects of an existing system to work out, but one of the most important, is a definition of the basis for action at each stage in the existing system, particularly one which distinguishes the actual basis for decision or action used from either the one originally intended or one which may sound logical. For example, one of the authors was once told by the manager of a stockroom that all items were purchased in carefully computed economical quantities based on price discounts and estimated purchasing cost, and that whenever the inventory on hand reached the reorder point, the average usage since the last order was computed as a basis for estimating the new reorder quantity. As a matter of fact, it was found that whenever the inventory of an item reached the reorder point, the stock clerk routinely ordered the same amount as the previous order, and the chief clerk routinely cut the size of every order, whenever necessary, so that its value was below the level requiring review by the purchasing committee.

When the chief clerk was asked why he did this, he pointed out that it took so long to get an order through the purchasing committee that this effectively doubled the lead time on the order and made his planning rather difficult. He felt that his system was reasonable, even though it meant buying many fast-moving items frequently in small quantities and at less favorable prices.

Digging out the details of an existing production-control system usually takes a great deal of patience and attention to detail in order to isolate discrepancies and to distinguish fact from fancy. In approaching this task, the analysis team should recognize that this is an important job that needs to be done well, but that it is not done directly to criticize the existing system or any person having a part in it. The team must understand the existing production-control system as an information system to know where it may impede the flow of material, and to understand the timing and delays in transmitting information, as a basis for understanding why the inventories that exist are there.

VISUAL DESCRIPTIVE TECHNIQUES

The important point of the work described above is to obtain a clear picture of the flow of material through the plant, of the information needed to keep it moving, and of how this information is presently organized, as well as how it might be organized. Sometimes graphical techniques are useful in recording the information obtained. A number of different techniques might be employed, one of which is outlined below.

Figure 11.1 outlines the operations, inventory or stock points, and the type of product flow for a manufacturer of household chemicals. As indicated, the flow lines show the type of flow, in this case whether the flow is of a batch type or a continuous-batch flow. The operation is fundamentally fairly simple. The raw materials are purchased and stored in tanks and dry warehouse space. These are drawn upon to mix and blend various formulas for products which the company markets. The materials arrive in shipments of a tank car or carload each, and the individual materials required in a particular formula are drawn on in sufficient quantity to make a full batch at one time. The blended batch is then fed to blended-stock storage points behind each of three packing lines. These storage points are for short-term storage only, to hold the batch produced at one point in time by the mixing and blending operation while it is being drawn down slowly in packaging. There are three packaging lines, depending upon the container size used. Since each blended-stock point contains only one stock at a time, the flow from the blended-stock point to packaging operation is shown as continuous.

From packaging, the flow is continuous into finished stocks, except for the fact that the particular product and package size may change from time to time. Packing materials are brought in in full shipments and stored in the warehouse. From there they are fed to the packaging lines in batches as required. Finished stocks are shipped to each of several branch warehouses in carload quantities, and from the branch warehouse shipments are made to customers on order.

Figure 11.2 shows the information flow of the existing production-control system superimposed on the operation and material flows. Customer orders are received at the branch warehouse for shipment. The branch warehouse orders replenishment shipments from the factory finished-stock control unit under a reorder point system. The branch warehouse also reports shipments monthly to the sales stock control unit in the home office. Based on these reports and the existing quarterly forecast, a program of production requirements by item is drawn up for the coming month. This is sent to the plant, which works out a detailed production schedule by item covering the forthcoming month. The production schedule is given to the packing-line foreman, who in turn places orders for blended stock with the mix-and-blend operation. The mix-and-blend foreman, in turn, requisitions authorized raw materials from raw stocks.

A monthly report is prepared at the factory showing raw and packaging materials on hand together with usage and receipts during the preceding

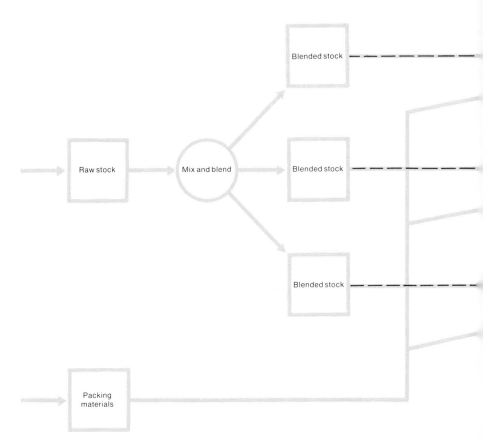

FIGURE 11.1 Material flow, household-chemicals manufacturer

months, and this is sent to the purchasing department. The purchasing department uses this together with the quarterly product sales forecast to place purchase orders. The purchasing department also receives reports of material stock-outs as they occur, as a basis for taking expediting action or placing additional orders.

Figure 11.2 is illustrative of a recording technique only; it is not necessarily intended to illustrate a good system. In fact, cursory inspection of Figure 11.2 will indicate that the system illustrated probably could be readily improved—for example, by using the reported production requirements for the coming month to schedule employment only, basing item schedules on short-term, e.g., day-to-day, reports of finished-stock shipments from the factory warehouse.

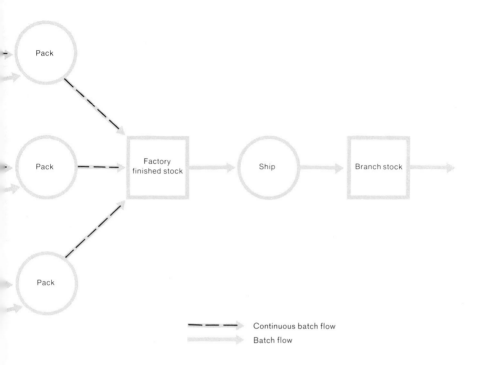

Figure 11.3 illustrates the use of the same charting technique with a somewhat more complex manufacturing operation. This process produces industrial tools of which about two-thirds are stock items and one-third is special items ordered by customers. Special items are either designed from the start or are modifications of stock items.

Raw stock flows into two points in batch shipments. Some of the stock is for blade manufacture. Blade stock is drawn down in batches to pass through the cut and heat-treating operations to go into finished-blade stock. From there individual types of finished-blade stock are sent in batches to the final-assembly operation, where the batch is held in floor stock awaiting assembly into finished tools.

Other raw stock and purchased components for chassis and motor manu-

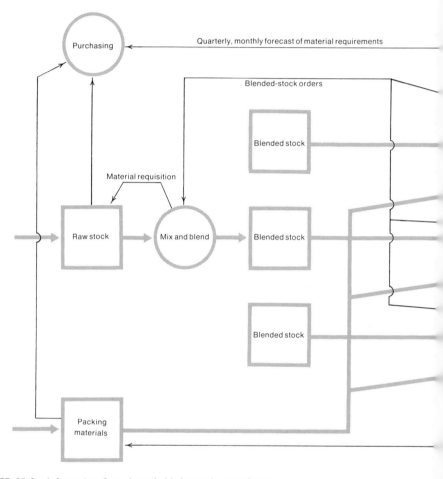

FIGURE 11.2   Information flow, household-chemicals manufacturer

facture are stocked until requisitioned in batches for manufacture of parts. Parts for frame assembly are manufactured on job order and move directly to a floor stock in the frame assembly operation to await processing. The frame assemblies in turn move under the job order to floor stock in final assembly.

Other parts, as completed, are put into a parts stock. This is drawn upon as required by three subassembly units, which are bench-assembly operations producing batches of each of the various types of subassembly stock. As each

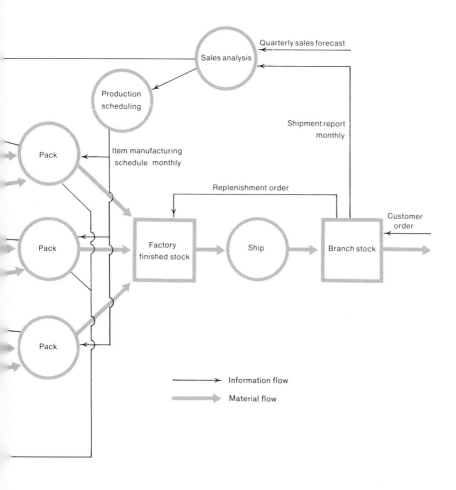

batch is completed, it is moved to a subassembly stock point, from which batches of subassemblies are moved as required to the final-assembly operation. Other parts move directly from parts stock to final-assembly floor stocks, where they are drawn upon in final-assembly operation. Completed tools move to a stock point awaiting test, and after being tested in batches, move either to finished stock, in the case of stock items, or are shipped to customers, in the case of specials.

Figure 11.4 shows the existing production-control system superimposed

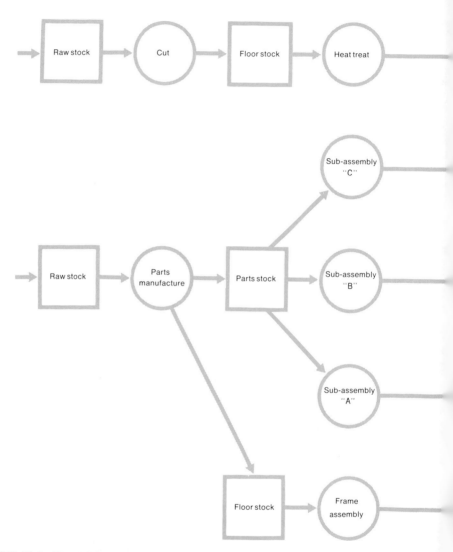

FIGURE 11.3 Material flow, industrial-equipment manufacturer

on the manufacturing flow. Customer orders for stock items are sent directly to the finished-stock room, from which the item is shipped. Customer orders for special items and replenishment orders for stock items, based on a stock reorder point—economical order quantity system, are both sent to the produc-

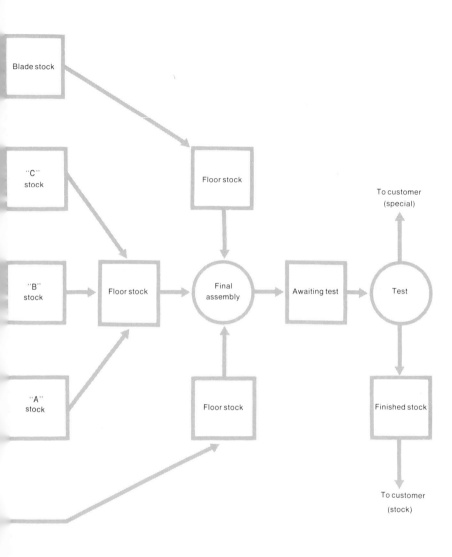

tion-engineering unit, where the necessary manufacturing order is prepared. The manufacturing order goes to the production-control unit which is responsible for loading equipment and assigning an estimated completion date to each operation. A copy of the manufacturing order in the form of a job

324

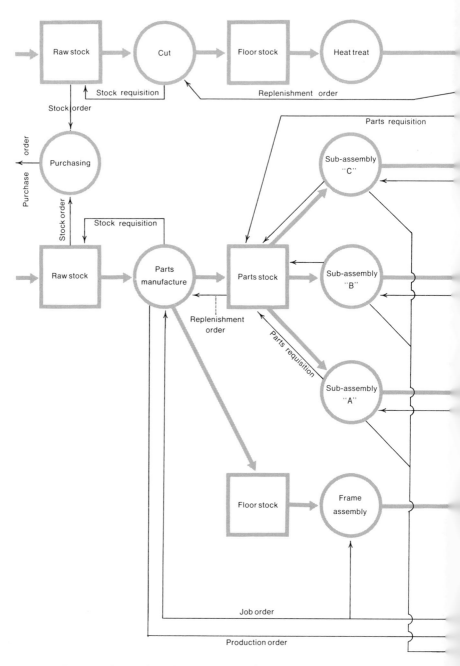

FIGURE 11.4 **Information flow, industrial-equipment manufacturer**

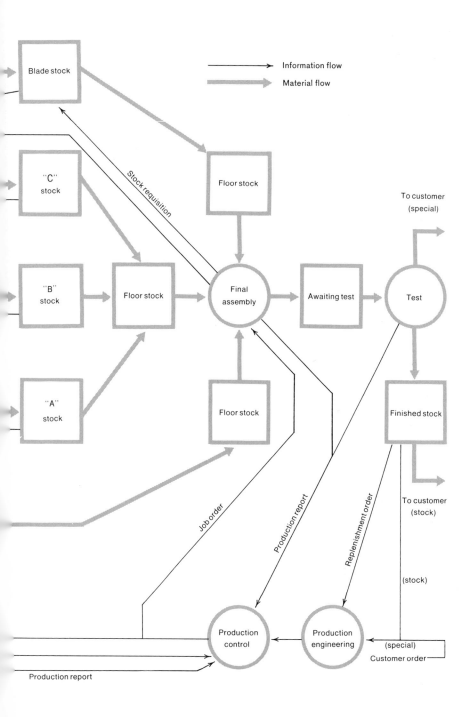

ticket is sent to each of the foremen in charge of final assembly, frame assembly, and parts manufacture.

The foremen in charge of final assembly and parts manufacture also receive material-requisition tickets for requisitioning raw-stock parts or components. Component and parts stocks are controlled on a reorder-point system with replenishment orders sent to the supplying operation via the production-control unit, which prepares the necessary job ticket and material requisitions. Raw stocks likewise are controlled on the basis of reorder points, with raw-stock reorders being sent to the purchasing department, which places the necessary purchase orders.

Once again, no attempt is made to justify the system indicated in Figure 11.4 as a good system in any sense for the operations shown. This is a schematic picture in outline form of the system as it existed. A number of difficulties might be found with it. For example, no demand forecasts are made, except in the sense that reorder points are established on various inventory items. Parts and subassembly operations are controlled against replenishment orders from inventory points, and no attempt is made to regulate these operations either on the basis of forecast demand or on the basis of actual customer demand. This, in fact, resulted in the build-up of sizable inventories with long order lead times from parts manufacture through test, as orders were allowed to build up at each stage to take up short-term fluctuations in demand on the various operating units.

FEATURES OF PRODUCTS AND PRODUCT DEMAND

A detailed study of a sample of products and product orders is useful after a general description of the production and distribution system has been obtained. Considerable detail is needed in making such a study, detail which is often not available. Frequently the necessary data, e.g., demand data, must be obtained by sampling or by inference from existing summary information. Where the product line is large, it is generally not possible to make anything like a complete study of the product line. A selection of items must be used. As far as possible, this should contain examples of different types of products flowing over different paths in the system. It should contain as well examples of products in high and low demand, together with a selection of special orders, if these are important, and, where seasonal variations in production are important, examples of seasonal products should also be included.

Probably the most important single type of information about sample products is data in as much detail as possible indicating characteristics of customer-demand variations. If order-by-order data showing the date of receipt and date of required shipment are available, so much the better.

Demand day by day or week by week is also useful. Often this information is not recorded in any accessible form, since the only reports reflecting demand may be sales or shipment information consolidated, for example, weekly or monthly. It should be emphasized, however, that data directly showing the characteristics of demand as received from customers is crucial. It is needed particularly to get quantitative estimates of the fluctuation characteristics in demand and the allowable delay in shipment of orders. Sometimes this information can be obtained on a sampling basis—e.g., order by order for a week, and perhaps week by week for a year—from stock records, inventory records, and the like.

A record of inventory balances for the sample of products is also useful, showing when and in what lots inventories were replenished, both for the end products themselves and for the parts from which they were made. Where possible, it is worth while to trace individual production orders for stock replenishment through the manufacturing system to find out, for example, what the lead time in replenishment was, whether the replenishment times are consistent or show substantial variations; and if there are substantial delays, to determine the causes for them to the extent possible. These data will provide further information on the question of the consistency of replenishment decisions with the control system presumed to exist.

VERIFICATION—THE EXPLANATION OF CURRENT INVENTORIES

The analysis team has available one important test of its understanding of the flow of product through the system, the types of planning and control decisions currently being made, and the basis used for these decisions. This is the question whether current inventories and lead times can be explained on the basis of the knowledge of the control system and the process which has been developed.

The analysis team may not necessarily think the existing system is the best possible, but they can view the combination of the present control system plus the manufacturing process as one mechanism for accomplishing a job. The analysis techniques which can be used to design an improved system and predict how it will operate should apply equally well to a description of the existing system. The team's ability to explain the characteristics of the existing system is a test of its understanding of the system or of the need to dig in further to find out how the planning and control decisions are actually made.

Until the team does understand the existing system, it is not in a good position to suggest modifications, since lack of understanding of the existing system and of its impact on operations may imply either that the team has not spotted certain essential characteristics of the operations or that there are decisions being made in some hidden way which they have not yet ferreted out. These decisions may continue to be made under a new system in a way which might wreck its effectiveness.

POLICY DECISIONS NEEDED

When the analysis team has developed an understanding of the flow of material through the plants and some quantitative estimates of the statistical characteristics of product demand, it is prepared to outline in a preliminary way the types of control decisions that are needed to keep the flow of products moving smoothly. Figure 1.1 (page 12) sketches out in a broad way the areas where planning and decisions are needed, but of course these must be detailed for the particular company.

For example, what policy decisions must be made? What tentative estimate is available for the value of capital or the return to be charged against inventory investment? How can service requirements be characterized, and what tentative estimates of requirements can be obtained? Are there any overriding policies governing employment stability? Generally the analysis team can get a preliminary statement of policies and policy costs of this type through discussions with the review committee. On the other hand, these must be recognized as tentative and subject to possible modification as the implications of the tentative choices are worked out. Furthermore, it may be expected that as conditions change in the future these policies and costs might appropriately be modified. The team must sketch out, therefore, the basis for testing the implications of these costs and the types of analyses which will have to be made periodically to give operating management a picture of the implications of alternative choices.

A review of the inventory functions in the system provides a good lead to the types of planning and control procedures which will be needed for routine operation. For example, if seasonal inventories are built up, or if products show strong seasonal tendencies, then a basis for laying out an operating plan in the face of seasonal fluctuations is required. Warehouse stocks at various levels in the system must be replenished. A number of types of replenishment schemes, such as those discussed in Chapters 6 and 8, might be employed.

As a first step, the points where replenishment rules are required must be identified. Where replenishment methods of a routine character are used, methods for reviewing and deciding when to adjust established inventory levels, reorder quantities, and the like will be needed. Where employment levels must be planned in advance, the basis for deciding what level of operation to plan is needed, and this decision must be made with respect to each employment pool which has been identified as important. Replenishment and adjustment decisions depend on the lead times between making a decision and having it become effective. These in turn depend on the processing time of the operation in question, the minimum advance notice required, and the delays in compiling, processing, and transmitting the information on which the decision is to be based.

Decisions concerning the particular item to make or the particular machine to use on a given order are important, and the nature of these decisions must be identified. Here again, it is essential to identify the minimum advance notice on such decisions that is required, and it is particularly important to separate decisions of this sort from questions concerning having the appropriate machine capacity available for demand. For example, decisions concerning the level of operation of an assembly line may be made from week to week or from month to month, while it may be possible to decide which items to send over the line as frequently as from day to day.

REQUIRED FORECASTS

As the nature of the types of decisions which must be made is spelled out and the lead time imposed by, for example, transit times, advance notice required to employees, processing time, or time to procure materials is determined, the types of forecasts required to operate the system will become evident. The analysis team will then be in a position to answer the questions concerning forecasts raised in Chapter 5, including a specification of the quantities which must be forecast—e.g., demand for operating times at the several operations or employment pools, demand for raw materials, demand for finished products at branch locations—and a measure of the span over which the forecasts must be made in view of the minimum lead times which exist. At this point the analysis team should become thoroughly familiar with the extent to which formal forecasts are currently being made, by whom they are made, what is forecast, and the span forecast.

At least two approaches to analyzing forecasts are fruitful. One approach is to measure past forecasts against actual demand in order to estimate the reliability of forecasts employing existing procedures. Where existing forecasts stop at end-product demand, the team can examine statistical methods for exploding product forecasts into forecasts of raw-material requirements and operating-level requirements.

Another approach is to use actual-demand figures to test various types of statistical or extrapolation forecasting methods. These figures may be particularly useful for short-term forecasts for stock-replenishment or short-term adjustments in operating levels. The fluctuation characteristics of product demand and the results of trial approaches to statistical forecasting will give an estimate of the expected reliability of forecasts of this type.

The immediate purpose of forecast studies at this stage is to obtain a "feel" for the reliability which can be expected in forecasts related to the span of time over which the forecast is made and the forecasting approach taken. This information is important in evaluating the timing of demand reports and the value of shortening the delay in transmitting actual-demand information to the control points where operating-level and inventory-replenishment decisions must be made. A secondary purpose, of course, is to initiate thinking about how forecasts should ultimately be made, i.e., by what method, by whom, and in what detail.

An understanding of the existing process and control system, the types of decisions that are required, and the types of forecasts needed puts the analysis team in a position to make a preliminary estimate of the importance of the various decisions in the system. Some estimate of the relative importance of these decisions is needed to guide the team in placing emphasis on the development of detailed or more sophisticated schemes for planning or control where these are important.

COSTS

So far, little has been said about costs. However, the investigation of the manufacturing process will give some guide to the relative importance of the various types of cost which may arise. In taking a first rough cut at approaches to setting up the various decision rules that are needed, approximate cost estimates are usually quite sufficient. They may be as crude as order-of-magnitude guesses or gross-range estimates.

In one case, for example, the process analysis showed that manufacturing operations could be adjusted quite flexibly to meet seasonal fluctuations in total demand. Approximate estimates of added costs of overtime operation and of inventory carrying costs indicated that the plan of operation for meeting seasonal demand could have a substantial influence on cost. It appeared quite worth while, therefore, to work out careful methods for balancing plant operation against inventory costs for setting up a preliminary operating plan.

On the other hand, in another case a preliminary analysis of a similar sort was made using techniques of the type described in Chapter 7, together with ranges of rough cost estimates. This analysis indicated that under a variety of cost assumptions operating and investment costs would not be greatly influenced one way or the other as between operating on a uniform-production plan with inventories taking up the full seasonal variation in demand, or operating under a plan designed to achieve a careful balance between inventory and operating costs. Since there were intangible advantages to the uniform type of plan, it was agreed that preliminary plans would be worked out under the assumption that uniform operation was most desirable. No further attempt was made to develop a more sophisticated seasonal-planning technique. This, by the way, eliminated the need to measure more accurately some of the costs, such as the cost of changing operating levels, which would have been required in a more sophisticated approach.

The importance of other types of decisions can be examined in a preliminary way. For example, in some circumstances the analysis team has found that the choice of run length or batch size has little effect on total cost as long as the batch size is within a broad range. The important thing to concentrate on in such a case may be handling demand fluctuations and making use of flexibility of run length to minimize safety stocks. In other cases, run length may have a very important influence on total cost because of the influence of heavy setup or training costs or productive-time losses while equipment is being adjusted. The team can also use demand characteristics to examine alternative types of replenishment rules.

Preliminary analyses of this sort can often be made using mathematical and statistical techniques directly, in effect to compute the operating characteristics of alternative approaches. On the other hand, demand characteristics and interrelationships among operating stages may make a purely analytical approach both difficult and unreliable. In this case it is often useful, in making a preliminary analysis, to set up a hypothetical manufacturing and control system on paper.[2] Samples can be drawn from a selection of actual or hypothetical customer orders to represent actual customer demand. These orders can be filled on paper, inventory balances can be maintained, operating adjustments may be made, and replenishment orders may be placed, under the rules which have been sketched out in a preliminary way. A "paper" trial of this sort gives the team a way of estimating how a tentative system might be expected to operate. Repeated trials varying control decisions and parameters such as the safety-stock level, reporting frequency, response number in operating-level controls, and the like will give the team a rough estimate of the relative importance of these various elements in the system.

DEVELOPMENT OF THE PROPOSED SYSTEM

Outlining the system

When the analysis team has examined in a preliminary fashion the importance of various types of decisions on over-all inventory and operating cost, it is in a position to sketch out the form that the system might ultimately take. The first job is to obtain more precise cost estimates in areas where they appear to be important. This is a difficult task, since the costs which are needed are often not available in easily identifiable form in cost-

---

[2] See pp. 333–337.

accounting records. The team must explore a number of sources for cost information, including cost-accounting records, records of employee turnover and training allowances, industrial-engineering estimates of time required in, for example, equipment change-overs, as well as the opinions and impressions of people at lower operating levels. In this connection one can only suggest (1) that costs obtained be reviewed critically with reference to the decisions for which they are required and the principles indicated in Chapter 3, (2) that independent estimates of cost elements be checked one against another where possible, and (3) that the sensitivity of decision rules to cost elements be checked.

The next task is to lay out the decision rule for routine use in making each planning, control, or replenishment decision. The selection of the particular rule in each case follows from the results of the preliminary analysis. At this point, too, the forecasts required, the basis for obtaining them, and the expected accuracy of forecasts must be specified. More detailed calculations and further paper trials may be used to pin down questions of timing, reporting frequency, bases for run-length calculations, degree of responsiveness of production operations to inventory fluctuations, and numerical methods for making preliminary operating plans where they are needed. These elements in combination provide the basis for estimating inventory balances expected at each stock point and the size of fluctuations in operating levels which may be anticipated when the proposed system is in operation.

During the preliminary stages of thinking about the ways in which the system might operate, it is probably worth while for the analysis team not to worry too much about practical considerations and procedures which might be used. Some thought along these lines will be inevitable. However, frequently the mistake is made that thinking about procedures starts too early, before the planning group has a definite idea of what the procedures are supposed to accomplish.

However, during the final stages of putting the proposed system together, procedural questions must be considered carefully. At this point it is worth while to speculate on the design of forms for making the necessary computations and reports and for transmitting information instructions. Part of the job of balancing out the final details of the system is to weigh the frequency and complexity of reports and computations against the operating and inventory savings which may result.

Product codes

During the course of the analysis the team must become familiar with the product-code system used by the company and with the information it contains. There are two points to be kept in mind here. First, can the information contained in the product code be exploited for purposes of the production-control system? Second, are any modifications or revisions in the code possible to improve its value as a production planning and control device?

Well-designed product codes make it much easier to consolidate information concerning given products, operations, or operating centers, and to identify what a particular piece of data refers to. If the coding system is to be useful, it is important that the codes be clear, specific, and as efficient as possible. The code should be unambiguous; i.e., a given code should mean the same thing to everyone using it, and a given product or operation should be coded identically by two or more different people. Efficiency in the code means that the size of the code should be as small as possible while still conveying the desired degree of detailed information. This is particularly important where punched-card equipment is used for the clerical-processing operation, since usually some compromise has to be made between the amount of detailed information desired on a given card and card capacity. An inefficient code uses up space which might otherwise be used for operating information.

For production planning and control purposes the code showing the end use of the product or the using industry is usually of no interest, except in so far as it may specify something about the manufacturing process. The code should, however, specify those product characteristics which determine the routing for manufacturing distribution and the types of people or equipment employed in processing it. It is often possible, in addition, to specify in the product code sufficient information about the characteristics of the product, such as size or dimensions, so that manufacturing time allowances can be applied automatically. This is, of course, of real value in costing. However, from the point of view of the production planning and control system, the important uses of the code are to show what operations the product passes through, what time load on these operations the product represents, and what stock points it affects, i.e., what parts and materials are used in its manufacture.

Testing the system

Tests of a proposed system have three functions. One is to demonstrate to the satisfaction of the analysis group and the management that the proposed system will work as anticipated. Another purpose is to work out flaws or difficulties in procedures. The third purpose is to train operating people who must use the system in the procedures and what they mean.

A number of approaches to testing a new system have been used, frequently in combination. One approach is to operate the system on paper, making use of past actual forecasts and actual customer demand. Another method is to run a paper trial or "simulation" using artificially generated demand data designed to have the general statistical characteristics of actual demand. A third approach is to install the system in a part of the operations and to let it run against current information parallel with the existing system, working out what decisions would be made, what inventory balances would have been, and what operating problems would have arisen had the decisions made routinely by the system actually been made. A fourth approach is to install the system to make the actual operating decisions covering a part of the product line, or perhaps one branch plant and the warehouses and customers it serves. All of these test methods have advantages and difficulties, from technical and managerial points of view.

SIMULATION ON ACTUAL DEMAND

Running a simulation against past actual demand may be done either by hand, using punched-card equipment, or on an internally programed computer. The scheme works essentially as follows. Preliminary production plans are drawn up according to the procedures as designed, using forecasts covering some past period. If actual forecasts are not available, they may have to be constructed according to the procedures laid down on the basis of earlier information. Such "forecasts," of course, should not be based on demand information for the period covered by the simulation. Inventory balances are established at each stock point in accordance with the proposed procedures and the estimated uncertainty in demand. Then the record of actual demand for the period is obtained in as much detail as possible. This is recorded and reported according to the proposed procedures, and "inventory balances" and "production level" and "loading" decisions are made as they would have been if the system had actually been in operation. The record of inventory balances, production changes, missed shipments, and other pertinent statistics is maintained for comparison with the actual operating performance during the period under test. This gives some measure of the efficiency of the system compared with that of existing procedures.

Where there are major sources of uncertainty other than in customer demand, care must be exercised to be sure the simulation gives a fair measure of system performance. Suppose, for example, that the transit time between factory and branch warehouse is highly variable. It is not possible generally to use the actual record of branch-replenishment orders and receipts, since the new system would presumably result in a different pattern of branch-replenishment orders. One way around this difficulty is to take a sample of branch-replenishment orders and construct a frequency distribution of observed shipment times based on actual experience. Then, whenever the simulation indicates that a branch-replenishment shipment is to be made, the shipping time for the particular order can be determined by drawing a number at random from the observed shipping time distribution.

To illustrate, suppose that the observed shipping times between a branch and a warehouse varied between 10 and 20 days according to the following pattern:

Observed lead time (days)	Number of instances
11	2
12	4
13	12
14	6
15	3
16	3
17	2
18	2
19	1
20	1
	36

We might divide the sample into 6 equal parts: shipping times of 11 and 12 days (the first part), 13 days (the next two parts), 14 days (the next group), 15 and 16 days (the next group), and 17 to 20 days (the final group). Then, any time the simulation showed a necessity for making a replenishment shipment we could roll a single die and choose a shipping time from the part of the distribution corresponding to the number turned up. For example, if the face showing 1 turned up, we might continue the calculation assuming the replenishment shipment arrived at the warehouse in 11 to 12 days. If a 4 turned up, we would assume that it would arrive in 14 days. If a 6 turned up, we would choose a shipping time between 17 and 20 days. In the last case, we might roll the die again to decide just which among these to pick. For example, if a 4 turned up on the second roll, we would pick 18 days as the assumed shipping time for calculating inventories on hand and customer orders which would be filled.

Random-number tables are available which can be used for choosing sample values from an observed distribution of this sort with greater ease and precision.[3] Where the simulations are carried out using punched-card or internally programed computer facilities, this type of random selection, or "Monte Carlo" process, can be included as a part of the calculation routine.

Simulations based on actual past customer demand avoid the necessity for interfering with current operations. It is also possible to run a trial covering a substantial period in a short time. For example, a full year's detailed operation might be simulated in a few hours or days, depending on the

[3] See, for example, RAND Corporation, *A Million Random Digits with 100,000 Normal Deviates*, The Free Press of Glencoe, New York, 1955.

detail of the simulation, the complexity of the system, and the computational facilities used. Furthermore, this type of test is sometimes convincing to operating people because the basic input, customer demand, is a sample of what the existing system has actually had to cope with. The results of the system also can be compared more or less directly with actual operating results.

This approach also has its difficulties and disadvantages. For one thing, if the same pattern of customer demand is used over and over again to try out modifications of the system, there is always the danger that the system variation or parameter values chosen may appear to be best because of some peculiar quirk in the sample of demand data used. From the point of view of operating management, particularly if the comparison between the simulation and past results looks favorable, there is sometimes the lingering feeling that a bit of hindsight may have crept into details of forecasts or control decisions which may bias the result. Then the question may come up whether conditions and customer-demand characteristics may have changed since the period studied, or whether the experience of the period encompasses the types of problems which can arise. Finally, this is still only a trial on paper, and the well-tested maxim about the proof of the pudding must be recognized.

MONTE CARLO SIMULATIONS

Simulations can also be made substituting artificially generated demand data for the actual record of customer demand. "Customer demand" can be generated using the sampling, or Monte Carlo, procedure illustrated above in connection with shipping times. For example, distributions might be set up, either hypothetical or based on observations, to reflect the variation in the number of customer orders received in a day, the number and variety and quantity of items ordered, and times when shipment is required. The approach is generally more valuable as an analysis tool than as a device for demonstrating the value of a proposed system. The distributions from which customer demand is generated can be varied to test out the operation of the system under various types of hypothesized conditions. This method is sometimes better adapted to high-speed computation, and since new random samples can be drawn for each test, it avoids the danger of warping the system design to fit a peculiar pattern of demand observed at some one time. On the other hand, care must be exercised to be sure that the characteristics of the artificially generated demand have some relation to actual circumstances. For example, if actual demand shows high correlation in number of orders or volume from, say, week to week, this sort of condition, which can have an important influence on inventory balances and operating levels, should be matched as closely as possible in the artificial samples.

The results of this approach sometimes are not particularly convincing to operating managers who may be attempting to estimate the worth of the proposed system. Management people are sometimes not too much impressed by a demonstration on customer demand which has only an indirect relation to reality. Furthermore, it is not so easy to compare estimated results using the proposed system with the results achieved under the existing method. This test method does, however, give a good basis for demonstrating the effect of possible changes in system characteristics or conditions imposed by policy.

SHADOW OPERATION

Sometimes it is possible to set up the proposed system in a plant or warehouse and let it operate to maintain dummy inventory records, reports, and requisitions based on demand as it comes to the unit from day to day. This type of test, where it is feasible, is sometimes a useful way of showing the people who must know how to operate the details of the system just how it works. It is also a very effective way of locating and working out procedural difficulties or methods for handling exceptional cases that may have been overlooked. It is one of the most effective ways of showing members of the analysis team and the people concerned with day-to-day operation that the system will work (if it will) and that it will cope with the problems that bulk largest in their minds.

The difficulties with this method of test are fairly evident. In the first place, it imposes an added burden on operating people and, necessarily, some interference with the normal flow of information in the plant or warehouse. In the second place, it may take a fairly long period before enough experience can be accumulated to provide a fair test. Finally, since it is still a simulation or artificial trial, if the system is different at all from the existing system, discrepancies are bound to develop with the way particular orders will be handled, items replenished, or employees and machines scheduled. Emergencies and chance events will interfere with the operation of the actual system, and this type of condition can be matched in a shadow trial only by introducing some sort of artificial emergency from time to time to attempt to simulate actual operations.

PARTIAL INSTALLATION

The use of the proposed system to make the actual day-to-day and longer-run decisions for a while for a part of the manufacturing and distribution system is the most severe test of feasibility. If the system works, it works. Thus this is frequently the most inviting type of test from the point of view of operating management. Certain serious difficulties with this method of test must be pointed out, however. For one thing, choosing the part of the total system in which to run the test is critical. Where the processing and distribution operations can be broken up into a number of independent parts, such as independent branch plants with satellite warehouses, this may be possible. Even within a plant it may be possible to identify a portion of the manufacturing processes which is independent of other activities, i.e., does not draw on common pools of employees or requisition materials from common stock points.

Where it is not possible to isolate a part of the manufacturing operations, care must be exercised in setting up the trial to show just how conflicts between the two parallel systems will be resolved. What is to be done, for example, if an order is placed under the new system for a part which turns out not to be in stock but which conceivably would have been there had the new system been used to control it or other operations drawing upon that part?

This type of trial also takes time. Any careful evaluation of what has been achieved is difficult. One can usually say whether the system works reasonably smoothly, and sometimes qualitative information on the impact on employment stability or customer service may be obtainable. However, this type of trial is generally not a good way of finding out whether the system will achieve anticipated inventory reductions or other cost advantages, except in a very approximate way. For example, changes in conditions during the course of any test of this type tend to invalidate any careful before-and-after comparison.

In summary, paper trial or simulation based on artificial demand samples is a useful analytical device for working out efficient system characteristics. Simulation using a sample of actual past demand is often an effective way of estimating the advantages and disadvantages of a system. Shadow trial under operating conditions is a good means for working out procedural difficulties and for teaching clerical personnel how the system operates. Installation and use of the system on a part of the company's operations, though not a particularly good test of economy or of a method for choosing the right design characteristics, is the most severe test of feasibility short of full-scale use.

OPERATING THE SYSTEM

Organizational alternatives

There are probably as many points of view on how the production-control function should be organized as there are companies in the business of buying, making, and selling goods. Some companies prefer a central-staff production planning and control department; others prefer a division of the function among operating units. Some decentralized companies with diverse lines still prefer a central control function, centered in one or more general-office units; others prefer a separate unit at each autonomous location or organization. The differences in viewpoint frequently reflect differences in individual and organizational personalities as much as a dispassionate view of the production planning and control function as such. This is probably as it should be.

Since the purpose of production planning and control is to arrive at a balance of the conflicting objectives of sales, production, and financial organizations, some companies believe the best solution is to set up a separate production planning and control unit. This may be true especially where the size and complexity of operations would make joint planning through conferences and discussions unwieldy. Since this activity must arrive at a balance among sales, production, and financial activities, it cannot be responsible wholly to any one of them.

One approach is to set up a central unit which reports to a general manager with responsibility for all functions. This may be the president or executive vice-president in a company of moderate size. Where operations are decentralized among a number of operating subsidiaries or divisions, a central unit may be established at each subsidiary headquarters. In addition, production and inventory control units may be established at each plant or warehouse to exercise detailed day-to-day control. Local units operate within the framework of plans made by the central unit and under the central unit's guidance for procedure and policy and cost determination.

The range of duties of the central unit will vary widely among companies. In some companies, this unit may be responsible for compilation of demand forecasts for annual or seasonal planning and for control of current sales and shipments data. In others, these may be left to the sales department, the central planning unit being responsible for converting these into production requirements. Since the size and accuracy of the demand forecast will have a strong influence on the service which can be provided customers, it is desirable to provide a regular channel whereby the sales organization can express its estimates and service needs if it does not prepare forecasts directly.[4]

Normally, a central planning unit will be responsible for setting planned operating levels in machine centers or manufacturing departments. Steps in this task include conversion or explosion of the demand forecast into an

---

[4] Forecasts here are deemed to mean maximum-demand forecasts or forecasts of expected demand with an estimate of forecasting accuracy. See Chap. 5.

estimate of production requirements, making allowances for in-process, in-transit, and protective or fluctuation stocks, and establishment of an operating budget to allow for any desirable build-up of seasonal stocks. The central unit is also often responsible for periodic, say, monthly, adjustment of plant or department operating budgets in the light of current inventory conditions.

In some companies, the central unit may be responsible for setting detailed schedules of production by item and even for machine loading. It is generally desirable to reserve these tasks for local units which can make short-term adjustments in the light of current inventory balances and operating conditions within the framework of operating levels established centrally. A central group will normally be responsible for projecting raw-material requirements as a basis for purchasing negotiations. Control over release dates may rest with the central unit, where coordination of supply to several plants is required, or it may be left to the local units, which may be better aware of detailed item usage.

The job of a central unit, as noted above, is to gather the requirements of production, sales, and financial interests and to reconcile these requirements in the form of a production plan and inventory standards. If it is to be effective, therefore, the plans and procedures it establishes must be adhered to by operating units, and its plans, once approved, must be supported by general management.

Many companies feel that it is neither practical nor essential to establish an independent production-planning unit. These companies divide responsibility among the several interested units, relying on formal committees to arrive at joint decisions. Where properly functioning, this system has many advantages. For one thing, it leaves direct responsibility for planning steps in the hands of those most directly concerned: the sales department for forecasting, the production department or plant management for setting and adjusting operating levels, etc. Also, this system can help speed up the flow of information on demand, inventory levels, and operating plans, since one intermediate step is eliminated.

This type of organization gets into difficulty principally when lack of a separate unit is interpreted in practice as lack of specific planning responsibility. At times the responsibility for a part of the planning task may not be clearly assigned, or it may not be recognized. For example, the sales organization may forecast demand, but the production organization may "second-guess" and plan against its own forecast or its revision of the sales department's forecast. Committee discussions to arrive at planning decisions may be time-consuming and may lead to unclear action. Another difficulty is that of making detailed planning and control procedures at the warehouse or plant-department level consistent with agreed-upon policy, with respect to inventory investment or service time, for example.

These disadvantages can be overcome in the design and installation of a system if:

1. Specific and detailed responsibilities are identified and assigned.
2. Procedures for making routine decisions are laid out.
3. Measures of performance are established.

Certain general principles governing the organization of this function can be noted. An organizational form that matches these should work; one that does not is headed for friction, if not for serious confusion. Production planning and control is not the sole concern of any single activity in a company, whether finance, manufacturing, or sales. It is a coordinate function and one in which each area, and general management as well, has an important stake. This must be recognized in the specification of any organizational authority and responsibilities. The operation of the production planning and control system will have a profound effect on the ability of each part of the organization to do its job.

A second principle which has an important influence on the efficiency of the system is this: The point of making a decision should be located where it will minimize the time needed to get the necessary information and transmit the decisions. Short-term decisions concerning which items to make or ship or what to do to balance stocks should be made where information on stock conditions and operating capacity is available and where the decision can be transmitted for action quickly and surely. Some companies try to set detailed machine loads or item schedules from distant central-office points. Others find it more economical to shorten the distance information has to travel by separating this decision from planning decisions and making it where the information is near at hand.

Principles governing organization of a production planning and control system can be put in the form of a series of questions:

Are necessary decisions and analysis functions spelled out? Policy or general-management decisions must be made, generally in balance. These decisions include charges for capital, employment policies, sales-service policies and decisions concerning risks to be assumed, e.g., on seasonal or short-lived merchandise. They must often be backed up by analyses showing the effect of alternative combinations of possible decisions. Preliminary plans and budgets must be laid out and accepted. Forecasts must be made at a number of levels. Employment levels must be controlled, machines and operations must be scheduled, orders must be filled. A fundamental part of the production planning and control design job is to specify precisely what decisions are needed, when, on what basis, and using what information.

Is someone designated to make each decision? Does he know this? Does each person understand the decisions he is expected to make? Does he know what is wanted and what the implications of the decision are? Does he know how frequently or when to make them? Where the decision is of a routine nature, say, sending a replenishment shipment under a base-stock system, does he know what information to use and what the procedure is for reaching the decision? Does he know whom to tell, and by what means?

Does the person making the decision get the information he needs in time and in form to use it? There are many devices for transmitting production planning and control data, ranging from the United States mail to high-speed facsimile or wire systems. None of these devices are effective unless the information to be transmitted is specified, has a common meaning at both ends, and arrives on time.

Does each person recognize when an emergency calling for nonroutine action arises? Does each know to whom it should be referred? No system for routine control can be expected to operate without occasional emergencies. In the face of demand uncertainties, the chance of process failure, or unavailability of raw materials, a system designed to cope with any eventuality would almost surely require uneconomically large inventories and stand-by capacity. The inventory risk levels define how frequently emergencies may arise. The persons responsible for routine decisions should know how to recognize and to whom to refer the emergencies that will arise.

Authority over inventories

Frequently there is argument as to who should control inventories. For example, should it be the sales organization or other unit that draws on the stocks and wants to be sure they are there, or the operation that supplies the stock point and wants to feed it economically? There is probably no resolution to this question as stated; the difficulty is that both have a legitimate interest. It is possible, however, to restate the question slightly and reach a solution. The user has to be sure that the material he needs will be there. He has a corresponding responsibility to state what his maximum and minimum requirements will be. Once these limits are accepted as reasonable, the supplier has the responsibility of meeting demand within these limits, making whatever use he can of the flexibility the inventory provides. Thus both have a share in the responsibility for and control over a stock unit. One specifies what the maximum and minimum demands on the stock unit will be; the other has the responsibility of keeping the stock unit replenished but not overloaded as long as demand stays within the specified limits.

Control over system operation

Up to now we have used the term "control" to refer to system reactions to differences between forecast and actual demand or inventories in the system. There is a broader meaning which applies: the steps needed to make sure that decisions made are carried out and to keep the system in tune with current conditions.

One type of control needed is to see that operations are working according to plan. To allow this type of control, the information system must incorporate reports of work done, e.g., job tickets with due and completion dates, and reports of effective operating hours against budgeted hours. Lists of inventory stock-outs and overdue replenishment orders may be prepared at stock points to initiate expediting action. A number of detailed forms and procedures for preparing reports of this type are in use, and descriptions of them can be found in the current literature. In designing these procedures it is important that the pertinent information go quickly to the person in the best position to act first. This is often the foreman of an operation, for whom a status report could be drawn up daily on the floor before job or production tickets are sent in. The foreman may want a report of jobs immediately ahead showing availability of materials. The right person may be an expediter who can use judgment in getting runs shifted about to achieve best balance in the face of an emergency.

A basic form of control is control over the movement of materials into and through the manufacturing and distribution system. The procedures will indicate what should be at a given stage in the system at any time, but is it there? Where the manufacturing system is the product-flow, or assembly-line, type, this type of control can be exercised readily on the line itself. Control over movement of goods to the line and control over movement in a job-shop-type organization can be achieved as a by-product of the dispatching system.

Some companies rely primarily on the departmental foremen to compare move tickets on orders which have arrived in their department for processing against the scheduled load of orders for the day or week ahead. Where an order has not arrived, they may have responsibility either to expedite the order directly with the department holding it or to refer the order to the production-control unit for following. In other cases, a daily or weekly report of orders processed or items produced compared with the load may be used. The report may be made out in advance and issued to the foreman, and in the spaces provided he will check those items or orders that are completed and will indicate action on uncompleted orders.

A secondary level of control over item replenishment can be built into the inventory-control records. Where some type of reorder system is used, e.g., on purchased items, a new order may be placed when the stock on hand and on order falls below the reorder point. The reorder point is normally set high enough, as discussed in Chapter 6, to allow for fluctuations in usage or deliveries. A second review point may also be set. When inventory on hand falls below this level, the item is flagged for expediting attention. This will allow for special action to prevent a shortage.

Reports of production or payroll hours worked or paid and hours "earned" in terms of good output versus budgeted level provide a control over conformance to the budget. The same type of control, actual versus budget, can be established over inventory levels. Each of the types of inventory and production control procedures discussed in preceding chapters provides an explicit standard or expected inventory operating level. These can be used as standards in evaluating the degree to which operations are being conducted according to system.

As a general principle, upper-management control devices should be drawn from the controls and reports used at lower levels. A favorite control device of upper management in many companies is the *inventory-turnover* ratio, the ratio of annual sales or cost of sales to average inventory. These ratios are sometimes deemed useful in giving management a quick appraisal of the inventory condition. The difficulty arises in deciding what a "good" turnover ratio is.

Ratios of this type do not give any direct insight into current performance versus plan. They may be useful in indicating trends, but here again they are valid only in comparison with a normal or expected ratio computed from plan.

Too often inventory ratios are substituted for a production and inventory plan. But to announce the policy that "inventories should turn six times annually" is hardly an effective way of indicating what general management expects in the way of operating performance. General management is interested in (1) a basis for arriving at a set of self-consistent financial and operating policies, (2) an operating plan and control system that is consistent with these policies, and (3) measures to show where and why operations are departing from plan.

Another type of control is needed to see that procedures are being followed and that up-to-date figures, e.g., for policy costs and restrictions, are being used. This is in part control over the training of employees operating the system and in part control over the procedures themselves. One sometimes finds that employees who are inadequately trained in how and why the system is set up will introduce "common-sense" or "short-cut" methods which frustrate the efficiency of the system. The chief clerk, mentioned earlier, who cut replenishment orders to avoid the purchasing committee is a case in point. Despite his intentions, which happened to have some merit, his "solution" was costing the company several times his salary.

Sometimes all possible care in preliminary procedures design will miss some apparently trivial point which can lead to trouble. A branch warehouse replenishment system using base-stock principles had apparently been carefully designed and had been tested in advance. In laying out procedures, however, the team had overlooked the problem of reported demand totaling to something other than full cartons. A clerk handling one set of branches decided to round off replenishment shipments to the next *lowest* full carton; this resulted effectively in a steady and unwanted reduction in the base-stock levels of the branches he handled. Another clerk decided to round off shipments to the next *highest* full carton; this led effectively to a steady and equally undesirable growth in the base-stock levels in his branches. A routine review of procedures brought this problem to light, and a procedure for carrying over partial carton lots to the next period was set up.

Control over procedures and their use is both a function of direct supervision and a continuing job for those members of the analysis team who have a hand in administration of the system.

A third type of control is a more general or analytical sort. Continuing records of forecasts compared with actual demand should be maintained. These should be examined from time to time to see that forecasts remain within the expected limits of accuracy and to determine whether more accurate forecasts are possible where accuracy is especially critical. Methods for setting safety-stock or base-stock levels or reorder points must be reviewed from time to time to see that they match current demand characteristics. Introduction of new products, processes, or facilities may require modification of existing procedures or development of new planning and control devices. Finally, performance in terms of inventory balances and operating levels versus plan or expected must be measured for general-management control.

Procedures and data-handling methods

Procedures for data handling and reporting should be set up with certain objectives firmly in mind. The most important of these are: (1) that the procedures should reflect precisely what the system design calls for; (2) that they should be easily adapted to changes or adjustment of policy, e.g., required customer-service levels, required investment earnings, or employment guarantees; (3) that they should be designed to flag exceptions or emergencies for attention; (4) that they should be easy to use, to minimize errors; (5) that they should be economical; (6) that they should be well adapted to auditing requirements; and (7) that information for statistical analysis should be accessible.

The effective design of procedures is extremely important, but a great deal might be said about techniques and types of aids and equipment available, most of which is outside the scope of this book. Available systems range from those designed around manual operation, using multiple-copy forms, high-speed filing devices, rapid duplicating methods and edge-punched cards, through punched-card systems, to systems employing high-speed internally programed computers. Selected references which discuss the characteristics and use of various types of equipment or procedures are given at the end of this chapter. However, when it comes to the design of procedures for a production planning and control system of real complexity, the help of an experienced, skilled procedures man is invaluable.

The manufacturers who supply various types of clerical equipment are characteristically quite willing to help adapt their products to a potential customer's needs. However, as a general rule they are not in a position to decide how the equipment should be used. This is fundamentally the job of the company—logical design of a system to meet the company's needs. When this is done, or well along, equipment suppliers can give valuable help in showing how their particular products can be used to implement the system.

More and more companies are turning to internally programed computers to handle information used in their production planning and control systems. This equipment is very powerful indeed. The tape or internal-storage capacity makes it possible to bring together in one or a very few files all the information—sales, shipments, forecasts, scheduled and completed production, costs—relating to a particular item. The computing capacity and opportunity for integrated files greatly assist in making product explosions to get requirements for operating times, parts or process items, and raw materials. More sophisticated decision rules, say, taking acount of joint product availability, keeping detailed records of progress on an order, or taking account of advance commitments and scheduled production in filling orders, are possible, whereas in a manual or punched-card system these might bog down because of the sheer volume of data storage and manipulation required. Programing flexibility makes it possible to include routine operating rules as a part of the regular computer operation in monitoring shipments, inventories, and production balances. Reports can be issued as required on an exception basis.

Some companies faced with production-control problems are looking to computers as the solution. Many of these companies are going to be disappointed. An internally programed computer is generally not an effective device for operating existing procedures. Clerical savings from the introduction of computers are usually modest, hardly worth the expense and effort of installing the equipment. Existing procedures have grown up about existing equipment and methods. They are not well adapted to take advantage of the flexibility which internally programed equipment can give. This type of equipment can handle routine decisions as part of its normal program, but it will only make the decisions and follow the decision rules that have been precisely and completely specified. A computer system will accept data in great bulk, but it will print out only what it is told to print.

The day may well come when companies will use flexible, high-speed computer systems widely to handle the routine clerical data and make the bulk of routine decisions in production planning and inventory control. The first companies to benefit will be those that have analyzed their production and distribution systems, those that have thought through the functions that inventories and the planning and control systems serve, and that have specified how the decisions are to be made to govern day-to-day operations in accordance with company objectives.

APPENDIX

DERIVATION OF ECONOMICAL ORDER- QUANTITY FORMULAS

INTRODUCTION

The circumstances surrounding the need to determine economical order quantities are described in Chapter 4, together with some convenient computing aids. This Appendix outlines the mathematical derivation of some of the more common order-quantity formulas.

The derivations described here are not novel in principle or, in most cases, in detail. A number of authors have derived similar formulas in a wide variety of cases.

THE BASIC CASE

Assume:

1. Sales or usage is constant, at a rate d per year.
2. The cost of placing an order (clerical, shipping, or setup cost) is a constant a. The unit cost of an item is a constant b.
3. The annual cost of carrying an item in stock one year is c.
4. An order is placed for the items to be available at the time inventory on hand reaches zero.

If a quantity q is obtained on each order, d/q orders per year must be placed. The average stock on hand will be one-half the order quantity $q/2$. The total annual cost of placing orders, purchasing materials, and holding inventory is given by

$$C = \frac{ad}{q} + bd + \frac{cq}{2}$$

Differentiating with respect to q gives

$$\frac{dC}{dq} = -\frac{ad}{q^2} + \frac{c}{2}$$

Setting dC/dq equal to zero gives

$$q = \sqrt{\frac{2ad}{c}} \tag{A.1}$$

the size of reorder for minimum total cost. (This is a minimum value, since $d^2C/dq^2 = 2ad/q^3$ is positive when $q = \sqrt{2ad/c}$.)

The optimum number of orders placed per year is given by

$$n = \frac{d}{q}$$

$$= \sqrt{\frac{dc}{2a}}$$

and the total cost under the optimum policy would be

$$C = a\sqrt{\frac{dc}{2a}} + bd + \frac{c}{2}\sqrt{\frac{2ad}{c}}$$

$$= bd + \sqrt{2adc}$$

The second term is, then, the total ordering and inventory cost per year.

Note that the average inventory carried $q/2$ is expressible as $\sqrt{ad/2c}$, i.e., as $w\sqrt{d}$. The reasoning given above is one basis for the frequently quoted "principle" that inventories should vary directly with the square root of sales.

SOME RELATED CASES

Refinement for Inventory Cost. Where the inventory cost per unit per unit time is primarily a charge for capital, the cost may be written as:

$$C = n(a + bq) + \frac{q}{2}\left[c' + \frac{i}{q}(a + bq)\right]$$

where $\qquad$ $c' =$ inventory unit cost other than capital

$i =$ imputed interest charge for capital in inventory

$(a + bq)/q =$ unit product cost, i.e., the unit value of inventory

Then the total cost C may be written as:

$$C = \frac{ad}{q} + bd + \frac{ia}{2} + \frac{(c + ib)}{2} q$$

and the minimum-cost order quantity is

$$q = \sqrt{\frac{2ad}{c' + ib}} \qquad (A.2)$$

Price Breaks. Frequently purchase quantities must be chosen not only with ordering and storage costs but also with vendors' discount schedules considered. In effect, this may require calculation of total annual cost at several price breaks. Suppose, for example, that we have a discount schedule as follows:

Quantity purchased	Unit price
$0 \le q < Q^1$	c^0
$Q^1 \le q < Q^2$	c^1
$\cdots\cdots\cdots$	$\cdots\cdots$
$Q^i \le q < Q^{i+1}$	$c^i \qquad c^i > c^{i+1}$
$\cdots\cdots\cdots$	

The optimum purchase quantity can be chosen as follows: First compute the optimum order quantity q^i for each c^i, using the formula given by Eq. (A.2) above. Since the optimum price bracket will have the order quantity $q^i < Q^{i+1}$ (otherwise lower total cost could be obtained by buying the quantity q^i at a lower unit price, e.g., c^{i+1}), the optimum can be found as follows:

1. Choose the highest i for which $Q^i \le q^i < Q^{i+1}$ (there will always be at least one such q^i); call this q^k.
2. Then test other discount levels c^j, $j > k$ by computing $C(j)$

$$C(j) = c^j d + \frac{ic^j Q^j}{2} + \frac{d}{Q^j} a$$

and comparing with

$$C(k) = c^k d + \frac{ic^k q^k}{2} \frac{da}{q^k}$$

The optimum discount level j will be given by the j for which $C(k) - C(j)$ is maximum.

Production Lead Time. Where material is ordered from a production line, the entire order quantity q may not go into inventory immediately but over a period of possibly several days or weeks. In this case the inventory will not increase by the full amount of the order or run quantity at one time. It will increase slowly over the course of the run, while production going into inventory exceeds usage going out. It will reach a maximum at the end of the run. If the length of the run extends over a substantial period, for example, if the item is in production half the time, more or less, this can have a substantial effect on the maximum inventory build-up and on the size of the economical run or order quantity. This can be seen as follows:

Let d be the sales rate per day and p ($>d$) the production rate per day when the item is being produced. The inventory balances versus time will be as shown in Figure A.1. During the production period (of length t), the inventory is increasing at a rate $p - d$. The inventory balance will be a maximum after t days, reaching a peak value of $(p - d)t$. The average inventory will be $(p - d)t/2$. Since $pt = q$,

$$(p - d)t/2 = \frac{q(p - d)}{2p}$$

$$= \frac{q}{2}\left(1 - \frac{d}{p}\right)$$

Under the assumptions noted in the first case, the total cost will be given by

$$C = \frac{ad}{q} + bd + \frac{cq}{2}\left(1 - \frac{d}{p}\right)$$

and the minimum-cost reorder quantity is given by

$$q = \sqrt{\frac{2ad}{c(1 - d/p)}} \qquad\qquad (A.3)$$

Where d and p are of the same order of magnitude, Eq. (A.3) can differ appreciably from Eq. (A.1).

In many circumstances, of course, the total order quantity is produced in a relatively very short time, compared with the time between runs. In such a case, the difference between (A.1) and (A.3) is negligible (since d/p is close to zero).

FIGURE A.1 Inventory balances versus time

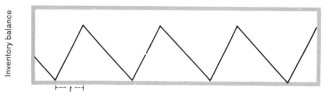

Time

Handling Cost. In some cases, the handling cost incurred may depend on the size of the inventory. For example, inventories over a fixed maximum may have to be stored in a nearby warehouse at a substantial cost per case of handling and trucking material stored outside, or production in excess of immediate needs of a given product may be specially packed and stored at a substantial extra-handling cost. If h is the unit cost of extra handling and I' is the critical point above which extra-handling cost is incurred, the total cost is given by

$$C = \frac{ad}{q} + bd + \frac{cq}{2}\left(1 - \frac{d}{p}\right) + \frac{dh}{q}(q - I') \qquad q \geq I' \tag{A.4}$$

$$= \frac{ad}{q} + bd + \frac{cq}{2}\left(1 - \frac{d}{p}\right) \qquad q < I' \tag{A.5}$$

From (A.4), the minimum-cost value of q is

$$Q' = \sqrt{\frac{2d(a - hI')}{c(1 - d/p)}} \tag{A.6}$$

and from (A.5),

$$Q'' = \sqrt{\frac{2ad}{c(1 - d/p)}} \tag{A.7}$$

Since $hI' \geq 0$, $Q'' \geq Q'$. If both Q' and Q'' are equal to or less than I', Q'' is the minimum-cost value; if both are equal to or greater than I', Q' is the minimum-cost value. If $Q' < I'$, $Q'' > I'$, then I' is the minimum-cost value.

These conditions can be used to determine when the usage rate justifies incurring the extra-handling cost. The amount

$$Q'' = \sqrt{\frac{2ad}{c(1 - d/p)}}$$

is to be made if Q'' is equal to or less than I'. This means that

$$\sqrt{\frac{2ad}{c(1 - d/p)}} \leq I'$$

and thus

$$d \leq \frac{c(I')^2 p}{2ap + c(I')^2}$$

If the amount Q' is to be made, then Q' is equal to or greater than I'; that is,

$$\sqrt{\frac{2d(a - hI')}{c(1 - d/p)}} \geq I'$$

In this case, then,

$$d \geq \frac{c(I')^2 p}{2p(a - hI') + c(I')^2}$$

Then the rule derived from Eqs. (A.6) and (A.7) can be summarized as:

When	Make
1. Usage, $d, \leq \dfrac{c(I')^2 p}{2ap + c(I')^2}$	$\sqrt{\dfrac{2ad}{c(1 - d/p)}}$
2. $\dfrac{c(I')^2 p}{2ap + c(I')^2} \leq d \leq \dfrac{c(I')^2 p}{2p(a - hI') + c(I')^2}$	I'
3. $d \geq \dfrac{c(I')^2 p}{2p(a - hI') + c(I')^2}$	$\sqrt{\dfrac{2d(a - hI')}{c(1 - d/p)}}$

THE MULTIPRODUCT CASE

Where a number of products are to be made in sequence on a single unit of equipment, the single-product model for lot-size determination (A.1) may be inadequate when applied to products independently. These may be inconsistent with each other or with machine availability.

In many cases it is desirable to make a sequence of products, with each product made once in each cycle. The only open question is the total length of the cycle through all products. In most cases, the sequence of products will be established by analysis of change-over costs from one product to another. The number of times the cycle is to be repeated must be determined.

Let
$$p_i = \text{production rate, product } i$$
$$d_i = \text{sales rate, product } i$$
$$t_i = \text{length of production, product } i$$
$$c_i = \text{inventory cost/unit/unit time, product } i$$
$$q_i = \text{order quantity, product } i$$
$$a_i + b_i q_i = \text{production cost of an amount } q_i, \text{ product } i$$
$$n = \text{number of cycles of production through all products}$$

The maximum inventory of product i will be given by $(p_i - d_i)t_i$; the average will be $(p_i - d_i)t_i/2$. Since $p_i t_i = q_i$ and $q_i = d_i/n$

$$\frac{(p_i - d_i)t_i}{2} = (p_i - d_i)\frac{q_i}{2p_i}$$

or

$$\frac{(p_i - d_i)t_i}{2} = (p_i - d_i)\frac{d_i}{2np_i}$$

$$= \frac{d_i}{2n}\left(1 - \frac{d_i}{p_i}\right)$$

The total cost for all products is given by

$$C = n\sum_i (a_i + b_iq_i) + \frac{1}{2n}\sum_i c_id_i\left(1 - \frac{d_i}{p_i}\right)$$

$$= n\sum_i\left(a_i + \frac{b_id_i}{n}\right) + \frac{1}{2n}\sum_i c_id_i\left(1 - \frac{d_i}{p_i}\right)$$

$$= n\sum_i a_i + \sum_i b_id_i + \frac{1}{2n}\sum_i c_id_i\left(1 - \frac{d_i}{p_i}\right)$$

Differentiating with respect to n and setting the result equal to zero yields the optimum number of cycles:

$$n = \sqrt{\frac{\sum_i c_id_i(1 - d_i/p_i)}{2\sum_i a_i}} \tag{A.8}$$

Since $q_i = d_i/n$, the optimum run length for product i is

$$q_i = \frac{d_i}{n}$$

$$= \sqrt{\frac{2d_i^2\sum_i a_i}{\sum_i c_id_i(1 - d_i/p_i)}} \tag{A.9}$$

When the number of products is one, (A.9) reduces to (A.3).
The total inventory of all products on hand will be

$$I = \sum_i I_i = 1/2\Sigma q_i(1 - d_i/p)$$

$$= 1/2\sqrt{\frac{2\Sigma a_i}{\Sigma c_id_i(1 - d_i/p)}}\ \Sigma d_i(1 - d_i/p)$$

The maximum inventory of product i is reached when a run is just completed:

$$\text{Max } I_i = q_i\left(1 - \frac{d_i}{p}\right)$$

$$= d_i\left(1 - \frac{d_i}{p}\right)\sqrt{\frac{2\Sigma a_i}{\Sigma c_id_i(1 - d_i/p)}}$$

The ratio of the maximum inventory of product i to the total inventory cycle I is given, therefore, by

$$a_i = \frac{2d_i(1 - d_i/p)}{\sum_i d_i(1 - d_i/p)}$$

The ratio a_i can be used in the case of uncertainty, for deciding when to stop a run of a given product and shift the unit over to another item: Whenever the ratio of inventory of the product i being made to total inventory reaches a_i, production is shifted to another item, either an item with no stock on hand or the item with the lowest ratio of stock on hand to usage rate.

Examples of circumstances where this type of control can be used include:

1. Change-over of a chemical process, in processing of several grades of a chemical or a petroleum product through a single unit into storage.
2. Shift of a packaging line, packaging the same material in various sizes, from one size pack to another.
3. Change-over of a die press from one item to another.

RUN LENGTH AND CAPACITY

Where the production requirement on a plant is a high proportion of the maximum available capacity, the limitation on setup and change-over time may impose a high hidden cost. For example, assume a series of products made on the same equipment. (Demand and production rates of the several products are expressed in homogeneous units, e.g., processing time, as before.) Using the same notation as in (A.8), the optimum number of change cycles would be

$$n = \sqrt{\frac{\sum_i c_i d_i(1 - d_i/p_i)}{2 \sum_i a_i}}$$

If d_i and p_i are expressed in units of amounts produced per unit time, then $p_1 = p_2 = \cdots = p_k = 1$. For illustration, assume $c_1 = c_2 = \cdots c_k = c$ and $d_i = d/k$ where $d = \Sigma d_i$ and k is the number of different products produced. Then assuming changes in d are reflected proportionately in d_i,

$$\text{Optimum } n = \sqrt{\frac{cd(1 - d/k)}{2 \sum_i a_i}} \tag{A.10}$$

shown graphically by the dashed line in Figure A.2.

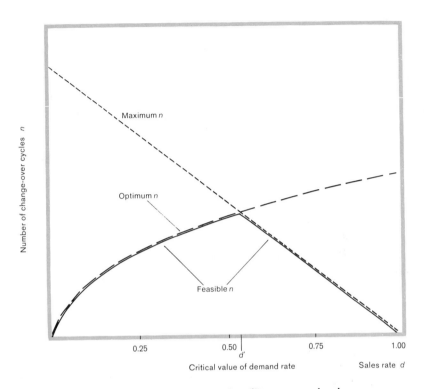

FIGURE A.2   Relation between sales and product change-over cycle role

The attainable number of change cycles, however, will depend on the requirement imposed by d on the productive time. The total required production time T' is given by

$$T' = d$$

Let t'' be the total time required on change-overs in one product cycle. Let T'' be the total time requirement for change-overs in a unit time period.

$$T'' = t''n$$

In a unit time interval,

$$T' + T'' \leq 1$$

or

$$T'' \leq 1 - T'$$
$$\leq 1 - d$$

Then, necessarily,

$$\text{Maximum } n \le \frac{1}{t''} (1 - d) \tag{A.11}$$

shown by the dotted line in Figure A.2.

When the demand d is sufficiently small so that the number of change-overs n given by (A.10) also satisfies (A.11), then (A.10) can be used. Where n determined by (A.10) does not satisfy (A.11), then

$$n = \frac{1}{t''} (1 - d) \tag{A.12}$$

The intersection occurs when

$$\frac{1}{t''} (1 - d) = \sqrt{\frac{cd(1 - d/k)}{2 \sum_i a_i}}$$

i.e., when the sales demand d equals the critical demand rate d' given by (letting $a = \Sigma a_i$):

$$d' = \frac{4a/t''^2 + c \pm \sqrt{8ac/t''^2(1 - 1/k) + c^2}}{4a/t''^2 + 2c/k}$$

The feasible number of change-overs as a function of the demand rate d is shown by the solid line in Figure A.2.

Let the unit variable cost of all products be the same, equal to b. Then the total cost is given by

$$C = an + bd + \frac{rbd}{2n} \left(1 - \frac{d}{k}\right)$$

where $ib = c$ is the unit carrying cost of inventory (assumed equal for all products for illustration) and $d/2n$ is the average inventory. Substituting from (A.10) and (A.12) for n, the cost becomes

$$C = \sqrt{2acd(1 - d/k)} + bd \qquad d \le d'$$

$$= \frac{a}{t''} (1 - d) + bd + \frac{ct''d}{(1 - d)} \left(1 - \frac{d}{k}\right) \qquad d > d'$$

The marginal cost of production would conventionally be thought of as b. However, in this case the marginal cost dC/dd is

$$C' = b + \left(1 - \frac{2d}{k}\right) \sqrt{\frac{ac}{2d(1 - d/k)}} \qquad d \le d'$$

$$\tag{A.13}$$

$$= b - \frac{a}{C} + \frac{ct''(1 - 2d/k + d^2/k)}{(1 - d)} \qquad d > d'$$

and as d approaches the plant capacity limit, C approaches infinity.

The situation is even more pronounced where substantial safety stocks are carried to protect against fluctuations in the rates of sale d_i. The total safety stock in a plant is frequently an increasing function of the sales rate d and the time between runs on a given product $1/n$. For example, the relation between safety stock S the sales rate, and cycle frequency might be

$$S = w \sqrt{\frac{d}{n}} \tag{A.14}$$

Substituting (A.12) in (A.14) gives

$$S = w \sqrt{\frac{d}{1-d}}$$

As d approaches 1, S (and the associated investment and storage costs) becomes very large.

In short, when the plant is loaded beyond the critical demand point d', the real marginal cost of production increases rapidly, even though the normal unit processing cost remains the same. This is due to the rapidly increasing inventory requirements, both to permit the necessarily longer runs or cycles and to protect against stock shortages between runs of an individual product. The cost function (A.13) is derived on the assumption that the unit cost of products is the same. When this assumption does not hold, the derivation is more complex, but the principle remains: Inventory requirements brought on by loss of flexibility drive the variable or marginal cost of production in the short run up rapidly as the load on the plant approaches theoretical capacity.

The impact of cycling times and capacity on the marginal production cost C' becomes particularly important where decisions concerning allocation of production are being made. If based only on shipping costs and the variable manufacturing cost b, decisions made—e.g., by linear-programing means—may lead to serious errors. In other circumstances, the effect of capacity limits on inventory requirements may justify increases in capacity even when the process is operating at a rate below the theoretical capacity.

B

PRODUCTION-
CONTROL
RULES

FORMAL STATEMENT OF CONTROL RULES

Simple Warehouse Rule. The reorder rule stated in Chapter 6 for replenishing warehouse inventories is expressible as:

$$q(i) = \sum_{k=1}^{U+1} d^*(i + k) - \sum_{k=1}^{U} q(i - k) - [I(i) - I^*]$$

where U = lead time (in periods)

$q(i)$ = amount ordered at the end of period i, available at the beginning of period $i + U + 1$

$d^*(i)$ = forecast demand for period i

$I(i)$ = inventory at the end of period i

I^* = planned inventory level

Simple Production Control Rule. Using similar notation, let

$p^*(i)$ = planned production for period i

$p(i)$ = production finally ordered for period i, available at the beginning of period $i + 1$

$\Delta p(i) = p(i) - p^*(i)$, correction or adjustment of production in period i

$I^*(i)$ = planned inventory level, end of period i

The identities hold:

$$I^\bullet(i) = I^\bullet(i-1) - d^\bullet(i) + p^\bullet(i-1)$$
$$I(i) = I(i-1) - d(i) + p(i+1)$$

and since U is the lead time,

$$p(i+U) = q(i)$$

Then the warehouse rule as a production-control rule takes the form

$$q(i) = p(i+U) = \sum_{j=0}^{U} p^*(i+j) - \sum_{j=0}^{U-1} p(i+j) - I(i) + I^*(i)$$

$$= p^*(i+U) - \sum_{j=0}^{U-1} \Delta p(i+j) - I(i) + I^*(i) \tag{B.1}$$

Damped Response Rule. The rule (B.1) can be thought of as consisting of two parts, the first term being the basic or original production plan and the remainder being a correction equal to the forecast discrepancy in inventory from plan. The discrepancy is made up of the current discrepancy less the corrections already allowed for through adjustment of intervening period production rates. The damped rule allows for correction of a fraction k of the inventory discrepancy in any period. The rule is given by:

$$q(i) = p(i+U) = p^*(i+U) - k\left[\sum_{j=0}^{U-1} \Delta p(i+j) + I(i) - I^*(i)\right] \tag{B.2}$$

Response Rule with Control Limits. An alternative to (B.2) may be defined as

$$p(i+U) = p^*(i+U) + \Delta p(i+U); \qquad |\Delta p| > L$$
$$= p^*(i+U) \qquad |\Delta p| \le L$$

where

$$\Delta p(i) = -k\left[\sum_{j=0}^{U-1} \Delta p(i+j) + I(i) - I^*(i)\right]$$

The limit L sets a lower limit on the size of change from plan to be considered.

EFFECT OF CONTROL NUMBER k ON INVENTORY REQUIREMENTS

A relation between the control number k and the distribution of inventory fluctuations about planned levels can be derived under the following assumptions.

Let

$$x(i) = d(i) - d^*(i)$$

Assume the $x(i)$ are independent random variables, with mean zero, and variance $t\sigma^2(x)$, where t is the length of each review period and $\sigma^2(x)$ is the variance between actual and forecast demand per unit time. Let $T = Ut$ be the lead time.

The control rule (B.2) gives

$$\Delta p(i + U) = -k \left[\sum_{j=0}^{U-1} \Delta p(i + j) + I(i) - I^*(i) \right]$$

Let

$$E(i + U) = \sum_{j=0}^{U-1} \Delta p(i + j) + I(i) - I^*(i)$$

Since

$$\begin{aligned} I(h) &= I(h - 1) - d(h) + p(h - 1) \\ I^*(h) &= I^*(h - 1) - d^*(h) + p^*(h - 1) \end{aligned} \Big\} \text{any } h$$

then

$$I(i + U) - I^*(i + U) = I(i) - I^*(i) - \sum_{j=1}^{U} x(i + j) + \sum_{j=0}^{U-1} \Delta p(i + j)$$

$$= E(i + U) - \sum_{j=1}^{U} x(i + j)$$

Since

$$\Delta p(i + U) = -kE(i + U) \tag{B.3}$$

then

$$\begin{aligned} E(i + U) &= E(i + U - 1) + \Delta p(i + U - 1) - \Delta p(i - 1) \\ &\quad - x(i) + \Delta p(i - 1) \\ &= E(i + U - 1)(1 - k) - x(i) \end{aligned}$$

and by continued iteration

$$E(i + U) = - \sum_{n=0}^{\infty} (1 - k)^n x(i - n) \tag{B.4}$$

Therefore

$$I(i + U) - I^*(i + U) = - \sum_{j=1}^{U} x(i + j) - \sum_{n=0}^{\infty} (1 - k)^n x(i - n)$$

Since the $x(i)$ are independent random variables, $y(i + U) = I(i + U) - I^*(i + U)$ will also be a random variable with mean $y = 0$

$$\sigma^2(y) = t\sigma^2(x) \left[U + \sum_{n=0}^{\infty} (1 - k)^{2n} \right]$$

$$= \sigma^2(x) \left[Ut + \frac{t}{2k - k^2} \right]$$

Then the standard deviation of inventories about planned levels will be

$$\sigma(y) = \sigma(x) \sqrt{T + \frac{t}{2k - k^2}}$$

$$= \sigma(x) \sqrt{\frac{T(2k - k^2) + t}{2k - k^2}}$$

If the planned inventories are set to protect against run-out a specified fraction of review periods, the reserve-stock requirements will equal

$$K\sigma(y) = K\sigma(x) \sqrt{\frac{T(2k - k^2) + t}{2k - k^2}}$$

EFFECT OF CONTROL NUMBER k ON PRODUCTION FLUCTUATIONS

The fluctuation of production from plan in any period is $\Delta p(i)$. Since by (B.3) and (B.4)

$$\Delta p(i) = -kE(i)$$

$$= -k \sum_{n=0}^{\infty} (1 - k)^n x(i - U - n)$$

and since the $x(i)$ are independent random variables, $\Delta p(i)$ will be a random variable with

mean $\Delta p = 0$

$$\sigma^2(\Delta p) = t\sigma^2(x)k^2 \sum_{n=0}^{\infty} (1 - k)^{2n}$$

$$= t\sigma^2(x) \left(\frac{k}{2 - k} \right)$$

The standard deviation of the distribution of production levels about plan will be

$$\sigma(\Delta p) = \sigma(x) \sqrt{\frac{kt}{2 - k}}$$

and the standard deviation of net adjustments from period to period, $\Delta p(i) - \Delta p(i-1)$, will be

$$\sigma(\Delta^2 p) = \sigma(x) \sqrt{\frac{2kt}{2-k}}$$

MAGNITUDE OF PRODUCTION ADJUSTMENTS

Where the forecast error per unit time is normally distributed with mean zero and variance $\sigma^2(x)$, net adjustments to the production level, $\Delta^2 p = \Delta p(i) - \Delta p(i-1)$, will be normally distributed with mean zero and variance

$$\sigma(\Delta^2 p) = \sigma(x) \sqrt{\frac{2kt}{2-k}}$$

The average magnitude or average absolute value of net adjustment will be

$$\overline{\Delta^2 p} = \frac{1}{\sigma(\Delta^2 p)\sqrt{2\pi}} \int_{-\infty}^{\infty} |\Delta^2 p| e^{-(\Delta^2 p)^2 / 2\sigma^2(\Delta^2 p)} \, d(\Delta^2 p)$$

$$= \frac{2}{\sigma(\Delta^2 p)\sqrt{2\pi}} \int_{0}^{\infty} (\Delta^2 p) e^{-(\Delta^2 p)^2 / 2\sigma^2(\Delta^2 p)} \, d(\Delta^2 p)$$

Letting

$$y = \frac{(\Delta^2 p)^2}{2\sigma^2(\Delta^2 p)} \qquad dy = \frac{(\Delta^2 p)\, d(\Delta^2 p)}{\sigma^2(\Delta^2 p)}$$

then

$$\overline{\Delta^2 p} = \sigma(\Delta^2 p) \sqrt{\frac{2}{\pi}} \int_{0}^{\infty} e^{-y} \, dy$$

$$= 2\sigma(x) \sqrt{\frac{kt}{\pi(2-k)}}$$

C

TECHNIQUES OF SEASONAL PLANNING

ADJUSTMENT OF DEMAND FORECASTS

In planning against highly seasonal sales, plans must be set early in the selling year to produce to build inventory for the peak-sales period. If early plans are set for higher-than-expected sales and these do not materialize, excessive costs of storage, obsolescence, and capital will be incurred; however, if early production plans are set to meet a sales volume at or below expected, it may become impossible to increase production later if high demand materializes during the peak season. An approximate method can be used for balancing the opposing risks of back-order or lost-sales costs and inventory costs. The objective is to adjust the sales forecast (presumably unbiased) to arrive at a production-requirements schedule which minimizes expected losses.

Assume cumulative sales forecast $D^*(t)$, expected sales up to time t, with a known or estimated distribution of errors about the forecast $f(x,t)$. The random variable x is defined by:

$$x = D(t) - D^*(t) \tag{C.1}$$

where $D(t)$ represents actual sales to time t. Figure C.1 illustrates a possible $D^*(t)$ in the case of a seasonal product. Assume two types of penalties:

1. A back-order penalty, taken as proportional to the amount by which cumulative demand exceeds cumulative production to time t. Let the unit cost of back orders be denoted by $s(t)$, which may vary with time.

2. An inventory cost, approximated as follows: Let sales at any given time be approximated as a linear function of time.

$$D = d(t)t \qquad (C.2)$$

Then when the inventory is at a level $I(t)$, the last unit of inventory will be sold out at a time $t = I/d$. Let the inventory penalty c be proportional to the size of the inventory times the time over which it is held. The penalty on the last unit will be $cI(t)/d(t)$ and on the total is $cI(t)^2/2d(t)$.

Let $S(t)$ be the adjustment to be made to the cumulative sales forecast in arriving at the production-requirements schedule $R(t)$.

$$D^*(t) + S(t) = R(t) \qquad (C.3)$$

FIGURE C.1   **Cumulative expected sales versus time of year**

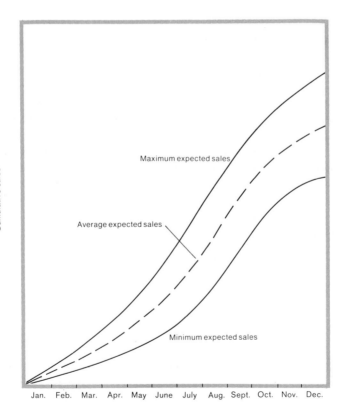

The back-order penalty may now be expressed as

$$s(x - S)$$

and since $I(t) = S(t) - x(t)$, the inventory penalty is

$$\frac{c(S - x)^2}{2d}$$

The total cost of the forecast error is given by:

$$C(t) = \int_{S(t)}^{\infty} s(t)[x - S(t)]f(x,t) \; dx + \int_{-\infty}^{S(t)} \frac{c}{2d(t)} [S(t) - x]^2 f(x,t) \; dx \qquad (C.4)$$

$$\frac{\delta C(t)}{\delta S(t)} = -s(t) \int_{S(t)}^{\infty} f(x,t) \; dx + \frac{c}{d(t)} [S(t) \int_{-\infty}^{S(t)} f(x,t) \; dx - \int_{-\infty}^{S(t)} xf(x,t) \; dx] \qquad (C.5)$$

To minimize $C(t)$, setting $\dfrac{\delta C(t)}{\delta S(t)} = 0$,

$$\frac{S(t) \int_{-\infty}^{S(t)} f(x,t) \; dx - \int_{-\infty}^{S(t)} xf(x,t) \; dx}{\int_{S(t)}^{\infty} f(x,t) \; dx} = \frac{s(t) \; d(t)}{c} \qquad (C.6)$$

Then (C.6) determines $S(t)$ as a function of the costs $s(t)$ and c, and the rate of demand $d(t)$. If $f(x,t)$ has the same form for all t, $S(t)$ can be graphed or tabulated as a function of $s(t)d(t)/c$ in suitable units—e.g., standard deviations where $f(x)$ is normal or percent of range where $f(x)$ is uniform. Figure C.2 illustrates such a graph for a case where x is uniformly distributed between two limits equidistant from $D^*(t)$.

The production-requirements schedule $R(t)$ is given by (C.3) where $S(t)$ is determined from (C.6). The production-requirements schedule may then be substituted for the sales forecast in working out the production plan.

THE LINEAR-PROGRAMING PROBLEM

The linear-programing problem may be stated as the minimization of a function

$$g(x) = \sum_{j=1}^{n} a_j x_j \qquad (C.7)$$

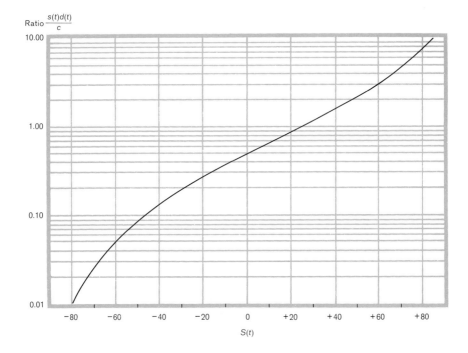

Ratio $\dfrac{s(t)d(t)}{c}$

$S(t)$

FIGURE C.2 Adjustment in cumulative estimated sales for values of $s(t)\ d(t)/c$

subject to the restrictions

$$x_j \geq 0 \qquad j = 1, 2, \ldots, n$$

$$f_i(x) = \sum_{j=1}^{n} b_{ij}x_j - c_i \geq 0 \qquad i = 1, 2, \ldots, m \tag{C.8}$$

A problem "dual" to (C.7), (C.8) is the maximization of the function

$$G(u) = \sum_{i=1}^{m} c_i u_i \tag{C.9}$$

subject to the restrictions

$$F_j(u) = \sum_{i=1}^{m} b_{ij}u_i - a_j \leq 0 \qquad i = 1, 2, \ldots, m$$

$$u_i \geq 0 \qquad j = 1, 2, \ldots, n \tag{C.10}$$

The "dual" problems (C.7), (C.8) and (C.9), (C.10) have the property that if, and only if, x is a minimizing solution of (C.7), (C.8) and u' is a maximizing solution of (C.9), (C.10) then[1]

$$g(x') = G(u') \tag{C.11}$$

If the x_i represent physical quantities and $g(x)$ a cost function to be minimized, then the u_i represent unit costs or prices. The nature of the u_i may be clearer following the discussion below. Furthermore, it can be shown that[1]

Either $u'_i = 0$ or $f(x') = 0$ $i = 1, 2, \ldots, m$

Either $x'_j = 0$ or $F_j(u') = 0$ $j = 1, 2, \ldots, n$ (C.12)

THE PRODUCTION PLAN AS A LINEAR PROGRAM

Let the production requirements be represented by the numbers $d(1)$, $d(2), \ldots, d(k)$, where $d(i)$ is the added requirement in the ith period. Let $h(i)$ be the maximum number of units of product which can be produced on regular time in the ith period and $w(i)$ the maximum production on overtime in the ith period. Let $I(i)$ be the inventory at the end of the ith period.

If $p(i)$ is the number of units produced on regular time and $y(i)$ is the number produced on overtime in the ith period, $I(i)$ may be expressed as:

$$I(i) = I(i - 1) + p(i) + y(i) - d(i)$$

$$= \sum_{j=1}^{i} p(j) + \sum_{j=1}^{i} y(j) - \sum_{j=1}^{i} d(j) \tag{C.13}$$

For simplicity, assume the opening inventory balance $I(o) = 0$. If not, the opening balance can be subtracted from the production requirement of the initial period [or periods if $I(o) > d(1)$] and the resulting $d(i)$ considered as production requirements.

The set of numbers $p(i)$ and $y(i)$, $p(i) \geq 0$, $y(i) \geq 0$; $i = 1, \ldots, k$, represents a production schedule. The cost of the schedule which is to be minimized may be expressed as:

[1] See John F. Magee, *Linear Programming in Production Scheduling, Studies in Operations Research—I*, Arthur D. Little, Inc., Cambridge, Mass., 1952; also T. C. Koopmans (ed.), *Activity Analysis of Production and Allocation*, Cowles Commission Monograph no. 13, John Wiley & Sons, Inc., New York, 1951.

$$C(p,y) = b \sum_{1}^{k} y(i) + c \sum_{1}^{k} I(i)$$

$$= b \sum_{1}^{k} y(i) + c \left\{ \sum_{i=1}^{k} \sum_{j=1}^{i} [p(j) + y(j) - d(j)] \right\} \tag{C.14}$$

$$= \sum_{i=1}^{k} c(k - i + 1)p(i) + \sum_{i=1}^{k} [(k - i + 1)c + b]y(i) + D$$

where $D = $ constant
$\quad b = $ overtime charge per unit of product
$\quad c = $ inventory carrying charge/unit/period
$\quad k = $ number of periods scheduled

The restrictions on the schedule are of the form:

Restrictions on regular production:

$$h(i) - p(i) \geq 0 \qquad i = 1, 2, \ldots, k$$

Restrictions on overtime production:

$$w(i) - y(i) \geq 0 \qquad i = 1, 2, \ldots, k \tag{C.15}$$

Restrictions on inventories:

$$\sum_{j=1}^{i} p(j) + \sum_{j=1}^{i} y(j) - \sum_{j=1}^{i} d(j) \geq 0 \qquad i = 1, 2, \ldots, k$$

Other kinds of problems or other modifications of restrictions can be formulated in linear-programing terms. Some illustrations include:

1. A "floor" might be put under the level of activity in each period. Restrictions of the form

$$p(i) - l(i) \geq 0 \qquad i = 1, 2, \ldots, k, h \geq l > 0 \tag{C.16}$$

might be added to (C.15).

2. The cost function might be modified to include a facilities cost proportional to the maximum production capacity or maximum inventory capacity used. For example, in the former case, (C.14) might be modified to

$$C(x,y,z) = C(x,y) + a_o z \tag{C.17}$$

with the restrictions on production in (C.15) modified to

$$h'(i)z - p(i) \geq 0 \qquad i = 1, 2, \ldots, k$$
$$w'(i)z - y(i) \geq 0 \qquad i = 1, 2, \ldots, k \tag{C.18}$$

where $\qquad a_o = $ unit cost of capacity

$$z = \text{amount of capacity to be installed (variable)}$$
$$h'(i), \ w'(i) = \text{monthly maximum outputs per unit of capacity}$$

3. A hiring, layoff, setup, or similar cost may be important. Let a' be the cost of adding a unit of production, a'' be the cost of removing a unit. The change in production level between period $(i-1)$ and (i) is

$$\frac{p(i)}{t(i)} - \frac{p(i-1)}{t(i-1)}$$

where $t(i) = $ number of working days in i

If $u(i)$ is the productive units added, and $v(i)$ is the number eliminated in period i, then

$$u(i) \geq 0$$
$$z(i) \geq 0$$
$$u(i) - \frac{p(i)}{t(i)} + \frac{p(i-1)}{t(i-1)} \geq 0 \qquad\qquad \text{(C.19)}$$
$$v(i) + \frac{p(i)}{t(i)} - \frac{p(i-1)}{t(i-1)} \geq 0$$

The restrictions (C.19) can be added to the original set and (C.14) modified to

$$C(p,y,u,v) = C(p,y) + a' \sum_{i=1}^{k} u(i) + a'' \sum_{i=1}^{k} z(i) \qquad\qquad \text{(C.20)}$$

4. The joint scheduling of two or more products through the same facilities can be set up in a manner analogous to (C.14), (C.15) with the addition of a product index, plus a set of restrictions superimposed to express the over-all capacity restrictions, e.g.,

$$h(i) - \sum_{j=1}^{k} p_j(i) \geq 0 \qquad i = 1, 2, \ldots, k \qquad\qquad \text{(C.21)}$$

5. The joint scheduling of successive operations illustrates the extension to a multistage or cascaded process. Let c_1 and b_1 be the unit inventory and overtime costs for process 1. Let c_2 and b_2 be the equivalent costs for process 2. Let $p_1(i), y_1(i), p_2(i), y_2(i)$ be the regular time and overtime outputs for processes 1 and 2, respectively, in period i, and let $d_2(i)$ be the sales forecast of product 2 in period i. The cost function to be minimized is given by

$$C(p,y) = b_1 \sum_{i=1}^{k} y_1(i) + b_2 \sum_{i=1}^{k} y_2(i) + c_1 \sum_{i=1}^{k} I_1(i) + c_2 \sum_{i=1}^{k} I_2(i) \qquad\qquad \text{(C.22)}$$

The inventories $I_1(i)$ and $I_2(i)$ are given by

$$I_1(i) = I_1(i-1) + p_1(i) + y_1(i) - p_2(i) - y_2(i)$$

$$= \sum_{j=1}^{i} p_1(j) + \sum_{j=1}^{i} y_1(j) - \sum_{j=1}^{i} p_2(j) - \sum_{j=1}^{i} y_2(j)$$

$$i = 1, 2, \ldots, k \quad \text{(C.23)}$$

$$I_2(i) = \sum_{j=1}^{i} p_2(j) + \sum_{j=1}^{i} y_2(j) - \sum_{j=1}^{i} d_2(j)$$

$$i = 1, 2, \ldots, k$$

Then $C(p,y)$ can be expressed as

$$C(p,y) = \sum_{i=1}^{k} b_1(k - i + 1)p_1(i) + \sum_{i=1}^{k} (b_2 - b_1)(k - i + 1)p_2(i)$$

$$+ \sum_{i=1}^{k} [b_1(k - i + 1) + c_1]y_1(i)$$

$$+ \sum_{i=1}^{k} [(b_2 - b_1)(k - i + 1) + c_2]y_2(i) + D \quad \text{(C.24)}$$

and the restrictions as

$$h_1(i) - p_1(i) \geq 0 \qquad i = 1, 2, \ldots, k$$
$$h_2(i) - p_2(i) \geq 0 \qquad i = 1, 2, \ldots, k$$
$$w_1(i) - y_1(i) \geq 0 \qquad i = 1, 2, \ldots, k$$
$$w_2(i) - y_2(i) \geq 0 \qquad i = 1, 2, \ldots, k$$

$$\sum_{j=1}^{i} p_1(j) + \sum_{j=1}^{i} y_1(j) - \sum_{j=1}^{i} p_2(j) - \sum_{j=1}^{i} y_2(j) \geq 0 \qquad i = 1, 2, \ldots, k$$

$$\sum_{j=1}^{i} p_2(j) + \sum_{j=1}^{i} y_2(j) - \sum_{j=1}^{i} d_2(j) \geq 0 \qquad i = 1, 2, \ldots, k \quad \text{(C.25)}$$

The $h_1(i)$, $h_2(i)$, $w_1(i)$, $w_2(i)$ are the maximum capacities, regular and overtime production, of operations 1 and 2 for period i. The cost function (C.24) together with the restrictions (C.25) defines a linear program which can be solved to obtain the optimum set of p and y.

CHECKING THE PROGRAM

The "dual" problem (C.9), (C.10) provides the means for checking the accuracy of computations. Note that if the computing procedures such as those outlined above are carried out accurately, the solution is a precise minimal solution to the program, not an approximate or near-minimal solution. The conditions (C.12) make it possible to assign values to the variable u_i in the problem dual to the particular planning problem considered and to establish relationships among these variables. Unless a set of numerical values can be assigned to the u_i consistent with the conditions (C.12), the plan is incorrectly computed. The following table shows the values of u_i which must hold in the case defined by (C.14), (C.15):

$p(i)$ Regular production	$y(i)$ Overtime production	$I(i)$ Inventory	u_i	u_{i+1}
$0 \leq p(i) \leq h(i)$	0		0	
$p(i) = h(i)$	0		$0 \leq u_i \leq b$	
$p(i) = h(i)$	$0 < y(i) < w(i)$		b	
$p(i) = h(i)$	$y(i) = w(i)$		b or greater	
		0		$u_{i+1} \leq u_i + c$
		$I(i) > 0$		$u_{i+1} = u_i + c$

If the schedule is correct, it must be possible to find a set of values u_i which satisfies the relations noted above. Similar tables can be worked out for the other scheduling problems described.

GLOSSARY
OF
PRODUCTION-
AND
INVENTORY-
CONTROL
TERMS[1]

ABC CLASSIFICATION Classification of the items in an inventory in decreasing order of annual dollar volume, split into three levels, called A, B, and C. Class A contains the items with the highest annual dollar volume and receives the most attention. The medium class B receives less attention, and class C, which contains the low-dollar volume items, is controlled routinely.

ACCURACY The degree of conformity of a calculated or measured estimate to the true value. The closer the estimate is to the true value, the greater the accuracy. (Note that this is not the same as PRECISION.)

ADAPTIVE FORECASTING An extension of EXPONENTIAL SMOOTHING that includes the use of transcendental fitting functions (e.g., exponential and trigonometric functions). Particularly useful for forecasting seasonal behavior. The coefficients of the fitting functions are revised after each observation of new data.

ANALYSIS OF DISTRIBUTION BY VALUE A type of VALUE ANALYSIS for a line of products, usually in the form of a plot of the cumulative frequency distribution of the annual dollar sales of each item in the product line. This

[1] Adapted from General Memorandum No. 33, Arthur D. Little, Inc., Cambridge, Mass., February, 1963.

plot generally shows a LOGNORMAL DISTRIBUTION and is useful in the estimation of required cycle stocks and safety stocks in an inventory.

ANTICIPATION STOCK   Stock built up to buffer seasonal fluctuations in sales or a planned intensive sales campaign, or to carry sales over a plant vacation or maintenance shutdown.

ARITHMETIC MEAN   The AVERAGE of a series of items obtained by dividing their sum by the total number of items. A generalized formula is

$$M = \frac{\sum\limits_{i=1}^{n} X_i}{n}$$

where there are n items X_i.

AVAILABLE STOCK   The algebraic sum of the stock on hand and the stock already on order, less any unfilled customer demand. Thus, available stock may be greater than, equal to, or less than the physical inventory and may even be negative if there are back orders.

AVERAGE   Any representative value of the central tendency of a group of values, such as the arithmetic mean, the geometric mean, the mode, or the median. The most common meaning of "average" is ARITHMETIC MEAN.

BACKLOG OF ORDERS   The sum of all unfilled orders waiting to be filled or processed.

BASE-STOCK SYSTEM   A fundamental method of inventory control which includes as special cases most of the systems in practice. In this system, when an order is received for any item it is used as a "picking ticket," and duplicate copies, called "replenishment orders," are sent back to all stages of production to initiate replenishment of stocks. Positive or negative orders called "base-stock orders" are also used from time to time to adjust the level of the base stock of each item. In actual practice, replenishment orders are usually accumulated when they are issued and are released at regular intervals.

BASIC STOCK   The desired level of the average inventory. Also known as normal or standard stock.

BREAK-EVEN POINT   The level of production or the volume of sales at which operations are neither profitable nor unprofitable.

BUFFER STOCK   Same as ANTICIPATION STOCK.

CARRYING COST   Cost of carrying inventory, usually defined as a percentage of the dollar value of inventory per unit of time (generally 1 year). Consists principally of four factors: cost of capital invested in inventory, taxes and insurance, obsolescence and spoilage, and space costs.

CASCADED SYSTEMS   Multistorage operations; the input to each stage is the output of a preceding stage, thereby causing interdependencies among the stages.

CHANGE-OVER COST   The sum of the SETUP COST and the tear-down cost for a manufacturing operation.

COMMITMENTS   Orders which have been accepted but not yet filled. They include back orders and are part of the BACKLOG.

COST OF CAPITAL INVESTED   The cost of capital invested in inventory is the product of three factors: the capital value of a unit of inventory, the time a unit is in inventory, and the charge, or imputed interest rate, placed against a dollar of invested cash.

CYCLE   The interval of time during which a system or process, such as seasonal demand or a manufacturing operation, periodically returns to similar initial conditions. In inventory control, a cycle is often taken to be the length of time between two replenishment shipments.

CYCLE STOCK   One of the two main components of any item inventory, the cycle stock is the more active part, i.e., that which depletes gradually and is replenished cyclically, when orders are received. The second part of the inventory is the SAFETY STOCK and is a cushion of protection against uncertainty in the demand or in the REPLENISHMENT LEAD TIME.

DECOUPLING INVENTORY   The inventory which is maintained between two operations in order to make it possible to control them independently. Also called line-balancing stock.

DEMAND   The expression of desire to purchase a commodity and willingness to pay for it. In inventory control, "demand" is different from "sales" because demand does not necessarily result in sales (i.e., if there is no stock, there will be no sale to satisfy demand).

DEMAND DISTRIBUTION A relative arrangement of a set of demand data. The data can be distributed over time (i.e., a TIME SERIES) or over the range of values assumed by the data (i.e., a FREQUENCY DISTRIBUTION).

DEMAND DURING A LEAD TIME The DEMAND expected over a time interval, the LEAD TIME. The lead time is measured in the same units as the forecast REVIEW PERIOD. For example, if the forecast of demand is reviewed every month, the lead time should be in months.

DEVIATION The algebraic difference between a particular number in a set of numbers and the average of that set of numbers.

DIRECT COST Cost which can be directly attributed to a particular job or operation. If the job were eliminated, the cost would disappear.

DISCRETE DEMAND DEMAND which occurs in integral multiples of some unit.

DISPATCHING In production operations, the function of releasing orders to the appropriate work centers.

DISTRIBUTION OF FORECAST ERRORS Tabulation of the calculated FORECAST ERROR according to the frequency of occurrence of each value. The errors in forecasting are, in many cases, normally distributed even when the observed data do not come from a NORMAL DISTRIBUTION.

DYNAMIC PROGRAMING A method of sequential decision making in which the result of the decision in each stage affords the best possible position to exploit the expected range of likely (yet unpredictable) outcomes in the following decision-making stages.

EOQ See ECONOMICAL ORDER QUANTITY.

ECONOMICAL LOT OR BATCH SIZE See ECONOMICAL ORDER QUANTITY.

ECONOMICAL ORDER QUANTITY (EOQ) The amount of a product which should be purchased or manufactured at one time in order to minimize the total cost involved, including the ordering costs (setup of machines, writing orders, checking receipts, etc.) and carrying costs (cost of capital invested, insurance, taxes, space, obsolescence, and spoilage). Also called "optimum lot size." The economical order quantity may be calculated from the equation

$$Q = \sqrt{\frac{2AS}{rv}}$$

where Q = quantity to be ordered
S = annual sales
A = ordering cost
r = carrying cost
v = unit cost

(Note that various assumptions are inherent in the use of the above equation.)

EXPECTED DEMAND An estimate of the average or mean DEMAND that should occur during some future period of time.

EXPECTED VALUE If x is any quantity calculated from a sample of observations, the expectation or expected value of x is the average value which would be obtained for x if it were calculated from an infinite number of samples of the same size drawn from the same population. If $f(x)$ is the frequency function of the variate x, then the expected value of x may be given by

$$E(x) = \bar{x} = \int_{-\infty}^{\infty} x\, f(x)\, dx = \sum_{-\infty}^{\infty} x\, f(x)$$

EXPONENTIAL SMOOTHING A weighted, moving-average technique in which past observations are geometrically discounted according to their age. The heaviest weight is assigned to the most recent data. The smoothing is termed "exponential" because data points are weighted in accordance with an exponential function of their age.

EXTRAPOLATION Estimation of the value of a FUNCTION for a value of the argument (independent variable) which is outside the range of all the values which are being used. This process may be contrasted with INTERPOLATION which is used when the required value of a function lies inside rather than outside the range of the tabulated values or given values of the argument.

FIFO See INVENTORY VALUATION.

FIRST-ORDER SMOOTHING Single EXPONENTIAL SMOOTHING as opposed to double exponential smoothing. First-order smoothing requires the use of only one past value, the previous singly smoothed value, whereas second-order smoothing requires the use of both the previous singly and doubly smoothed values.

FIXED COST Cost which is not affected by changes in the volume of business activity, as opposed to VARIABLE COST.

FIXED-INTERVAL REORDER SYSTEM A periodic reordering system in which the time interval between orders, such as a week, a month, or a quarter, is fixed but the size of the order is not fixed, and orders vary according to usage since the last review. This type of inventory-control system is employed where it is convenient to examine inventory stocks on a fixed time cycle, such as in warehouse control systems, in systems where orders are placed mechanically, or in handling inventories involving a very large variety of items under some form of clerical control. Also called fixed-reorder cycle system.

FIXED-ORDER SYSTEM An inventory-control system in which the size of the order is fixed, but the time interval between orders depends on actual demand. The practice of ordering a fixed quantity when needed assumes that individual inventories are under constant watch. This system consists of placing an order of a fixed quantity (the REORDER QUANTITY) whenever the amount on hand plus the amount on order falls to or below a specified level (the ORDER POINT or REORDER POINT). Also called the TWO-BIN SYSTEM in common factory or stockroom use.

FLOAT (1) In-process inventory, (2) an extra quantity due to batch production, or, sometimes, (3) cycle stock. See IN-PROCESS INVENTORY.

FLOOR STOCKS Stocks of inexpensive production parts held in the factory, from which production workers can draw without requisitions.

FLUCTUATION STOCKS Same as SAFETY STOCKS.

FORECAST The EXTRAPOLATION of the past into the future. It is usually an objective computation involving data, as opposed to a PREDICTION, which is a subjective estimate and is management's anticipation of changes and of new factors influencing demand.

FORECAST ERROR   Represented as e_t, the algebraic difference between the current observation x_t and the forecast $_xt_{-\tau}$ made τ periods ago. That is,

$$e_t = x_t - _xt_{-\tau}$$

FREQUENCY CURVE   A graphic representation of a FREQUENCY DISTRIBUTION, i.e., of a set of frequencies of various tabulated values of a variable. The vertical coordinate of the curve is proportional to the frequency for the various values of the variable which are noted on the horizontal coordinate. Customarily, the area under the curve depicts the total frequency while the ratio of the area over an interval to the total area is the relative frequency. Sometimes called the density function.

FREQUENCY DISTRIBUTION   A table or mathematical function that indicates the frequency with which repeated measurements of a variable would fall into each of any number of subdivisions of the allowable range of the variable. The subdivisions are usually called classes and are often used on the horizontal axis of a FREQUENCY CURVE.

FUNCTION   In business, a job, task, or possibly a process. In mathematics, an algebraic expression describing the relation between two or more variables, the function taking on a definite value, or values, when special values are assigned to the argument(s), or independent variable(s), of the function. If there is one independent variable, the dependent variable y may be determined explicitly by the equation $y = f(x)$ or implicitly by $f(x,y) = 0$. If there are several independent variables, the forms are $y = f(x_1, x_2, \ldots, x_n)$ or $f(x_1, x_2, \ldots, x_n, y) = 0$.

GROSS MARGIN   Gross profit, usually expressed as a percentage of net sales.

GROSS PROFIT   Net revenue minus cost of goods sold, before consideration of administrative or selling expenses.

HANDLING COST   The cost involved in handling inventory. In some cases, the handling cost incurred may depend on the size of the inventory. For example, inventories over a fixed maximum may have to be stored in a nearby warehouse at substantial cost per case for handling and trucking material stored outside, or production in excess of immediate needs of a given product may be specially packed and stored at a substantial extra-handling cost.

HISTOGRAM   A graph of contiguous vertical bars representing a FRE-

QUENCY DISTRIBUTION in which the groups or classes of items are marked at equal intervals in ascending order on the x axis, and the number of items in each class is indicated by a horizontal line segment drawn above the x axis at a height equal to the number of items in the class.

IMPUTED COST   Cost which is indirectly estimated and which is attributed rather than directly measured.

INDIRECT COST   Cost which is not directly incurred by a particular job or operation. Certain utility costs, such as plant heating, are often indirect. An indirect cost can be either a FIXED COST or a VARIABLE COST.

IN-PROCESS INVENTORY   Inventories needed because of the time required to move goods from one location to another, in the plant or outside. Generally, in-process inventories are goods being worked on, such as the product moving along an assembly line.

INTERPOLATION   The process of finding a value of a function between two known values by a procedure other than the relationship which is given by the function itself. Interpolation may be performed numerically or graphically.

INVENTORY   Stock-keeping items which are held in a stock point and which serve to decouple successive operations in the process of manufacturing a product and getting it to the consumer. The basic decoupling function is served by inventories of two types: (1) inventories necessary because it takes time to complete an operation and to move the product from one stage to another—IN-PROCESS and MOVEMENT INVENTORIES; (2) inventories employed for organizational purposes, such as to let one unit schedule its operations more or less independently of another—ORGANIZATION INVENTORIES. Inventories may consist of finished goods ready for sale, they may be parts or intermediate products, or they may be raw materials.

INVENTORY CONTROL   The technique of maintaining stock-keeping items at desired levels, whether they be raw materials, goods in process, or finished products.

INVENTORY MANAGEMENT   The branch of business management concerned with the development of policies to which the firm's inventory is meant to conform.

INVENTORY POLICY Specific expression by the management of the firm's desires regarding inventory.

INVENTORY VALUATION The value of the inventory at *either* its cost *or* its market value. Because inventory value can change with time, some recognition must be taken of the age distribution of inventory. Therefore, the cost value of inventory, under accounting practice, is usually computed on a first-in-first-out (FIFO) or a last-in-first-out (LIFO) basis to establish the cost of goods sold.

JOB-SHOP OPERATION A functional organization whose departments or work centers are organized around particular types of equipment or operations, such as drilling, forging, spinning, or assembly. Products flow through departments in batches corresponding to individual customer orders, which may be finished stock orders on the plant or, in the extreme, individual customer orders.

LIFO See INVENTORY VALUATION.

LEAD TIME The time interval from the date an order is released until the first receipt. In inventory control, there are often several different lead times to consider, such as the processing lead time (time for an order to be processed), delivery lead time (time for an order to be delivered), or replenishment lead time. In a FIXED-INTERVAL REORDER SYSTEM, the replenishment lead time begins when an order to replenish stock is released, and lasts until the item is delivered to stock, ready for filling customer demand. Since replenishment orders are released only at regular intervals in this type of system, one review period (the interval between the regular reviews) must be added to the replenishment lead time to get the total lead time that must be considered in setting reorder points. In a FIXED-ORDER SYSTEM, where a replenishment order can be released at any time, the lead time is exactly the time required to deliver the item to stock (i.e., the replenishment lead time is equal to the total lead time).

LEVEL OF SERVICE A measure of the demand that is routinely satisfied by inventory, e.g., the fraction of orders filled from stock; the fraction of dollar demand filled from stock.

LINE-BALANCING STOCK See DECOUPLING INVENTORY.

LINEAR PROGRAMING Mathematical techniques for solving a general class of optimization problems through minimization (or maximization) of a linear function subject to linear constraints. For example, in blending aviation fuel, many grades of commercial gasoline may be available. Prices and octane ratings, as well as upper limits on capacities of input materials which can be used to produce various grades of fuel, are given. The problem is to blend the various commercial gasolines in such a way that: (1) cost will be minimized (profit will be maximized), (2) a specified optimum octane rating will be met, and (3) the need for additional storage capacity will be avoided.

LOGISTIC CURVE A growth curve used to describe functions which continually increase, gradually at first, more rapidly in the middle growth period, and slowly again nearer the end, reaching a saturation point eventually. A symmetrical logistic curve follows the equation

$$y = \frac{k}{1 + e^{a+bx}} \qquad b < 0$$

LOGNORMAL DISTRIBUTION A distribution in which the logarithm of the variable is normally distributed. Whereas the NORMAL DISTRIBUTION may be thought of as being generated as the sum of several small independent events, the lognormal distribution results from the product of several small independent events.

LOT-SIZE INVENTORY Inventories which are maintained whenever quantity price discounts, shipping costs, or setup costs, etc., make it more economical to purchase or produce in larger lots than are needed for immediate purposes.

MARGINAL COST The additional OUT-OF-POCKET COSTS incurred by increasing the level of output of some operation by one unit.

MAXIMUM REASONABLE DEMAND The maximum reasonable demand (during a lead time) is the sum of the expected demand and an allowance for protection against the uncertainty inherent in any FORECAST. The allowance for error is the product of the SAFETY FACTOR and the STANDARD DEVIATION of the errors in forecasting over a lead time. That is,

Expected demand
+ Safety factor × Standard deviation
―――――――――――――――――――――――
= Maximum reasonable demand

MEAN   See ARITHMETIC MEAN.

MEDIAN   The middle value in a set of measured values when the items are arranged in order of magnitude. If there is no middle value, the median is the average of the two middle values.

MIN-MAX SYSTEM   In inventory control, a particular FIXED-INTERVAL REORDER SYSTEM which consists of reviewing stocks at regular intervals but placing a replenishment order only when stocks on hand plus on order have fallen to (or below) some specified order point (minimum). When this occurs, an order is placed to bring the amount on hand plus on order up to a specified ceiling level (maximum). See (s, S) INVENTORY POLICY.

MODE   The most frequently occurring value in a set of measured values.

MODEL   Representation of a process or system that attempts to relate (usually mathematically) some or all of the variables in the system in such a way that an increased understanding of the system is attained. Frequently the model is used to forecast the result of some particular strategy of controlling the real system.

MONTE CARLO TECHNIQUE   Any procedure that involves random-sampling techniques to obtain a probabilistic approximation to the solution of a mathematical or physical problem. In general, the estimated quantity is a statistical parameter, the sampling is made from an artificial population that is in some sense a model of the physical system itself, and the mathematical expressions involved in such models are built up of one or more probability distribution functions. Artificial customer-demand data can be generated by using the Monte Carlo technique, and the distributions from which customer demand is generated can be varied to test the operation of a system under various types of hypothesized conditions.

MOVEMENT INVENTORY   A type of IN-PROCESS INVENTORY which arises because of the time required to move goods from one place to another.

MOVING AVERAGE   An arithmetic average of the last n observations over time which places more (and equal) weight on the n current observations than on those obtained longer than n periods ago.

NOISE   The unpredictable difference between the observed data and the "true process."

NOMOGRAM   A computational aid consisting of two or more scales drawn and arranged so that the results of calculations may be found by the linear connection of points on them. Also called an "alignment chart."

NORMAL DISTRIBUTION (Gaussian distribution)   A symmetrical distribution with mean μ and standard deviation σ which appears as a bell-shaped curve when graphed. The mathematical expression is

$$f(x) = \frac{1}{\sigma\sqrt{2}} \exp \left[\frac{-(x - \mu)^2}{2\sigma^2} \right]$$

OPERATIONS RESEARCH   Quantitative analysis of purposeful (i.e., military, industrial, or administrative) operations with intent to derive an integrated understanding of the factors controlling operational systems and for the purpose of supplying management with an objective basis on which to make decisions. Frequently involves representing the operation or the system by a mathematical MODEL.

OPPORTUNITY COST   The return on capital that could have resulted had capital been used for some purpose other than its present use. Sometimes refers to the best alternative use of the capital; at other times, to the average return from feasible alternatives.

OPTIMUM LOT SIZE   See ECONOMICAL ORDER QUANTITY.

ORDERING COST   The costs used in calculating ECONOMICAL ORDER QUANTITIES which increase as the number of orders placed increases. Includes costs related to the clerical work of preparing, issuing, following and receiving orders, the physical handling of goods, receiving orders, inspections, and machine setup costs, if the order is being manufactured.

ORDER POINT   The inventory level such that if the total stock on hand plus on order falls to or below it, action is taken to replenish the stock. Equivalent to REORDER POINT and TRIGGER LEVEL.

ORDER-POINT, ORDER-QUANTITY SYSTEM   FIXED-ORDER SYSTEM.

ORGANIZATION INVENTORIES   Inventories maintained between various stages of production for organizational purposes, such as to allow one processing unit to schedule its operations more or less independently of another and thereby help achieve smoother production operations. The three main types of organization inventories are LOT-SIZE INVENTORIES, SAFETY STOCKS, and ANTICIPATION STOCKS.

OUT-OF-POCKET COSTS   The net additional costs incurred when some change is made in business operations.

PERIODIC-REORDERING METHOD   FIXED-INTERVAL REORDER SYSTEM.

PERPETUAL INVENTORY RECORD   A document on which each inventory transaction is posted so that a current record of the inventory is maintained. Note that if there are delays in posting, the record can be misleading.

POPULATION   See UNIVERSE.

PRECISION   The degree of reproducibility of the calculations or measurements produced by a process. The smaller the standard deviation of the results, the higher the precision. Precision does not imply ACCURACY.

PREDICTION   Management's intuitive anticipation of changes and of new factors influencing the market, as opposed to a FORECAST, which is an objective projection of the past into the future.

PRESENT VALUE   The value of an anticipated future stream of payments. Equal to the amount of capital which, if available now, could be invested at the going rate of interest and would earn exactly the anticipated stream of payments.

PROBABILITY   Numerically, a quantity between 0 and 1 that states the fraction of trials (of an experiment repeated many times) in which a particular result would occur. This number can either be a subjective guess or be based upon the empirical results of actual trials.

PROBABILITY DISTRIBUTION   A table of numbers or a mathematical expression which states the probability of each of all possible outcomes of an experiment occurring.

PRODUCTION CONTROL, PRODUCTION PLANNING   The function of planning and controlling the production cycle to assure that personnel and facilities are economically utilized, and that products are manufactured within time and cost limits.

PROTECTIVE INVENTORY   SAFETY STOCK.

QUEUE   A sequence of elements, one waiting behind the other; a waiting line.

QUEUEING THEORY The mathematical theory describing the behavior of a queue (distribution of waiting times, lengths of queue) and relating this behavior to queue discipline (rules of operation), input or arrival characteristics, and the service facilities for the queue.

RANDOM NUMBERS A sequence of integers or group of numbers (often in the form of a table) which show no relationship to each other anywhere in the sequence. All integers have an equal chance of occurring at any point in the sequence.

RANGE The algebraic difference between the largest and the smallest numbers in a set of numbers.

REGRESSION ANALYSIS A technique for determining the tendency for the mean value of one variable, for given values of one or more other variables, to vary with the other variables.

REGRESSION COEFFICIENTS The constant coefficients contained in each of the terms involving the independent variables in a REGRESSION EQUATION. For example, in the regression equation $Y = a + bx_1 + cx_2 + dx_3$, $a, b, c,$ and d are the regression coefficients.

REGRESSION CURVE The curve (usually graphed) that best relates certain data according to certain rules of REGRESSION ANALYSIS.

REGRESSION EQUATION A function that indicates how the average value of a dependent variable, for given values of one or more independent variables, varies with relation to the independent variables.

RELATIVE FORECAST ERROR See FORECAST ERROR.

REORDER POINT The ORDER POINT. Also called reorder level.

REORDER QUANTITY In a FIXED-ORDER SYSTEM of inventory control, the fixed quantity which should be ordered each time the available stock (on hand plus on order) falls below the ORDER POINT.

REPLENISHMENT LEAD TIME The time that elapses between placing an order for merchandise and receiving the merchandise so that it is available for use. Also see LEAD TIME.

RETURN ON INVESTMENT Ratio of the profit earned in a period of time to the capital required to produce the profit.

REVIEW PERIOD The time between successive examinations of the inventory to determine what should be reordered.

ROUTINE CONTROL SYSTEM A control system that operates according to design and which relies on management. Any action to handle exceptional situations.

RUN-OUT LIST A list of items to be scheduled into production, sequenced by the dates at which the present available stock is expected to be exhausted.

SKU STOCK-KEEPING UNIT.

SAFETY FACTOR A numerical multiplier of the FORECAST ERROR, used to establish the level of safety stock and chosen to provide a particular level of service.

SAFETY STOCK The average amount of stock on hand when a replenishment quantity is received. Its purpose is to protect against the uncertainty in demand and in the length of the REPLENISHMENT LEAD TIME. Safety stock and CYCLE STOCK are the two main components of any inventory.

SAMPLE A set of objects or things from a larger set called a UNIVERSE (or population). Unless otherwise specified, all samples are assumed to be random samples, i.e., each item in the universe has an equal chance of being drawn.

SECULAR TREND A long-term trend that persists over many observations.

SEQUENCING Determining the order in which a manufacturing facility is to process a number of different jobs in order to achieve certain objectives.

SERVICE FUNCTION A mathematical relationship of the SAFETY FACTOR to service level, i.e., to the fraction of demand that is routinely met from stock. Expressed mathematically, the service function is the expectation of one tail of a distribution function:

$$E(t > h) = \int_{h}^{\infty} (t - h)p(t)\ dt$$

SERVICE TIME The time required to serve the customer (i.e., fill his demand) after he places demand on an inventory.

SERVO SYSTEM A control mechanism linking a system's input and output, designed to feed back amplified output to regulate the operation of the system in conformance with planned operation.

SETUP COST The OUT-OF-POCKET COSTS associated with a machine setup that would increase or decrease if the number of setups was increased or decreased.

SHORTAGE COST The marginal profit that is lost on each item demanded but not immediately available in stock. Care must be taken to isolate all of the additional profit that would have occurred had the item been sold at the time it was demanded. In addition, a customer whose demand is not satisfied may, in the future, reduce his potential demand at this particular establishment.

SIMULATION The technique of utilizing representative or artificial operating and demand data to reproduce, under test, various conditions that are likely to occur in the actual performance of a system. Frequently used to test the ACCURACY of a theoretical MODEL or to examine the behavior of a system under different operating policies or conditions.

SLACK TIME The time allowance for contingencies in excess of the time usually required to carry out a process.

SLOPE OF A LINE The change in the vertical height of a line drawn on a graph as one moves out a unit distance along the horizontal axis.

SMOOTHING Averaging by a mathematical process or by curve fitting, such as the method of least squares or EXPONENTIAL SMOOTHING.

SMOOTHING CONSTANT In exponential smoothing, the fraction of the difference between the actual result and the forecasted result that is then added to the previous smoothed value to arrive at a new smoothed value. See EXPONENTIAL SMOOTHING.

SPECULATION INVENTORY Another form of ANTICIPATION STOCK.

(s, S) INVENTORY POLICY A two-level control system in which a replenishment order is issued if the available stock is equal to or less than the ORDER POINT s (the lower level), and in which the amount ordered is equal to S (the upper level) minus the available stock.

STANDARD DEVIATION   A measure of the dispersion of data about the mean value, which indicates the degree to which the fluctuations occur. Mathematically, the standard deviation of a SAMPLE of observations is

$$\sigma = \sqrt{\frac{\sum_{i=1}^{n} (x_i - X)^2}{n - 1}}$$

where x_i = individual readings
$\quad\quad\ \ n$ = number of such readings
$\quad\quad\ \ X$ = mean of the readings

If the mean μ of the UNIVERSE is known, X is replaced by μ and $n - 1$ by n. The standard deviation is the square root of the variance.

STANDARD INVENTORY   The normal or BASIC STOCK.

STATIONARY DISTRIBUTION   A PROBABILITY or FREQUENCY DISTRIBUTION describing the occurrence of a particular event over time, in which the parameters (e.g., MEAN and STANDARD DEVIATION) remain constant. Such a distribution shows no seasonal or SECULAR TREND.

STATISTIC   A quantity obtained from SAMPLE observations, such as the MEAN (X) or STANDARD DEVIATION (s), which may be used to estimate a UNIVERSE PARAMETER (such as μ or σ).

STEADY STATE   Condition of a system whose behavior has settled down so that various operating characteristics can be described by stationary distributions, as opposed to the initial, transient state of a system.

STOCHASTIC VARIATION   Random variation; implies the existence of a RANDOM variable that may assume each of its values with a definite PROBABILITY.

STOCK-KEEPING UNIT (SKU)   An item of stock that is completely specified as to style, size, color, location, etc.

SYSTEM   A group of objects or procedures purposefully organized and interconnected to perform a desired function in a desired way.

TIME SERIES   A sequence of numbers (in either tabular or graphical form) representing the repeated measurement of some phenomena over some time period.

TREND   A linear function of time.

TRIGGER LEVEL   See ORDER POINT.

TURNOVER (OF STOCK)   The ratio of total sales during a specific time period (generally 1 year) to the average inventory on hand during that time period. Can be applied to an individual SKU or to the aggregate inventory.

TWO-BIN SYSTEM (OF INVENTORY CONTROL)   A type of FIXED-ORDER SYSTEM in which inventory is physically or conceptually carried in two bins. A replenishment quantity is ordered when the first bin is empty. When the material is received, the second bin is refilled, and the excess is put into the working bin.

UNIFORM DISTRIBUTION   A distribution in which the independent variable has a constant probability of assuming any particular value over some possible range of the variable. Mathematically, this distribution is expressed as

$$f(x) = \frac{1}{b - a} \qquad \text{for } a \leq x \leq b$$

UNIVERSE   The population, or larger set of objects or things, from which SAMPLES are drawn. Usually assumed to be infinitely large, or at least very large relative to the sample.

VALUE ANALYSIS   The procedure of examining each element of a product or process to determine whether it can be made better or cheaper. A type of value analysis is known as ANALYSIS OF DISTRIBUTION BY VALUE.

VARIABLE COST   A cost which varies when the volume of an operation is varied, as opposed to those costs which remain fixed.

VARIANCE   The square of the standard deviation. See STANDARD DEVIATION.

WAITING-LINE THEORY   Equivalent to QUEUEING THEORY.

WEIGHTED AVERAGE   An average of several components, each having its own average, obtained by adding up the product of the average of each component times the fraction of total items that are within that component. A generalized formula is

$$A = \frac{\displaystyle\sum_{i=1}^{n} w_i x_i}{\displaystyle\sum_{i=1}^{n} w_i}$$

The numbers w_i are called the weights. If they are all equal, the weighted average reduces to the ARITHMETIC MEAN.

INDEX